Hair Trigger 34

A STORY WORKSHOP ANTHOLOGY

D1511622

COLUMBIA COLLEGE CHICAGO   CHICAGO 2012

FICTION WRITING DEPARTMENT

600 SOUTH MICHIGAN AVENUE

CHICAGO, ILLINOIS 60605-1996

FICTIONWRITING@COLUM.EDU

312.369.7611

Christopher Semel photographs courtesy Catherine Edelman Gallery, Chicago, from *Brothers* series. The photographs were produced between 2009-2010.

Sarah Faust photographs courtesy Catherine Edelman Gallery, Chicago, from *My Mother* series. The photographs were produced between 2002-2009.

Hair Trigger 34
Copyright ©2012, Columbia College Chicago
Story Workshop® is a service mark (U.S. Patent and Trademark Office Registration No. 1,343,415) of John Schultz.

Fiction Writing Department
fax 312-369-8043
phone 312-369-7611
fictionwriting@colum.edu

Columbia College Chicago
600 South Michigan Avenue
Chicago, IL 60605-1996

ISBN 0-929911-42-3

THE DAVID FRIEDMAN MEMORIAL AWARD

The David Friedman Award offers a cash prize to the best story or essay published in *Hair Trigger* each year. Our thanks go to David Friedman's family, which established this fund in fall 2002 as a memorial to their son, a talented writer and painter, as well as an alumnus of Columbia College Chicago and a great friend to the Fiction Writing Department's students and faculty.

Table of Contents

Preface & Acknowledgments

WELCOME TO THE THIRTY-FOURTH EDITION OF *HAIR TRIGGER,* THE COLUMBIA College Fiction Writing Department's annual anthology of student writing, featuring the best of the best in work produced in Story Workshop® and other classes in the undergraduate and graduate Fiction Writing Department programs at Columbia College Chicago. During the three decades since the magazine was founded by former chair and Story Workshop originator John Schultz, it has established itself as one of the top journals of its kind in the country. In addition to garnering many top national awards—among them first-place prizes from the Association of Writers and Writing Programs, the Coordinating Council of Literary Magazines, and the Columbia University Scholastic Press Association—*Hair Trigger* has published the work of over 175 individual award winners, many of whom have gone on to successful careers in writing and publishing, as well as a variety of other writing-related professions. The Fiction Writing Department is proud of those students, as it is of the many other students in classes whose work perhaps did not make it into the magazine's pages but who nonetheless played a part in fostering the creative, energetic, and supportive environment that has become the hallmark of the program.

As with previous issues of the magazine, *Hair Trigger 34* collects prose fiction, plays, and creative nonfiction writing by undergraduate BA and BFA students, and by graduate students in the MFA in Creative Writing–Fiction, MA in the Teaching of Writing, and Combined MFA/MA Degree programs. These works come from core Story Workshop classes—Introduction to Fiction Writing, Fiction Writing I and II, Prose Forms, Advanced Fiction, and Advanced Prose Forms—as well as from Fiction Seminars, Critical Reading and Writing classes, and a wide variety of creative nonfiction, playwriting, genre fiction, publishing, electronic applications, and other Specialty Writing classes taught with sound complementary approaches. The success of the Story Workshop method and those other approaches used in the Fiction Writing Department program is reflected in the broad range of voices, subjects, forms, and cultural/linguistic backgrounds represented in all editions of *Hair Trigger* during its illustrious history, including the edition you are holding in your hands.

An exhaustive and rigorous selection process ensures that no excellent story—whatever its voice, subject, form, or approach—will be overlooked. Student editors in our College Literary Magazine Publishing class work for a semester with a faculty advisor who helps them reveal their unconscious as well as conscious biases, form into diverse teams, read submissions, and decide which should be given to the full group for consideration. Those manuscripts passed ahead in the process are read by all editors, who then begin the hard work of deciding which pieces should go into the final magazine. Instructors may appeal a rejected piece for another reading and further discussion by student editors who, along with Faculty Advisor Chris Maul Rice and *Hair Trigger* supervisor Shawn Shiflett, are responsible for making the final decisions. For space reasons, we are unable to include many first-rate stories, essays, and plays each year; but over the magazine's history, this thorough, fair process has ensured that the very best work will eventually see the light of day. Respect for the reader, for content, for form, for point of view and language, for vividness of telling, and for dramatic interaction characterize the selections printed in this volume, and we believe that the diversity represented in the pages of *Hair Trigger 34* stands as a distinct and refreshing contrast to the so-called "workshop story" found in many other writing programs. Our appreciation goes to the student editors, chosen for their own ability as writers and readers. Congratulations and thanks to Chris Maul Rice, who was chiefly responsible as Faculty Advisor for supervising undergraduate and graduate student editors in the overall selection and production process for *Hair Trigger 34*, to full-time faculty Shawn Shiflett, who oversees *Hair Trigger* for the Fiction Writing Department, and to Production Manager Linda Naslund, whose leadership of the production team and commitment to quality have for so many years been largely responsible for ensuring the magazine's tradition of excellence.

Thanks to Acting Chair Patricia Ann McNair, Associate Chair Gary Johnson, and to faculty members Andy Allegretti, Don Gennaro De Grazia, Ann Hemenway, Eric May, Joe Meno, Nami Mun, Audrey Niffenegger, Alexis Pride, Lisa Schlesinger, Shawn Shiflett, Sam Weller, John Schultz, and Betty Shiflett for consulting on matters affecting the student editors' complex selection process—as well as to the many other excellent adjunct and visiting teacher-writers in the Fiction Writing program.

Thanks to Mary Forde, Assistant Vice President for Creative Services, and to Corey Plazak, Stefan Coisson, and Edward Thomas for print and cover design and artwork layout. Particular thanks go to Deborah Siegel, Rob Duffer, and Nicole Chakalis for copyediting, proofreading, and supervising critical aspects of production. And special thanks to Mica "Poonce Ponce" Racine, who has long given us invaluable assistance in production and design of *Hair Trigger* and other projects.

Our profound gratitude goes to Warrick Carter, President of Columbia College Chicago; to

Louise Love, Vice President for Academic Affairs and Interim Provost; and to Eliza Nichols, Dean of the School of Fine and Performing Arts, for their continuing support and encouragement of this program. We owe a debt, above all, to the over 750 students registered for classes in the Fiction Writing Department each semester from whose writing the selected pieces in this volume were gleaned.

We sincerely hope that you enjoy the original and inventive work appearing in this edition of *Hair Trigger*.

Randall Albers, Chair
Fiction Writing Department

Hair Trigger 34 Student Editors
Jenele Anderson
A.J. Camarena
Aimee Goluszka
Noelle Hufnagel
Matt Martin
Michael Meyer
Frankie Migacz
Jessie Morrison
Jonathan Natzke
Dorothy Schultz
Cynthia Vargas

Hair Trigger 34 Faculty Advisor
Chris Maul Rice

Teacher Appreciation Week

Jessie Morrison

And I'm not the kind that likes to tell you/
Just what you want me to/
You're not the kind that needs to tell me/
About the birds and the bees
—New Order, "Age of Consent"

TEACHER APPRECIATION WEEK AT JAMIESON COLLEGE PREP WAS HELD EVERY year during the bleak days of early February. On Monday, officers from Student Council came around during first period and offered the teachers cups of Starbucks coffee, but the year that Liz Stratford began her affair with one of her students, they forgot to wheel their cart down the languages hallway and no one in her department got any. On Tuesday, an ice cream sundae bar was offered in the faculty lounge during lunch periods, and Liz helped herself to three scoops of chocolate frozen yogurt doused in caramel and puffs of whipped cream. She ate every bite, and even licked the Styrofoam bowl, and that would have been worth it, except eating ice cream at 10:30 in the morning didn't seem to agree with her, and she'd had to excuse herself from fifth period Spanish II to relieve her crippling diarrhea in the coed faculty bathroom. Wednesday was a faculty jeans day, Thursday was an early release schedule, and the whole school had Friday off—which, of course, was far better than the coffee, the ice cream, or the jeans. Liz was looking forward to a snug afternoon on the couch, hidden under the blankets and watching baby mama drama on *The Maury Show*, and was in good spirits when she arrived to school Thursday morning.

On her way to the languages office, she ran into a small crowd of teachers gathered around the main bulletin board. Janice Hudgins, the eccentric, braless, studio art instructor, was working the crowd, beaming and pointing. Hanging on the wall, framed in black poster board, were paintings of various Jamieson teachers. The portraits were remarkably well done, rendered, Janice was saying, by the Honors Studio Arts class. They were meant as homage to students' favorite teachers, and the project had been kept secret over the course of several months so they could be unveiled during Teacher Appreciation Week.

Hanging in one corner was a portrait of English teacher Bill Zuckerman, his expression both haggard and kind, brandishing a fat piece of chalk at a freshly diagrammed sentence. Below that was Gary Powers, potbellied, avuncular, examining a large oak leaf with a magnifying glass. The artist who had rendered Elaine Mackey had kindly painted the buck-toothed science department chair smiling with her mouth closed. She was dressed in a lab coat and was proffering a bubbling beaker, her eyes twinkling over a pair of reading glasses. In the very middle, and larger than the rest, was a portrait of Francine Dowling, a popular English teacher who'd been killed in a car accident just a month earlier. The portrait depicted Francine sitting at a desk piled high with papers, her curly blond hair spilling out in a messy halo around her face. She was resting her chin in one hand. In the other, she balanced a tattered copy of *Romeo and Juliet*. She smirked out at the world, and the expression on her face was so close to the one that Liz remembered from faculty meetings that goose bumps rose up her arms. Above the portrait, in neat gold-painted writing, a small banner read: *Ms. Dowling 1976-2010 "Angels are bright still, though the brightest fell"* —Macbeth . . . *We miss you.* A few teachers were gazing at Francine's likeness and wiping away tears.

Suddenly, Liz felt a shudder of recognition as she scanned across the bulletin board and came across a pair of her own eyes. In the portrait, she was wearing her favorite shirt, the pink and gray striped button-down from Macy's, except the artist had taken the liberty of unbuttoning the top two buttons so that a provocative line of cleavage, faint but unmistakable, began at the place where her shirt came together.

Liz was stunned. Unlike the other teachers on the wall, she had never been the type of educator who inspired love in her students. She was never interviewed for the school paper; she was never quoted in the student yearbook; alumni never came to visit her. She was the type of teacher who students forgot about nearly the moment they walked out of her class. She didn't get the sense that they disliked her, necessarily, but she wasn't a *performer* like some of the other teachers. She spent a lot of time behind her podium. Her department chair had encouraged her, after her last observation, to "get out there in the thick of things," "circulate around your classroom," "create a more student-centered environment." But the learning of a language, Liz felt, was an orderly process, mathematical, almost; how mastery of one concept was essential to moving onto the next level of comprehension. There was the past tense, the present, and later, the subjunctive; the various cases, the vocabulary, the fluency and pronunciation. It all required constant drilling and emphasizing skills, and that was why she didn't waste time playing Tortuga like Sra. Pintor did, or teaching Latino culture in a ridiculous sombrero and holding maracas, cooking empañadas for an entire class, like Sr. Gomez. Nor, like Sra. Richmond, did she give out pesetas, red-paper fake money that was plastered with Sra. Richmond's own bovine face, which students could acquire through various forms of hoop-jumping, and then cash in on the days they didn't do their homework. It was all gimmicky, in her opinion, not to mention a disgrace to Latino cultures everywhere and an affront to the sizable population of Latino students who attended Jamieson College Prep. Furthermore, Liz would be willing to bet that when *her* students came out of a year's worth of her class, they wouldn't have pesetas or empañadas to show for it; they wouldn't know how to salsa, but they'd be able to communicate in Spanish, and last time she'd checked, wasn't *that* the goal of the class?

The trade-off of her pedagogy, though, was that students didn't like her very much, which, she had to admit, was something that bothered her a great deal. So when she saw her picture hanging on the wall among the faces of other beloved faculty members, she was both stunned and pleased, because she couldn't even begin to guess at what student might have painted her, or why. And it was clear that the artist had been watching her, *studying* her, so much so that they could not have created a more accurate portrait than if she'd commissioned one herself. She *liked* it—it was honest, and yet it presented her in the best possible light: vulnerable but pretty, serious but not severe. She only possessed one other portrait of herself: a caricature that her father had bought for her at Great America when she was thirteen; in it, her head was enormous, her braces an exaggerated grill; the bump on her nose jutted out almost as far as her simian forehead. She hadn't thought it possible that the cartoonist could make her look even more grotesque than she felt in her cage of adolescence, but sure enough he'd done it, and even though she begged her dad not to, he'd hung it up in the living room, right above his piano. He genuinely thought his daughter looked beautiful in the portrait, and Liz remembered the incident clearly because it was the first time she really understood the delusive power of love.

She thought about asking her students outright who'd painted her, but she felt that she might come off as accusatory, and she also didn't want to embarrass anyone. She felt, instinctively, that the sensual nature of the painting—the unbuttoned blouse, the cleavage, the elongated eyelashes—indicated that the artist was a boy. But there was a sensitivity in the work, an intuitive understanding, that pointed towards a more female perspective. It had to be an older student, since underclassmen weren't allowed to take Honors Studio Art, so that eliminated her two Spanish I classes. There were a few juniors in Spanish II, but one of them, Andy Frank, openly disliked Liz because of a bad grade she'd given him on a vocabulary project, and the other, Jenny Fricka, had dysgraphia, and Liz doubted that someone whose handwriting was so horrendous it qualified as a learning disability would have that kind of skill with a paintbrush.

So that left her two AP Spanish IV classes: thirty-five students in all, an overachieving, sensitive bunch. The artist had to be in one of those, and she was determined to find out who it was. The class had just finished reading Marquez's short story, "Un Señor Muy Viejo Con Unas Alas Enormas," and that afternoon, as they sat bent over their reading quizzes, Liz took the opportunity to scrutinize each of them. But no pair of eyes flicked up in her direction; they all seemed engrossed in their work. When the bell rang, and they all filed indifferently past her desk to turn in their quizzes, Liz began to think that perhaps the artist had only chosen her because their favorite teacher had already been chosen by someone else, or worse, because her face was simple and uncomplicated and relatively easy to draw. But if that was true, why did the portrait contain such depth, such accuracy? The artist, whoever it was, had managed to capture a certain sadness in her, a truth, and the riddle of who had created it succeeded in haunting her for the entirety of her long weekend.

The following Monday morning, as Liz headed to the languages hallway towards her office, she again passed by herself, the lonely expression unchanged, the chalk-line cleavage still provocatively in place. It made her unaccountably sad, the idea of herself pinned to the wall all weekend like a dead butterfly, staring out into an empty hallway with the lights turned out. It was still early; kids were only beginning to trickle in. Faculty members picked their way down the slippery hallways with faces buried in scarves, and she furtively lifted a corner to search for a signature, a set of initials, to give her a clue. The portrait was unsigned. She began to casually ask around the department office for information, but didn't want to sound too interested; if they could see what a big deal it was to her, they would feel sorry for her: Gomez and Pintor and Richmond, all of whom regularly received Christmas presents from students, who were high-fived in the hallway, who were asked to write college letters of recommendation, and whose faces all hung on the bulletin board, alongside her own.

When the bell rang at 3:00, she found herself walking upstream through the crowds, headed in the direction of the fine arts hallway. Liz had worked at the school for over ten years, but had never actually been in the art studio. It was a dusty room, with a large row of windows that looked out onto the parking lot and flooded the space with gray light. Outside, it was snowing a little bit, the depressing, anemic kind of snowfall you can only get in February, when everything about winter has lost its charm. The room itself, though, contrasted with the depressing scene outside: it was warm, cozy, and messy, with bits of paper on the floor, tubes of paint and trays of chalk and colored pencils crammed on shelves against the walls. It smelled of fresh paper, acrylic, and the earthy, nostalgic saltiness of modeling clay. Student artwork was displayed everywhere—Chinese lanterns, sculptures made of lumpy ceramic and clay, copper wire animals, and portraits of all kinds. There were abstract geometric shapes, landscapes, still-lifes, architectural blueprints, collages, photographs in color and black-and-white. A group of girls with dyed hair and stripey, mismatched clothing was gathered around a cloth dummy, pinning up a dress that appeared to be made out of flattened pop cans.

Janice Hudgins stood in the middle of the room, bent over a table where one of Liz's AP Spanish students, Carlos Fernandez, sat before a chalk canvas, so absorbed in his work that he didn't seem to notice that Janice's left breast, unfettered by a bra beneath the thin material of her sweater, was swinging pendulously near his cheek. Liz knocked, gently, on the door-frame.

"Ms. Stratford!" Janice said, straightening up. "Well! What brings you up to our neck of the woods?"

"Hi, Janice," Liz said, looking around the unfamiliar room. "Hey, I just wanted to thank you for that nice surprise on Thursday. For the paintings. What a nice idea."

"Weren't they just *wonderful?*" Janice extended her arms, her protuberant nipples nodding along enthusiastically. "But don't thank me—you should thank your portraitist! He did a wonderful job, didn't he?"

So, it was a "he" after all. She'd been right about that.

"Well, I'd like to thank him," Liz said, "if I knew who it was."

"What? Well, he's standing right here, isn't he?"

Bewildered, Liz looked around the room. There were the three girls around the dummy, their backs turned to her. And there was Carlos Fernandez.

"Carlos?"

He was a senior, with dark hair that fell in his face, an attractive, childish face that was sometimes marred with an outbreak of zits. He sat in the back of her class, rarely raised his hand, and because he was a native Spanish speaker, she'd often gotten the distinct feeling from him, the way he looked at her without really looking, his silence in class, his slouched demeanor, that he was mocking her and her careful Gringa attempts at rolling r's. When he saw Liz in the hallways, he greeted her with a curt "hey," or, if he was with his friends, a group of equally languid punk rock kids, he ignored her completely. Even now, he continued scribbling furiously, refusing to meet her gaze. And yet, if it was true, this boy had painted her in a manner so intimate and true that even now, as she stood in the doorway watching him, she felt a blush creeping up her neck.

Liz was thirty-five years old—in good health and not at all old, but the problem with working in a high school, surrounded by hordes of perpetual teenagers, was that it made her *feel* old. She'd been twenty-two when she first started teaching, just a couple years older than the upperclassmen. She was now halfway through her eleventh year at Jamieson, and each year that passed the students were eternally young, optimistic, eager, and unburdened by regret, while her own aging process seemed to accelerate, as if everyone around her had discovered a fountain of youth from which she was not allowed to drink. She remembered feeling, in her twenties, that the energy of her students was contagious. It infused itself in her own life. In those first teaching years, she'd never been more attractive to the opposite sex—not a weekend went by without a date, and sometimes she'd juggled as many as three or four guys at a time. Lately, though, the energy of her students simply filled her with envy, and poisoned even her own teenage memories, which now felt so vague and quaint and far away. She hadn't been on a date in over eight months.

Sometimes, she played a hypothetical game with herself, acceptable, she reasoned, because there wasn't a chance that she'd ever actually play it in real life. The game was this: *If* she were still in high school, which of her students would she have a crush on? She discovered that she had a type: popular athletes, big boys with close-shaved, neat haircuts, who wore their jerseys on Fridays and comfortably called out answers without raising their hands; boys who, even if they didn't know the correct answer, somehow gave it with such authority that it seemed like it was right.

The kind of boys who never gave her a second glance when she actually *was* in high school.

She entertained herself with questions like, If I was still eighteen, who would I want to go to prom with? If I was eighteen, who would I imagine kissing? And more and more lately, she'd been allowing herself to think other, more intimate questions about some of the boys that sat before her each day, tripping earnestly over their Spanish pronunciations. Sometimes she felt guilty, but she also felt secretly smug that, being thirty-five, having slept with eight men, having been in three long-term relationships, it was a virtual guarantee that she knew more about sex, had had more of it—at least numbers-wise—than even the most testosterone-riddled senior in the school. She knew that she should be moving on from her most recent disastrous breakup with Kent by putting herself out there with men her own age instead of spending her Saturday nights watching *Saturday Night Live* accompanied by a carton of boxed wine and engaging in increasingly strange fantasies. But it still didn't stop her from thinking them.

Carlos Fernandez was not the type of boy that she would have liked if she were in high school. Up until now, she had never looked at him in AP Spanish IV and wondered.

But now, when she looked down at him as he worked with his chalks, his face obscured by a sheath of dark hair, and she thought of that line of cleavage, the sensitive rendering of her face fashioned by his smooth hands, she realized that our tastes change as we grow older.

It's a sign of maturity.

It was all hypothetical, of course. She would never *act* on it. She'd never acted on anything risky in her whole life, even when she *was* a teenager. But when Carlos finally stopped his scribbling, put his pencil down, and slowly, deliberately, raised his dark eyes to meet hers, a bolt of warmth spread from her chest down between her legs, a sudden and dangerous attraction, and she murmured a fumbling thank you before retreating back into the sea of children in the hallway.

The quickest way to begin a love affair with a student is to believe unequivocally that you are not the type of person who would ever do such a thing. This belief, coupled with an unfamiliarity with who you really are, allows you to put yourself in situations that a more honest person would recognize as dangerous and, therefore, avoid. Someone who wasn't purposefully naïve, for example, would not have lingered in the fine arts hallway, gazing for a long time at amateur drawings of hands and feet, waiting for the building to clear. And after the hallways had cleared, a more responsible adult, one less shot-through with loneliness and misdirected narcissism, would not have seen the boy who had painted her and, feigning surprise, asked him where he lived, and finding that it was not too far out of the way, offered him a ride home.

"Are you sure that isn't weird?" he asked, as they fell into step and headed toward his locker where he could get his coat and his books—one of which, she saw, was the collected stories of Gabriel Garcia Marquez that she herself had assigned.

"It's snowing," she said. "And freezing. Do you really want to have to wait for the bus?"

Carlos looked out the hallway window at the whirling snow and shrugged.

"Did you like that story?" she asked, pointing at the book.

"It was OK," he said. He turned his back to her, put on his winter hat, pulled it low over his eyes, slung his bag over one shoulder and started walking quickly in the direction of the parking lot so that Liz had no choice but to hurry behind him. She couldn't understand it—his behavior towards her indicated either complete indifference or active contempt. It didn't seem to fit. Why would you spend all that time drawing someone you despised? How could you depict them so beautifully and honestly if you didn't feel any connection to them?

At first, they were silent as they sat side by side in her Toyota, waiting for the engine to warm. Outside, snow swirled, and they exhaled in icy puffs that soon fogged the windshield. Finally, Liz put the car in gear, and when she pulled out of the parking lot, she asked him, "Why did you paint me?"

Carlos shrugged. "I don't know."

She was quiet for a moment. "You did a really beautiful job. I didn't know you were so artistic."

Silence. They turned onto Milwaukee Avenue.

"Can I ask you something, Carlos?" she said finally. "Am I a good teacher? I mean, do the kids like me?"

She needed, badly, for him to tell her that they did. But he didn't say anything for at least half a minute. Finally, he conceded, "Well, they don't *dis*like you."

"But—well—*you* must like me, right?" she continued hopefully. "Because, you know, you painted me."

"You were never supposed to see that," he said roughly. It was the first sign of emotion she had elicited from him. He had his phone out now, and was glaring down at it and texting someone with fast fingers. "Mrs. Hudgins didn't tell us she was hanging those up. She hung up the ones that got As. But she never asked us if she could."

"Did you not want me to see it?" she asked carefully.

"No!" he looked up from his phone and directed his glare at her. "Why?"

"Because it was private. My friends all saw it, and they keep making fun of me about it, saying I have, you know, a crush on you or something."

Liz weighed her options and risks, a lifetime of not taking risks, a lifetime of not asking questions.

She looked at him. They were stopped at a red light. "Do you?"

His face was red, but it could have been from the cold or the wind or from an acne medication. He looked out the window at a Burger King parking lot with supreme concentration. "I think you're pretty, if that's what you mean."

She should have told him that was very sweet of him to say. She should have told him that was nice to hear, if a little inappropriate, and that he was going to make some lucky girl in the senior class very happy. But vanity won out, and as the light turned green and they accelerated softly through the snowy intersection, she said, "Well, I think you're handsome, Carlos."

Handsome. Pretty. The words seemed to perch between the two of them for the rest of the silent car ride, stuffed uncomfortably in the cup holders.

When she pulled in front of the yellow-brick apartment building where he lived, she watched as he gathered up his things, suddenly not wanting to see him go.

"So, who do you live with?"

"My mom and sister. Well, my sister's only here on weekends—she got a scholarship to a boarding school in Indiana, and she stays in the dorms during the week."

"What about your mom?"

"She works at night, so I don't get to see her very much."

"And your dad?"

Carlos shrugged. "Haven't seen him since I was a kid."

"You're alone a lot then, huh?"

"Yeah, I guess."

"What do you eat for dinner?"

"I don't know. Cereal, sometimes. Sometimes my mom makes me a plate and puts it in the fridge."

She touched his arm gently, in the same way his mother might. "I don't like that thought—of you eating dinner by yourself. You're too young to be alone all the time like that."

He laughed a little. "What," he said, "you want to come up and make me dinner or something?"

Being upstairs was jarring for both of them. Carlos's demeanor changed dramatically once they were inside. He was no longer surly and guarded, but self-conscious and shy; he kept straightening things and apologizing because the small rooms smelled strongly of Glad Air Freshener and cat pee and fried food and his mother's spicy perfume. He stood around the kitchen, watching his teacher as she rummaged through cabinets, while a small orange tabby wound its way around his legs.

"You don't have much in this house in the way of food, do you?" she said.

He bent down and picked up the cat. "Told you."

Liz was determined to find something for him to eat in the barren cupboards and sparse refrigerator. She'd never had much maternal instinct, but now that she was alone with Carlos in the quiet, warm apartment, she was feeling a sudden and strong desire to nurture him. She finally gathered the supplies for grilled cheeses and Campbell's tomato soup. They ate together, quietly, in the small, narrow kitchen. Outside, the gray afternoon faded into an uneasy darkness.

It happened so seamlessly it almost felt natural. When they finished eating, Carlos stuck his long, skinny legs out straight in front of him and his feet brushed Liz's shins beneath the table. He made no effort to move them, but left them there, resting, his feet warm beneath his socks. It was an invitation, however subtle, and so, marveling at the disconnect between the things her head was telling her and the things her body was doing, Liz leaned over the crumb-dusted plates and empty soup bowls, cupped Carlos's face in her hands, and drew it towards her own. She kissed him with closed lips, then opened her mouth wider to let his pressing tongue inside, a sloppy kiss from a young boy who hadn't had many kissing years quite yet.

When they'd stood up, still kissing across the table, and she'd pushed him gently against the refrigerator, a few coupons on magnets fluttering to the ground, and pressed the full length of her body against his and felt him rising against her, she whispered, because she had to, "We shouldn't be doing this," but she was relieved when he said, almost choking on his want, "I don't care," because then it felt that it was ridiculous to say that she was taking advantage of anyone. She remembered herself at seventeen, perhaps naïve about some things, but still fully grown and certainly not a *child*. In less than a year, Carlos would be old enough to fight in Afghanistan, to die there, even, and so it seemed ridiculous, this arbitrary age thing, when you came right down to it. When he ran his hands down her waist, she reminded herself that the American public, so puritanical and hypocritical about sex, certainly hadn't come to a consensus about when one truly leaves their childhood behind: you can drive at sixteen, vote at eighteen, drink at twenty-one, and none of it made sense; it was meaningless semantics; Carlos was a person and Liz was a person and in medieval times, he'd already be married and she'd already be dead; and if they discovered that they loved each other, then wouldn't it be a waste to turn their backs on it because modern soap boxers had decided that they belonged to two different stages of life and that it was taboo to intersect, on a sexual level, those two arbitrary stages of being? And wasn't it true, she told herself stubbornly as Carlos took her by the hand and led her into his dark bedroom, with its unmade twin bed and guitar case leaning against a dresser where T-shirts and jeans spilled out of open drawers, that the very idea of a teenager was a social construct, invented sometime last century when people no longer had to help out with farm work and could afford to go to school for a bit longer?

Thus dispatching the voice of her conscience with such logic, she fell onto the bed, he on top of her, and she felt herself moan at the weight of him—how long had it been since she'd last lain under a man?—but when she pulled his sweatshirt over his head and looked upon his thin, frail body, the tiny, delicate nipples, the ladder of chest bone, the absence of hair except for two small, dark tufts under his arms, her conscience awoke. His body was shaking, either from pleasure or fear, she couldn't tell, but either way it was too late; the needs of her body and the desire to finally fulfill a reckless wish for returned youth had won out. She asked him before he entered her, without really caring what the answer was, whether he was a virgin, and he told her he wasn't and she suspected that he was lying, but she still didn't care. If she was taking something from him that couldn't be given back, then so be it. She would tell herself later he wanted it even more than she did. And when he soon began to shudder, grabbing at her hair in stunned pleasure, she began whispering tenderly in his ear, "This is our secret; we can never tell; we can never tell," and he nodded promises, agreeing to anything at that moment if it meant that what had just happened might happen again.

They began seeing each other as many as three times a week. Sometimes, she would linger in the language office after school, and if he walked by and looked at her through the windows, she knew that instead of going home, she would drive in the opposite direction, to his mother's apartment. Other times, she would leave school and pick him up at the 7-Eleven two blocks from school. Once, wild with the forbiddenness of it all, they made love right there in her car behind the 7-Eleven, right next to the Dumpsters, and she'd driven him home in satisfied silence. It was a happy time, so happy that she managed to forgive herself for the criminality of it. The fear of getting caught never really went away, but it was tamped down easily by her delusions. She'd been so lonely for so long, and she felt that she deserved this long-awaited happiness. She rehearsed her justifications so often that she almost wished there was someone who knew about it to challenge her. Her only wish was that Carlos was eighteen, but his birthday was in June, and if they could last that long . . . well, who knew where things might go from there.

But in a way, it was only sex. A woman her age ought to have realized that, ought to have known better, but she had justifications for that too: they *couldn't* go places together, they *couldn't* talk on the phone, they *couldn't* get to know each other's families. And so, their entire life together centered around those hours after school in his twin bed, and yet that life was more fulfilling for her than even what she'd had most recently with

Kent. Carlos was the silent type; she never worried that he would be indiscreet, that he would brag to his friends about his conquest, and it amazed her how well he could play his part: in class, he was the same brooding, back-row presence as ever; the only difference was that he no longer seemed to sneer at her. He continued to turn in his homework with the same above average but not superior effort; he continued to earn Bs.

Alone together, he was someone else entirely. He was guileless and overflowing with feeling; he held her tightly, possessively, and in the four weeks that it lasted, he seemed to grow up right before her eyes: a fumbling, inexperienced lover in the first week, a confident, commandeering lover by the end, unafraid to try new things, asking for whatever he wanted and getting it.

One afternoon in early March, when it was still bitterly, unseasonably cold, Liz and Carlos were lying naked in his bed, while outside, wind rattled the thin panes of his bedroom windows.

"I still haven't gotten over that fact," he was saying, trailing a finger down her bare arm, "that every day I have to sit there and watch you teach, when all I'm doing is picturing you naked. I mean—lots of kids probably picture their teachers naked; it's just that I can't believe I actually get to *see* it." He lifted the covers and examined the length of her body.

"Don't!" Liz squealed, pulling them back around her. "You know I'm self-conscious."

"I know," he said, lifting to peak again. "But I don't get why."

He reached underneath the blanket to squeeze her waist. She loved the way he could not keep his hands off her, how he buried his hands in the folds of her body like he was kneading dough.

"Because I'm *old*, and the only other bodies you've seen are *young*."

"You're not *that* old. And you're also gorgeous."

She curled up against his thin, smooth body, warmed by the compliment. When he said tender things to her, it was always with an earnestness that she felt could not have been replicated by a man her own age.

"You know, you have a lot more to lose from this than I do," he said.

"I know that."

"So why risk it? Why risk your job and your reputation and everything else, just for me?" It was a good question, one that she'd considered often on her drives home alone through the dark winter streets. She leaned on an elbow and looked at him.

"Well, I've been trying not to say things around you like, 'when you get older,'" she said, "but it's true: when you get older, it's a lot harder to find people who really understand you. It's a lot rarer than you might think."

"And you feel like I understand you?"

She nodded. He was watching her intently.

"Do you love me?" he asked.

"Would it scare you if I said yes?"

"No."

"Then yes. Yes, I love you. Do you love me?"

"Yeah."

He pulled her on top of him again, dragging her breasts across his face, and entered her for the second time that afternoon. When they were finished, they drifted off to a peaceful sleep, nested beneath his blankets like a pair of baby birds.

She awoke in the disorienting, sudden light—someone must have turned a switch. She sat up, squinting, and saw a woman standing in the doorway.

"Ma," she heard Carlos begin, and the pleading, childish fear in his voice triggered her recognition: she'd seen the woman at parent-teacher conferences, a kindly face, nodding and answering in the short, clipped responses of the immigrant. Liz sat bolt upright, feeling exactly the way she'd felt at age twenty, when her car had spun out of control on the Kennedy during a snowstorm: absolute and total fear for her life, waiting for the impact, and the bright white lights, and then nothingness or heaven or hell. Instead, the car had swung past an oncoming semi by inches and slid gently into a snow-softened ditch.

Carlos's mother began to shout, and as Liz tripped out of the tangle of bed sheets, reaching blindly for a scrap of clothing, utterly naked, she found herself translating the woman's words into English out of habit. Most of them were curses.

Carlos, sitting up in bed now, was defending Liz wildly, also yelling in Spanish, the kind of native, rapid Spanish that he had never used in class. She was used to stilted exchanges between her heavily accented white or black students and herself; she'd forgotten how quick and undulating the language sounded when spoken by native speakers. It almost mesmerized her; under different circumstances she might have stopped and just listened, but then Mrs. Fernandez picked up a dusty Little League trophy from Carlos's dresser and hurled it in her direction. She ducked and it smashed into the wall, chipping paint. There were more screams, more objects thrown, Carlos hopping out of bed, an assault of pennies and nickels and dimes that his mother had produced from her jeans pockets. Crouching, Liz swept up pieces of clothing blindly from the carpeted floor. Then she took a deep breath and, covering her face with a shirt, slipped through the doorway past Carlos's mother, who tried to block her but was too heavy and too short and too slow. Wild with adrenaline, Liz tripped and fell in the front room, hitting her chin on the coffee table, but stumbled back to her feet, grabbed her purse, and bolted down the stairs and out the front door.

Outside, it was so cold, and the tree branches, bare and skeletal, emptied of life, swayed ominously. The streets were slicked with dirty ice and she ran towards the street, forgetting where she'd parked, the cold pulsing up from the sidewalk and numbing her bare feet so she was half-running, half-hobbling. Piles of snow, discolored and molded by snowplows into deformed mountains, gaped at her, and she turned around, half expecting Carlos's mother to be coming behind her—she could still hear the screaming—but instead she saw her car and started the engine with fumbling fingers, blasted the heat which only blew stale, freezing air that made her bare nipples ache, and she pulled away and found a gas station where, ignoring the strange faces outside the car, faces mute and uniform, wrapped in scarves and drooping hats, she pulled on the clothes she had salvaged: a T-shirt of Carlos's, soft and smelling of him, her pink underwear, a black pencil skirt she'd worn to work, but no nylons, no bra, no shoes, no coat.

When she got home, she crunched through the snow in her bare feet, up the steps of her apartment building which had never felt longer, and crawled under a throw blanket on the couch, dripping and sobbing and clutching her silent phone until she could feel her feet and hands again.

One thing was for sure, she decided, huddled under the blanket: she could not go to work tomorrow. What if Mrs. Fernandez recognized her face? Liz thought about repercussions. If they caught her, she might go to jail. She would certainly never teach again. She might have to register as a sex offender, might have to go door to door and tell her neighbors to keep their children away from her. All of her worst nightmares would come true, and for what? Had it been worth it, that month of passion? Had it been love? She'd been so sure only hours ago, but now she wasn't so sure anymore. She wasn't thinking of Carlos's misery; he was young, and the victim, and would bounce back. She was thinking, now, only of herself.

She called in sick for two days until, mercifully, the weekend came. She never left her apartment once. She read the online newspapers obsessively and watched the morning, afternoon, and evening news. She half expected the cops to show up at her door, or the principal to make a condemnatory phone call. She checked her work email with grim obsessiveness: if it were to come to light, she wanted to know right away. But the only email she received of a personal nature was from Sra. Pintor, who informed her that the substitute could not find the DVD for *La Casa de Bernarda Alba,* and the students had been given a free period instead. "Recuperate pronto!" Pintor had added at the end, and the bright innocence of the well-wishing, as well as the mundane nature of the email, made Liz feel even worse. It brought to her attention the fact that it would never so much as cross the minds of teachers like Pintor or Gomez or Richmond to compromise their integrity or to slide into perversion with a student in order to feel loved or validated. They gained their students' affection the old-fashioned way: by being kind and interesting and fair. The contrast made Liz realize her failings not just as a teacher but as a human being. The fact that Pintor thought Liz would *care* that a DVD had gone missing—as if this might be Pintor's definition of a bad day at work—sent her dissolving into torrents of tears.

She did not hear from Carlos—why would she? She'd never even given him her phone number, so as to diminish the evidence and prevent them from getting caught. Yet she'd expected, or perhaps hoped, that he would have managed to track it down. But the truth was, she only wanted to speak to him to find out if his mother knew, and if she did, whether she would tell. She loathed herself for being so self-serving, but she figured, how many teenage boys get caught with girls in their beds? If Mrs. Fernandez hadn't recognized her (and with no word in four days, she was beginning to hold out hope), the matter might have already blown over in their household. He'd been right: it was she who had something to lose from this whole mess, not him. She resented him for it, would have hated him if she'd had the energy. *He'd* been the one to start it. Of all the teachers in the school, he'd drawn her. He'd unbuttoned her shirt with his paintbrush, for God's sake. He'd seen her desperation and he'd tempted her. Yes, she'd offered him a ride home, but *he'd* invited her upstairs. *He'd* rested his legs against hers. The kid was almost eighteen. He'd known exactly what he was doing. And now it was *her* whose life was going to ruin.

But at the same time, she felt a worsening guilt, like she'd stepped in something cold and it was seeping into her blood. She dreaded seeing him again. It would remind her of her shame, her descent into hedonism and lies, how far she would go to be assured she was still attractive. She had no desire to touch him ever again. She cried almost continuously, not really for what had happened that night, but for what had always been happening to her, every moment since the day she'd begun to teach high school, which was that her life was moving forward, aging, ending, while somewhere, everywhere, there would always be people who were young. Why hadn't she chosen to break the rules and lie and cheat and fall for the wrong man when she herself was seventeen, when almost any bad behavior could be chalked up to age? What excuse, at thirty-five, did she have?

On Monday, having not heard otherwise, Liz went to work. Her hands trembled on the steering wheel; she pulled over to the side of the road once to throw up the banana she'd eaten for breakfast. She'd imagined every possible public scene, every ignominious humiliation. When she arrived at school, she walked past the bulletin board, her heart sinking, and saw that the portraits had all been taken down and replaced with angular, penciled blueprints from Beginning Architecture. In the department office, no one looked at her strangely; no one avoided her eyes; they all asked if she was feeling better. She nodded, woodenly, murmured something about the stomach flu, barely bothered to pretend to lie anymore. She waited for someone to say Carlos's name; if they had, she would have confessed all instantly.

But nobody did. The bell rang for first period, and her freshmen greeted her as usual. Nobody asked where she had been. The class was conducted with compete normalcy. She introduced the new vocabulary list, household items II: pillow, tablecloth, dresser. The students drearily repeated the words after her: *almohada, mantel, aparador.* She checked in the homework. Three students had failed to complete it. She dutifully marked a zero next to each of their names in her gradebook. They weren't apologetic, and she wasn't angry. It was just the way things happened.

Second period Spanish I was much the same, except this time eight students hadn't completed their homework, and she felt compelled to halfheartedly reprimand the class and remind them that the end of the third quarter was three weeks away. Then she continued with household items: mattress, fan, light bulb. They repeated dutifully: *colchon, ventilador, bombilla.*

By lunchtime, she felt a weariness inside her that reached to her depths. It was exhausting, waiting for a mocking look from a student, or for the appearance of Dr. Jones, the school principal, at her classroom door. It was exhausting waiting for seventh period AP Spanish, and for the sleepy, dark, knowing eyes of Carlos in the back of the room. Would he wait for her after class and explain developments? Would he tell her his mother hadn't known? Would he tell her he was grounded? Would he go back to his sneering? Would he tell her he still loved her? Would she have to tell him that it was over?

She had not considered that perhaps he would not be there at all. His desk sat empty, silent, without explanation. She thought of asking her students where he was, but didn't trust herself to speak his name without giving it all away. They continued to read from Marquez's short stories, this time, "Un Dia de Estos,"—"One of These Days." She forced herself not to look at the empty desk in the corner, not to wait like a hopeful dog for him to appear in the doorway.

He wasn't there the next day either, or the one after that. Liz thought she would go mad, but she didn't dare ask his whereabouts. She suffered in silence and they read more Garcia Marquez. Finally, that Friday, at the end of the day, she received an email from the registrar's office. It read:

Subject: Notice of Student Withdrawal
Teachers,
Student Carlos Fernandez ID 135095 has withdrawn from all classes effective March 7, 2010. Please send student's current grade to the registrar's office and update your class list.

There was nothing more, no explanation, no forwarding address. He was gone from her class, gone from Jamieson, gone from her life. She emailed the registrar's office with the only meager gift to him she could think of: she changed his grade from a B- to an A. She hoped that he would see it on his transcript and take it as a secret message of goodwill.

She began to wonder: was it possible that she would get away with it, that she had done something that should have destroyed her life and yet mercifully her sin would go unaccounted? Did this happen often: did bad deeds go unpunished? Up until Carlos, she'd always operated under the assumption that you didn't get away with anything. How different might her life have been if she'd discovered earlier that sometimes you did? Though she ached to know where and why he had gone, if he was all right, her desire to assure his well-being was eclipsed by the sheer joy of realizing that her life was not going to fall apart, that she would not be raked across the coals of public opinion, turned out for a harlot, fired, and arrested. She went into the faculty bathroom, locked herself in a stall, put her head in her hands and cried with relief.

After school, as she walked to her car, her bag filled with quizzes to grade over the weekend, she smiled to herself. It was sunny and the sun was warm, the first time she'd felt warm sun on her face since perhaps early November. Spring was coming, and she felt free of her burden. As she unlocked her car, a black pickup truck pulled into the parking lot and stopped abruptly, blocking her in. A young girl, perhaps a student at Jamieson, swung open the door and climbed out of the passenger seat. She was tiny, with legs the thickness of Liz's arms in skintight jeans and boots with white fur around the cuffs. She wore a shiny puffy jacket and had long, straight, raven-black hair. Liz recognized the dark, sleepy eyes instantly.

Carlos's sister uttered one syllable; "Cunt," with such vicious hatred that Liz stepped back, dropping her school bag. Then the girl reached up with a small fist and swung. The blow was surprisingly forceful—she was wearing three gold plated rings, and Liz fell backwards onto the curb, seeing swirls of white light and feeling a bursting in her nose and flood of warm, ferric blood. Then the girl spat, not on Liz but on the ground right next to her head, and climbed back into the pickup, which peeled out of the parking lot and down Milwaukee Avenue.

Instantly, Sra. Pintor was hovering over her.

"I saw the whole thing!" she cried, helping Liz back to her feet. "My God, I think your nose is broken!"

Liz reached up. Something in her face indeed felt broken, and the blood flowed in thick gouts from both nostrils so she couldn't breathe.

"Do you *know* that person? I'm calling the police. Shit! I should've gotten the license plate number, but I can describe the girl anyway. Did you *know* her? We've got to take you to a hospital—"

Liz waved her away.

"I'm fine," she said. Her eyes stung with tears. She reached into her bag and pulled out a Household Items II Quiz, tore it in half, rolled it into two tight cylinders and gently stuffed them in her nose.

"We need to take you to a hospital, or at the very least to the police station!"

"I'm going home," Liz said flatly.

"But you've been *assaulted!*"

Sra. Pintor tried to put an arm around Liz's shoulder and Liz pushed her roughly away.

"I don't want your help, Maria," she yelled. "And I'm going home." She climbed into her car and skidded into reverse and out onto the street, leaving Maria Pintor, in her black, chalk-dusted slacks and naïve, innocent face, gaping in the faculty parking lot.

She managed to last three more months, until the end of the year, before putting in for her resignation. It was too exhausting, waiting and waiting for Carlos's sister to show up again, or his mother, or the boy himself. Her nose, which now squeaked audibly whenever she smiled, was a constant reminder that there were others who knew, and that whatever had happened to Carlos—wherever he'd gone—his family blamed her. She did not believe in herself as a teacher anymore, nor trust in herself as a person. In June, she took a job at a bank, increasing her salary by forty percent. The work was much easier and quieter and more tedious; whereas before she had been encouraged to circle the classroom, now nothing was asked of her but to stay behind a window, counting crisp increments of other people's money.

She was unhappy; she didn't know how much she'd loved her job until she'd left it: the riotous volume in the hallways, the newfound boyfriends and girlfriends smiling gummily and unself-consciously at each other on the benches outside of school, the cacophonous slamming of lockers during passing periods, the pep rallies and the cookie bakes, the fundraisers and assemblies and variety shows; the student-teacher volleyball games, the walk-a-thons, the field trips. Surrounded by adults all the time now, the only time she saw high school students was on the bus, and the change in perspective made her realize, with a shiver of self-disgust, that they really were still just kids.

Five years after she quit her job at Jamieson, she was at a restaurant, eating a salad on her lunch break with a friend from the bank. She recognized Carlos the moment he opened the door, even though he was a young man now—twenty-three, with a close-shaved beard that was popular among twenty-somethings. He wasn't high school skinny anymore, had gained some weight in his arms and shoulders and belly. He was still very young though, and handsome. The old sullenness and the skater clothes were gone, and he was dressed in a way that indicated success had either arrived or was not very far off. He was accompanied by a pretty girl with dark, thick hair, skin the color of his own, and red-glossed lips. She was hugely pregnant, with a heavy belly, a high ass, and swelling breasts that nestled together in a low-cut blue maternity dress. A small chip of diamond flashed on her left hand.

Liz could not turn away in time: Carlos looked at her directly. There was a tremor of recognition on his face, and she reached up and smoothed her hair self-consciously, thanking God that she'd just been to see her colorist, wishing she'd reapplied gloss to her lips, whose color without it was a pale, anemic pink; happy that she was sitting so that he would not see the thickening in her own middle, reminding herself that she was involved with someone seriously now: Allen, who worked in the bank's regional offices, who was forty-six and divorced, balding, kind, but with a tendency to fall asleep during movies, reminding herself that she was successful and content and that life had gotten much better for her since that mixed-up time. Carlos glanced at her for only a moment, and the look in his still-sleepy eyes was inscrutable. Then he put a protective arm around his lovely fiancée, drew her close to him, whispered something into her shiny hair, and the two of them, laughing privately, turned around and walked out of the restaurant.

Sheltered

Noelle Aleksandra Hufnagel

FOR ONE, ALBERT FREAKING EINSTEIN, THAT'S WHO. I BET HE NEVER HAD TO EAT sad, soggy Cheerios for breakfast every morning because his dad was hell-bent on giving him a hard time. No, I'm guessing he got to eat in peace. The theory of relativity? $E=mc^2$? Atomic bombs? Cake walk. I'm over here, thirty years old, trying to dodge daggers of disapproval from my old man, and I already know it's a losing battle.

I swear it's always the same routine with him. As soon as the cereal hits the bowl, his hawk eyes hone in on me from the dining room, following my every movement in the kitchen, tracking me like I'm some kind of known felon, like if I'm left unsupervised for too long I'll be tempted to steal something of value, pocket it, and run off to the nearest pawn shop, only we don't even own anything of real value. Our house is a catch-all for anything unwanted, second-hand, bargain-basement, used and abandoned.

My dad is one of these people, these Dumpster divers, trolling the streets of Chicago in search of discarded treasures. Most of what he finds he spruces up and sells off—he owns his own antique shop in Andersonville—but everything else he brings home with him, adding to our shabby-shit decorating motif. It's a real point of contention between us.

Take our gem of a dining-room table, for example. A real monster, this table. It looks like something that belongs in one of those murder mystery mansions. Someone should've been killed on this table. Someone might've been killed on this table. He found it in an alleyway and snatched it right up, accepting the fact that both leaf extensions had long since been locked and rusted into place, acknowledging that the dimensions were far too big for our narrow house in Rogers Park, forgiving the inevitable white scuff marks from the backs of our mismatched chairs banging up against the maroon-painted walls, thinking all of these things were somehow worth it, imagining the table was what we'd been missing for so long; it was the answer to something, a way of helping us to become one of those big, happy families who eat meals together and talk to one another and share our hopes and dreams and all that *Brady* nonsense.

The table was a pipe dream from the get-go, but my dad wouldn't hear a word about it. I told him once: Listen, I know a guy, an Amish fella—he's got the beard, the goofy hat, the whole nine—and all he does all day is make tables. Big ones, small ones, round ones, square ones. You name it, this guy has built it. Good-quality, solid tables. Only the best woods. He owes me a favor, so all you've got to do is tell him what you want and he'll make it. No problem. A real custom operation. And you want to know what my dad said in return? Without even looking up at me, he said, "We got a table." That was it. End of conversation.

I mean, maybe it was a little less absurd when it was still the four of us living under one roof. We could spread out, get in some decent elbow room, invite people over without someone having to hold the bread basket. But then my ma split, twenty or so years ago, sneaking out under the cover of darkness, hoping to find herself or whatever. She ended up in Las Vegas, of all places, the one city where people always seem to lose more than they ever find. A couple months later, she sent us a postcard with a crummy picture of Cher on the front and a message on the back that read: I'm not coming back. She kept to her word, too, because we haven't seen her since. She just disappeared. Then, my older sister, Isabella, who basically raised me, left as soon as she turned eighteen, leapfrogging from one boyfriend to the next, from one bed to the next, most likely trying to find someone to take care of her for a change. Now it's just me and my old man, and we look like a couple of chumps stood up for dinner, a couple of people with too much table between them.

And you wanna know what really busts my chops? My dad has always been able to see the value in junk, a stranger's lousy pile of trash left in a random back alleyway, but when he looks at me, his own son, his flesh and blood, he's never been able to see anything that amounts to very much. Nothing of value anyway. To him, I'm a lost cause. I shouldn't let it get to me, but it does. It gets to me.

Even with the forced distance, the extra cushion of separation, I can tell it's going to be one of those mornings where my dad is all angry looks and shakes of the head and long exhalations of disappointment.

"You were up late last night," he says.

I lean against the archway leading into the dining room and nod, slurping the milk from my spoon because I know it drives him crazy.

He sits in his usual spot at the far head of the table, filling out a cross-word puzzle in the *Tribune*. I don't even know how he gets back there. I wonder about it sometimes. In all these years, I've never actually seen the progression of it, the effort it must require to sit in this particular seat, crammed against the wall. I imagine there's got to be climbing, crawling, maybe even a little clenching. It's possible, I suppose, given his small stature, that he swings from the chandelier or slides on his stomach across the surface of the table. But there's no sign of a struggle. His mustard-colored dress shirt remains wrinkle-free. His green tie hangs in place, the knot tight and centered just below his Adam's apple. His tan slacks maintain a good, crisp pleating down the front. It's some kind of unsolved mystery.

"Basement's a wreck," he says. "What the hell you been doing down there?"

I shrug. "Nothing."

"Looks like something to me." He raises his gold-rimmed glasses, resting them in the permanent grooves of his wrinkled brow, a look I've grown accustomed to receiving from him. "You've got a pile of wires and pipes and tools. That's not nothing, Lucas."

"What were you doing downstairs, anyway?" I ask.

"I'll go wherever I damn-well please. This is my house. I pay the bills." He lowers his glasses to the bridge of his nose. "And I won't have you building anything illegal under my roof."

All I can do is roll my eyes and laugh. "What? You think I'm building a bomb?"

My dad's face remains serious, stern. "I don't know what to think anymore, Lucas."

"Well, you can relax. I'm working on a few different inventions." I take another bite of cereal, swallowing. "That's all."

"Always something with you, isn't it?" He points the end of his pen at me. "You're a grown adult, for Christ's sake. You shouldn't still be living at home, building toy contraptions in the basement."

"They're not toys, OK? They're prototypes."

He places a hand on top of his head, brushing a few strands of gray hair over his bald spot. "I've been watching a lot of these crime shows lately and none of these parents seem to have a damn clue what's going on with their kids. That won't be me, Lucas. I won't have you make a fool out of me."

"I have to get ready for work." I walk back into the kitchen, dumping the rest of my cereal into the sink.

"Having big ideas doesn't make a person any less small, Lucas. You'd do well to remember that."

"Nice talk," I say, and head down the basement stairs.

Before the door slams closed at the top, I hear him call out, "I don't want that crap in my house anymore. You hear me?"

The basement isn't much to look at. It consists of an open area with low ceilings, wood-paneled walls, and a concrete floor covered in accent rugs. The only door leads to a small bathroom tucked beneath the stairs. A row of three beams divides the room. On the left side, wedged between two end tables, is a cream-colored sofa-bed that faces an old television set with a large rabbit-ear antenna on top, both of which stopped working about a decade ago. Aside from a few hanging bulbs, the only light comes from a small egress window. On the right side, there's a plastic foldout table cluttered with my recent unfinished inventions. They're all top secret, of course. None of them work, but it's only a matter of time.

The way I see it, all anyone needs is one great idea, one stroke of genius, to go down in history, to be labeled as extraordinary, to change the world, to make a mark. One great idea has the potential to erase all the real lousy ones. That's the way it works, maybe. So that's what I've been trying to do. I'm trying to get it right, for once.

I sprawl out across the thin mattress, lying on my back and crossing my arms behind my head, staring at a poster of Einstein hanging on the wall—his hair electric, his mustache bushy, and his tongue sticking out. In the picture, he looks like he's laughing at someone, probably for underestimating him, for thinking he was nothing more than a fool. The picture usually makes me smile, but now it feels like he's mocking me, like he knows something I don't.

I touch a small patch of white hair on my head, the size of a half-dollar, just above my right ear. It appeared when I was ten, a drastic contrast to the rest of my dark brown hair. My ma told me it was the mark of a genius. She gave me the poster and said, "Be big, Lucas. Be larger than life. That way, I'll be able to see you wherever I am." She left us a few days later. After she was gone, my dad told me the mark was from running around and banging my head into walls. He suggested I move into the basement. I've been down here ever since, hidden below the house where no one can see me.

The animal shelter where I work has a reputation for being home to all the defective animals no one wants anymore. None of those special breed mixes or fluffy kittens. Not at this joint. The animals here have used up all nine lives and then some. We've got missing limbs and weird bald spots, gnawed ears and nervous tics, near-death and plain just-won't-die. The longest living resident of the bunch—a black Lab with a white underbelly—just so happens to be blind, deaf, and dumb. A real trifecta of dysfunction. If this dog had a choice, she'd probably order herself up a final meal consisting of Kibbles & Bits with diced suicide pills à la Kevorkian. But this is a no-kill animal shelter, so unless some poor sap wants to adopt an antique animal—a last ditch effort at redemption—the Lab and the rest of her furry reject friends are stuck here for the long haul.

It all makes for a real slow day, especially since I'm usually the only one here. I mean, I'm not saying I run the place, but I basically run the place. Mostly, I pass the time reading magazines, surfing the Internet, or, like now, settling in for a quick rest of the eyes. I do some of my best thinking when I'm asleep. I'm leaning against the wall behind the reception desk, my legs kicked up on a filing cabinet, daydreaming about winning the Nobel Prize again, when a voice yells, "Alakazam!" and jerks me from my slumber.

I shoot upright, almost toppling over as the springs in the chair propel me forward into a standing position. A boy, about seven or eight, appears in front of me wearing a black top hat and cape over a pair of dirty, jean overalls. He's all cheeks, this kid, his whole face clenched tight, resembling the scrunched-up end of a water balloon. His skin is a pale white, ghost-like, and his arms are raised and tensed, squeezing an imaginary box of air between his hands.

"Jeez, kid, you about gave me a heart attack. What the hell is your problem?"

In a robotic voice, he says, "I-am-smooshing-you-with-my-mind."

"Why would you do that?"

He opens one eye, looking me up and down in a really creepy, uncomfortable way. "I-am-the-great-and-powerful-Oswald."

"Yeah, and I'm the bored-and-losing-interest-Lucas. A pleasure, I'm sure." I fake shake the air. "What kind of name is Oswald, anyway?" I flick his top hat, causing it to fall backwards, revealing an over-gelled mop of shaggy, black hair.

He snatches the hat from the ground and pulls it back down snug on his head. "It's my grandpa's name."

"Well, it's lame." I swipe the wand hooked into the kid's side belt loop. "What's with the getup, anyway?" I ask, swatting at the air like a composer leading his symphony.

"Hey, be careful with that!" the kid shouts, leaping up and trying to grab the wand from my hand. "You don't know how to use it. It's powerful. You could discriminate me."

"I think you probably mean *disintegrate*, Houdini. And I wouldn't do that. You, on the other hand, I'm not so sure." I tap him on the shoulder with the wand, glancing out the bay window near the waiting area. The sidewalk in front of the shelter is empty. April in the city is the worst. The weather can't figure out what it wants to do. The rain finally stopped, but the sky is still casting a gloomy shadow over everything. "So while you're out smooshing people for no good reason, where are your parents?"

"I made them disappear," he says, crossing his arms and staring down at his once-white sneakers, now muddy, with a water-line halfway up the toe. His shoelaces, untied, look like slimy worms slithering across the tile.

"Then why don't you do a little hocus-pocus and make them reappear?"

"I can't. I've tried." He shrugs. "I live with my grandpa now."

"And where's that exactly?"

"Not far. He won't notice I'm gone. I put a spell on him. He can't move from the couch until after dark."

"You don't say." I adjust my glasses on the bridge of my nose. "You walked here then? Or did you pull yourself out of a hat?"

"I walked. This time." The kid takes a step closer. "But we're wasting time. I have a shelter emergency. I made my fish, Rabbit, jump out of his tank, only I didn't know I did it, and when I went back into my room, I found him on the carpet. I'm not sure how long he was out of the water, but I thought you would have some special equipment here I could use to fix him."

"Whoa, whoa, whoa." I hold my hands up in front of my chest. "You have a rabbit or a fish?"

"I have a fish named Rabbit."

"Who names their fish Rabbit?"

"He's my assistant."

"Listen, kid, we don't really do fish here." I motion over my shoulder with the wand. "Mostly dogs and cats. And most of them are just waiting around to die."

He takes a step backwards. "They come here to die?"

"I didn't mean die, exactly. We don't kill them, OK, kid? We just give them a place to stay until they don't need one anymore." I sit down in the swivel chair, rubbing my forehead. "What I'm trying to say here is that we're a shelter, not a vet. I mean, I'm almost a veterinarian. I've been taking these night classes for the past ten or so years so my dad will get off my back and let me live with him rent free. I just have to take these final tests, for certification or whatever, but I haven't really gotten around to it yet. The truth is, I'm really an inventor. Like, a future Einstein, maybe. You know who Einstein is, don't ya, kid?"

"I can't be a magician without an assistant," he says, giving me these real pathetic, puppy-dog eyes. He looks like a wet Chihuahua, this kid. "Rabbit is my only friend. I don't think I can perform without him."

I feel for the kid. I really do. I know what it's like to be on your own, trying to be bigger than you really are, trying to be noticed. I roll the chair forward, walking my legs closer to him. "I guess I could take a look at him or whatever. It couldn't hurt, right?"

The kid reaches behind his back, struggling with something below his cape. Then, he yells, "Abracadabra!" and pulls his hand forward. In his palm, he cradles a plastic Baggie filled with water, closed at the top with a rubber band. A large goldfish floats inside. He's missing his left eye, but he's sucking air from the water and his gills are opening and closing, which I consider a good sign.

"He's still alive," I say, taking the bag from him.

"Yeah, I know." The kid rolls his eyes and wipes his nose with the back of his hand. "But he doesn't swim straight anymore. And he looks more see-through than usual."

"Sure, sure. That can happen with these fish-out-of-water-type incidents, probably." I hold the bag up over my head with one hand and adjust my glasses with the other. "It's possible this missing eye has something to do with it. It might be messing with his balance."

The kid starts waving his arms erratically in the air. I think maybe he's having a seizure or something. I'm about to tell him not to swallow his tongue, when he yells, "Presto chango!" and holds out his little hand, revealing a black speck in the middle of his palm.

"No, shit." I lean forward. "Is that the missing eyeball?" I use my index finger to gently scoop up the fish eye like a contact lens. "I'll be damned."

"Can you reattach it?"

"I don't know, little man. I'll probably have to run a series of tests first," I say, knowing full well this fish has seen better days and probably doesn't stand a chance. "He'll have to stay with me overnight. For observation."

"Oh." The kid walks over to the curtain hanging from the doorway at the right of the reception desk. He peeks through the slit in the fabric and stares down the long hallway leading to the back kennels. "Will he be OK back there?"

I nod. "It's safe. I won't let him out of my sight." I start rummaging around the desk drawers looking for a pen and paper to write down the kid's phone number. But when I turn around again, he's gone, just like a real magician.

On the corner of the reception desk, a vase that once held fake flowers for decoration now holds the little magician's sick fish. I filled it up with fresh water, tossed a piece of lettuce in there from my bologna sandwich, and taped pieces of crisscrossed string across the top in case he got any more suicidal thoughts, pointing to the glass and warning, "Not on my watch, pal."

I've been keeping close tabs on him throughout the day—not much else to do around here after cleaning out the cages and making sure the animals are fed and watered. The fish doesn't appear to be getting any better, though. He almost looks worse. It's like he has a weight in his belly pulling him to the side. He keeps staring at me with his one good eye, looking at me to do something. I can't have a dead fish on my hands when this kid shows back up again. I don't think I can deal with disappointing another person. My dad is enough to handle.

After finishing my final rounds just after seven, I lock up the animal shelter and head over to the high-rise on Lakeshore where my buddy Mikey lives, carrying the vase with the sick fish along for the ride.

Mikey's place is on my way home—there's a bus stop out front, anyway—but even if it wasn't, I'd still stop by to check in on him. There are over three thousand ways to die, and Mikey knows them all by heart, which is only odd if you don't know Mikey. I've known him since the third grade. He used to live in the house next door to me. We'd get into all kinds of trouble together, most of which was my fault. His ma would always tell me, "I pray for you the most, Lucas." But I sure wish she'd prayed a little less for me and a little more for Mikey. Maybe then he wouldn't have been struck by lightning out on that baseball field when we were thirteen. Maybe it would've been me instead. I was the reason we were out there in the first place. I was avoiding going home, as usual, avoiding my dad, avoiding sitting at that lousy table. It should've been me. I've always felt real guilty about that.

Mikey's heart stopped beating for six long minutes before the paramedics finally brought him back to life. The only problem is, I don't think they brought him all the way back, if you know what I mean. He spent a lot of time in and out of hospitals for one surgery after another. I guess that's when he became real obsessed with learning about death. Every time I'd visit him, he'd ask me to bring him another medical book from the library. These books were the only things that seemed to make him feel any better, so I kept bringing them, and he kept asking for more. I hoped that he'd eventually stop reading them, but he's still at it some seventeen years later. I guess he hasn't found the answer he's looking for yet.

After a good minute or so of knocking and calling out his name from the hallway, I finally hear shuffling inside the apartment. He unlocks the deadbolt, unhooks the chain, and cracks open the door. He looks the same as always. He only wears sweatpants anymore, rotating between a few pairs in various shades of gray, along with an off-white T-shirt and a red hoodie.

He gives me the once-over, his stare lingering for a moment on the fish in the vase tucked under my arm. Then, he clears his throat. "Lucas, I'm busy," he says, resting a hand on top of his blond curls, flattened on one side.

"I won't stay long," I say, and invite myself into the apartment. "Did you go to work today, man?"

He shakes his head. "No, I took a personal day."

While I watch the animal rejects, Mikey cares for the furry elite, tying bows around the necks of poodles and spraying perfume behind the ears of cute pugs. He works for his ma at this doggy day care and spa. It's a real racket, this place. But people love their damn animals. I swear they'll pay anything. I mean, hell, my dad used to give Isabella five bucks allowance to watch me after school for the week, and she didn't even really do anything but read her magazines and make mac and cheese when I asked. That just goes to show you how little my dad thinks of me, I guess.

"So, what do you know about fish?" I ask.

"I know they die," he says, reclaiming his seat on the sagging, brown couch pushed up against the wall. "We all die, eventually."

"Right, right. But what kills them, usually?"

"You name it. Too warm. Too cold. Fed too much. Not fed enough. Disease. Infection. Stress. They're delicate little creatures. We're all just a bunch of delicate little creatures."

Mikey picks up an Atari joystick from the floor and returns to his game of Pitfall. He's had this thing since we were kids, and it's the only game he ever plays. He never beats it, though. He's actually pretty awful at it. Even now, instead of maneuvering his character through the jungle, leaping over water holes and quicksand and crocodile heads, he simply allows his character to cling to a vine, swinging back and forth over a bottomless tar pit, dangling him over death's door, like he's afraid to let go, afraid to move forward.

Mikey's mood and all-around demeanor changes depending on the weekly obituaries, improving or declining based on the likelihood of a person's demise. He has far less problem with the timeliness of it. A teen. A child. A baby. These deaths are tragic, unbearable, hard to imagine. But Mikey has learned to accept them as an unfortunate occurrence of life. Horrible, all too frequent, but possible just the same.

It's those deaths that defy the odds, the ones that are so rare you only ever hear about them happening somewhere else in the world, not to someone you know, not to your neighbor, the runner, the athlete who always smiles when he passes you in the hallway, and then one morning he wakes up in the middle of the night with a stomach ache, takes a couple of Tums, and three hours later, he's dead. *Bam!* Just like that. Age thirty-eight. Heart attack. Stuff like that will ruin Mikey's entire week, maybe even his month, making him question everything, pushing him closer to the edge.

I place the vase on his coffee table, next to a book about infectious diseases, and grab a stack of newspapers—only the obituary sections remaining—and toss them on the hardwood floor next to the others.

"So, um, what if one were to jump out of his tank? Could he live through it?"

"Depends. He's stared down the barrel of a gun. Not an easy thing to come back from." His eyes follow the swaying character on the television screen. "Some people think it should be simple. You're alive. It's a gift or a miracle or whatever. But it's a big deal to cheat death."

"Mikey, man, there was no barrel. He touched carpet for a few minutes, OK? It wasn't the apocalypse."

"That's what you think." He takes a deep breath, tilting his head back against the couch cushion. "Listen, I've read cases where a goldfish has survived anywhere from seven to thirteen hours out of water. It's rare. If their gills remain moist, they stand a chance."

"Let's say this fish survived the out-of-tank part. He gets tossed back into some water and he's in there sucking air again. Is he in the clear?"

Mikey rests the controller on the ground and leans forward, staring into the glass vase. "Not that simple. There's risk of infection. Probably treatable. The real problem is the shock. He's been on the other side. He doesn't see things the same anymore. You gotta make sure he doesn't get too stressed out."

"Sure, sure. Would losing an eye be stressful?"

Mikey looks over his shoulder at me. "What do you think, Lucas?"

"But does he need it to survive?"

"No, Lucas. No one needs their eyes to survive. Just another nice-to-have luxury, I suppose." He sighs. "Whose fish is this, anyway?"

"Belongs to a kid magician. He came into the shelter today."

Mikey leans back. "Why all the interest?"

"I don't know. He doesn't really have anyone else," I say, and stand. "I better get going, man. I'll leave you to it."

"See you tomorrow, maybe."

Before closing the door behind me, I watch as Mikey walks to the window, staring outside at the falling rain with a glazed-over look on his face. Mikey, I realize, is kind of like my sick fish, and I have no idea how to help him, either.

When I get home, it's after ten. The garage door is still open, which is unusual. My dad has strict rules about keeping the house locked up. He has strict rules about everything. As I make my way closer, I notice some boxes lined up in neat little rows of three in the empty space where my ma used to park her car, each box clearly labeled with black permanent marker: Lucas—To Take.

The security light kicks on, shining down on me in the dark. I stand in the driveway for a moment, looking at all my belongings from the basement, realizing immediately that my old man is finally giving me the boot. I should've known he was planning on chucking me from the nest. Of course, some notice would've been nice. Even landlords give two weeks. But maybe that's how these things work: a surprise attack.

With one hand holding onto the vase sheltered beneath my jacket, I use the other to pull out my keys. The house is dark inside, except for the glow of a television set in the living room. I can see a silhouette of my dad behind the curtains. When I shove my key into the lock, it doesn't budge, though I figured that would be the case. Even though I only have two keys on the ring—a gold one for the shelter and a silver one for the house—I double check to make sure I didn't mix them up. Then, I ring the doorbell.

My dad answers the door, opening it just enough to peer outside. He looks me up and down with his usual disapproving stare and says, "Your stuff is in the garage."

"Yeah, I see that," I say. "You're not going to let me in?"

He shakes his head, his eyes tired and swollen, and moves to shut the door.

"I thought we had a deal. I get to stay in the basement rent free while I'm in school. What happened to investing in my future?"

"You've been in school for the past ten years. It's time to cut my losses. This is for your own good, Lucas."

"I'm not going to blow anything up, you know."

"It's time," he says.

"Can't you wait until tomorrow to chuck me? I don't have anywhere to go."

"I'm sure you'll figure something out." He shuts the door, turning the deadbolt.

My sister, Isabella, works as a cashier at a Jewel grocery store a few blocks away. I stop by to pick up a few essentials—toothbrush, toothpaste, and deodorant—and maybe convince her to let me stay with her for awhile, wherever that is these days.

The store is empty, except for a few scattered people picking out apples or pacing the frozen foods aisle in search of the right flavor ice cream. Isabella stands at express checkout lane two, one of three cashiers, flipping through a magazine to pass the time. Her ash-blond hair is pulled back into a ponytail and her bangs are hanging in her eyes, covering a birthmark on her forehead in the form of a misshapen butterfly. She looks so much like our ma.

I place my basket of items on the conveyer belt. "Dad gave me the boot."

"I'm surprised it took him this long," she says, scanning barcodes.

"What's with the fish?" she asks, pointing to the vase.

"Medical experiment stuff."

"Looks dead."

"He's not."

"Looks it."

"He's going to be fine."

"You're the expert," she says, placing my items into a brown paper bag and folding over the top like she did my sack lunch for all those years.

"Any chance I can crash at your place?"

"I'm in between places right now."

This is her way of saying she's in between boyfriends.

She reaches into her purse, stashed under the register and pulls out her wallet. "Can't you stay at Mikey's?" she asks, swiping her debit card through the machine and punching in her pin.

"Maybe. I don't know. It's pretty depressing over there."

"What's the difference? You're over there all the time anyway. You guys have been practically inseparable since you were kids. Probably do him some good to have someone else around."

She's got a point, I guess. Mikey and I have always been a kind of tag-team operation. I'm sure we wouldn't have gotten this far without each other.

"You guys can circle the drain together," she says and hands me the paper bag along with twenty bucks. "You'll go over there, right?"

"Yeah, sure thing," I say, even though we both know it's a lie, and I grab the bag, exiting through the automatic doors.

I catch a bus to the pet supplies store on Ashland before they close. A bell dings overhead as I walk inside and a teenaged boy, Tyler, dressed in khaki pants, a black T-shirt, and a red vest, emerges from one of the aisles, looking like I just ruined his night. He glances at his watch and rolls his eyes, crossing his tattooed arms and slumping against a pallet of bagged dog food.

"We're about to lock up, man. What can I get ya?"

"I need a fish like this one." I raise the vase in the air, a little water spilling over the edge and soaking into my sleeve. "Only I need one with two eyes that can swim straight and stuff."

He leans forward, squinting. "He's still alive."

I roll my eyes. "Yeah, I know."

"He sure doesn't look right, though. What's wrong with him?"

"Jumper." I raise my eyebrows. "He survived the fall, but if he gets too stressed out, he's a goner."

Tyler motions for me to follow him to the wall of aquariums at the back of the store. "Fish usually jump ship when they're having trouble breathing." He shakes his head and laughs. "Ironic, huh? Idiots."

"Sure, I don't know."

"So why do you want another one already?"

"I figured it would do him some good to have another fish in there with him. Help keep him calm." I shrug. "Besides, if he doesn't make it, I'll have a backup as a precautionary measure." The fish stares at me with his one good eye, straining to gulp water. "A magician needs an assistant, you know. Even if it is just a fish."

Tyler rubs the back of his head. "Whatever, dude." He grabs a green fish net and a plastic bag. "Just tell me which one you want. That band Swindler is playing tonight at Metro. I don't wanna be late."

The streetlamp in front of the animal shelter flickers, the light distorting my shadow into weird shapes against the side of the brick building. I take long strides down the alleyway, sloshing through the puddles to the back door. Once inside, I punch in my code on the numbered wall panel to silence the soft beeping. The last thing I need is the overhead alarm to sound and wake everyone on the block, announcing my reject status to the world.

I don't bother turning on any lights, my eyes having already adjusted to the dark. The building is arranged into various areas of isolation, dividing the animals based on factors like adoption potential and health status. The dogs and cats are kept on opposite ends from each other, separated in the middle by a row of examination rooms and storage closets. There's a roll-away cot stored in the medical lab in case someone has to stay overnight and observe one of the animals. I figure it'll do the trick for a while, until I can come up with a more permanent option.

Before hitting the sack, I decide to check in on some of the dogs to make sure they're still breathing. In the back canine area, there are twenty metal cages, ten on each side. Aside from a few soft whimpers, none of the dogs bark at my presence, probably hoping I've returned to break them loose. Either that or they've just given up altogether. No more fight left, you know. I can relate.

That's when I see him—the little magician curled up inside one of the cages, his arm and half his cape wrapped around the blind, deaf, and dumb black Lab, both of them fast asleep in a kind of cocoon.

I crouch down, setting the grocery bag and the vase of fish on the linoleum floor next to the cage. "Oswald, buddy, wake up," I say, and gently knock against the metal cage with my knuckles.

The kid rubs his eyes and looks up at me, a red splotch on his face from where his cheek rested on his arm. "You're back. Where did you go?"

"What are you doing in there? Your gramps is probably worried."

"I called and told him I was staying at a friend's house."

"I thought you didn't have any friends," I say, realizing immediately that he means me. I am his friend. We're friends now.

He points to the dog. "She was scared when you left. Someone put a spell on her, I think. I was trying to undo it." He yawns. "How's Rabbit?"

"I'm still running tests," I say, motioning to the vase on the ground. "But listen, Oswald, you can't stay in here, man."

"I don't mind," he says. "I'm not allowed outside alone when it's dark. My powers don't work well at night."

"They don't, huh? Well, it is late. Maybe it'd be OK if we waited until morning to take you home." I grab a few blankets from one of the cabinets along the wall and spread them out on the floor, lying down on top of them. "It's kinda nice to have someone else around to talk to other than the animals."

Oswald snuggles back up to the dog and begins stroking her fur in long motions, starting at the top of her head and working down to the tail.

"You know, I'm building this invention. Beginning stages. Still have a lot of kinks to work out. But it's this automated arm-like contraption that would hook onto the cages and pet the animals when no one's around."

"That's a good idea."

"Really?" I ask, grinning. "You think so?"

He shrugs. "I don't know."

"Yeah, the only problem is, I don't think it would make them any less lonely. I'm guessing they'd know the difference between a replica and the real thing."

"Better than nothing," the kid says, closing his eyes and wrapping his arm around the dog's belly.

"Maybe you're right," I say.

A drop of water lands on my cheek, drawing my attention to the cloud-shaped water mark on the ceiling tile. I roll over onto my side, pressing my back against the metal cage and sliding the vase below the slow drip. The two fish are huddled together near the bottom. The fish with one eye is still sucking air, his gills pumping away. He looks stronger already. I get the sense that he's going to make it. He's going to be OK. I close my eyes, listening to the rain ping against the roof of the animal shelter, and mouth the words "presto chango" over and over again, hoping to catch a break, hoping for a little bit of magic.

The Thunder God

Michael J. Meyer

WHEN WE BROKE INTO THE HOUSE, I THOUGHT IT WOULD BE ROMANTIC.

"It's technically squatting, Angela," Johnny said as we passed the city limits. "We're just broke, not actually homeless."

"I know."

Jacksonville shrank in the rearview mirror until I couldn't see the Mayo Clinic anymore. An illuminated billboard read "Atlantian Gardens, Next Exit. Your Seaside Legend Awaits." As we drove along the beach front lined with sandbags, toward the housing development where we would sleep that night, I watched the shapes of windows merge into a constellation of lights. A pall of thunderclouds crawled over the ocean toward the glow where the familiar square of my brother's hospital room had gone dark last spring. There had been nothing to see—regular room with a new patient, just like Johnny said—but he drove me all the way from Illinois anyway, and now there was nowhere else to go.

"You gonna be all right?" Johnny said. He kept his eyes vigilant on the curving road, but reached across the gearshift to awkwardly squeeze my knee.

"We're gonna crash one of these McMansions before the fucking yuppies move in," he said. "It's totally romantic."

"OK," I said.

That was how Johnny took care of me. When my dog Tuesday died, he left me alone to mope around my room and empty a box of tissues. That night though, he climbed up the trellis to my window with a pair of stolen kittens cradled in his shirt like balled-up socks. They were tiny, with eyes not even open yet, and we named them Jello and Biafra. That was the night I told Johnny I loved him.

When their eyes never opened, Johnny went with me to the forest preserve to bury the kittens, but he never apologized. He just dug two neat holes and drove me home.

When our headlights crawled onto the cul-de-sac, the unfinished subdivision looked like a row of Christmas presents wrapped up in white paper. They faced away from the beach where thick, anvil-shaped clouds swelled over the water. A few houses had siding and lawns already, and Johnny picked one with French doors and an iron gate. His plan to get in was to climb up to a window and come down to let me in—which he explained as I was boosting him up on top of the garage.

"What do you want me to do?" I said.

He stuck his head over the ledge of the roof and his unwashed black hair hung dangling over his eyes. "You're lookout, remember?"

I was always lookout. That was Johnny's way of including me, but he was really just keeping me out of the way while he did something dangerous or stupid. I watched from the ground as Johnny wrapped his scarecrow legs around the drain pipe and scrambled up the side of the house. Everything made too much noise: the gutter groaned as he pulled himself up, the roof tiles crackled under his feet, and the window screeched as he opened it. I crouched into my sweatshirt, and hunched down behind a garden wall to watch the street for headlights. A siren wailed somewhere and I flinched.

"But what if I see someone?" I called up to him.

Johnny already had one foot inside the window and he shrugged. "Then we're screwed," he said, and disappeared into the house.

I watched the windows of the house for the movement of Johnny's shadow, something to tell me that he was OK, that he hadn't broken his leg in the dark, or set off a security system, or cracked his head open on the stairs, and that I wouldn't have to call an ambulance or ride to a police station and explain to an impatient man with a pen who I was and where I was supposed to be. We had come to visit the place where my brother died, and now we were trespassing because Johnny didn't know what to do with me. It was getting harder to think of this trip as romantic. If it wasn't, somehow that wouldn't be Johnny's fault.

He'd been inside for a long time, leaving me standing on a stranger's deck while dark clouds oozed toward shore and made the ocean uneasy. Waves rushed to escape them and one by one collapsed on the sand. The palms in the yard shuddered and the empty mansions seemed nervous, fluttering their house wrap with the anticipation of a storm.

I had been afraid of thunderstorms since the summer I turned six, when lightning struck our garage during my birthday party. Dad had hung white Christmas lights over the deck, and just as we sat down to eat cake off paper plates, just as my brother said it looked like rain, a white roar cut a scar down the side of our garage and the Christmas lights exploded in a hail of glass. I remember hiding under the picnic table as rain began to fall, unwilling to speak or move because I was certain the sky had condemned me.

It was during weather like this when my brother Ben promised he could keep me safe. Lightning would strike elsewhere, the walls of the house would hold up against the wind, and tomorrow we would still be alive. That was years ago, when I was small and my brother was still strong enough to be magic. I pulled up my hood against the wind and looked up into the dark face of the house.

"Don't be afraid," I said, and tried to sound convincing. "The storm will come, and then it will pass. We just have to stick together and be brave until it's over."

When Johnny appeared in the patio door I felt a skip of relief, like I'd been airborne and now my feet were on solid ground.

"Check it out," he said. He had a blanket from the car thrown over his shoulder and a pair of six-packs hooked in his fingers. When Johnny pushed the hood off my forehead and led me inside by the hand, I was shocked by how much I still needed someone to ground me.

We sat and smoked on the deck with the blanket pulled over us, kicking empty beer cans into the dry pool and listening to the clatter echo off the concrete walls. Past the railing, the waves were gray and agitated, throwing themselves toward the ledge and shattering into spray against the rocks. The anvil clouds were heavy and ready to drop, and they seemed to pulse. I felt the wind hold its breath and my spine straightened into a rod. Far out over the water, the clouds flared purple and a forked tongue of lightning connected the ocean and the sky for the length of a heartbeat. I grabbed Johnny's hand and squeezed my eyes shut, counting like my brother taught me, and listening for the voice of thunder. *One, two, three . . .*

I remembered the laughter in Ben's voice from a night years before when I crawled into his bed after a thunderclap frightened me awake.

"Come on out, sissy-cat. It's farther away than you think."

Ben reached into the blankets, hooked his arms under mine, and hoisted me up onto the window box next to him. It had been so black outside I could only see the clawed shape of the maple tree in our backyard. Ben had poured over books on weather phenomena and tried to explain them to me in a way I could understand, that lightning was a natural electrical phenomenon and not out to get me, but science was as real to me as magic. All I wanted my brother to do was make it stop.

That night he said, "OK."

My brother rubbed his palms together, then lifted me into his lap and lowered his cheek next to mine to stare down the storm. His breathing slowed and his eyes slid closed, deep into a trance. He raised an arm above his head, extending one finger toward the sky, and I clutched my blanket, not daring to look away. Outside, the wind paused, the maple tree settled down, and the rain slowed to a gentle patter. The world was waiting for his command.

With a slash of his finger, Ben drew a line through our window and a silver blade of lightning slit the sky. The windowpanes shuddered with thunder, I shrieked and turned away, and in the flash of ghostly light, I understood the whole room: Ben's bare walls, the outlines of dust in the shape of his posters, the stack of empty boxes under his bed, the shirts in plastic hanging in his closet, my brother's bones pressing through the surface of his skin—and in that moment I knew my brother was leaving me. His breath shuddered out all at once as he sank back against the wall with an exhausted smile.

"How did you do that?" I whispered.

Ben's blue eyes crackled with excitement, and something like a promise. "Because I'm the Thunder God."

I was certain that first lightning bolt had severed something invisible that tied our family together because soon after, our parents separated and

Ben stayed with Dad, his real father. After they moved to Chicago though, it was storms that held us together. When lightning would strike near my house, I'd call my father in tears, begging him to put Ben on the phone, and when my brother laughed I could hear the same rumble of thunder through the phone.

"I'm taking care of it," he'd say. "The Thunder God has got your back."

My brother knew more about the weather than anyone, so it had to be true. He drew pictures of clouds and quoted me their secret names—the white horse tails of cirrus uncinus and the towering castle turrets of cumulus castellanus. He could guess the temperature outside to a degree, he knew days before it would rain, and with his microscope Ben had showed me the crystal geography of snowflakes. Lightning and thunder were creatures I wasn't sure Ben could control, but I still wanted him to be the Thunder God.

I didn't believe in any higher power and lightning still shook the sweat from my skin, but when a storm meant the chance to hear my brother's voice, I prayed every night for rain. A thunderstorm would bring us closer when my house was empty, and as Ben and I each sat at a window, holding the phone to our ears and waiting for a flash. Then we would count together, his whisper on top of mine, until the voice of thunder bridged the space between us and filled our rooms to the walls.

Far away from me, Ben began to weaken. He had always been sickly, and then he was just sick, with something doctors couldn't agree to diagnose but were sure could not be cured. Whatever "it" was, autoimmune, cancer, or genetic dysfunction, Ben's body was rejecting itself. As I got older, grew taller and only a little bit fuller, Ben slipped farther away. When I was switching from training bras to the real deal, Ben was getting a port installed in his chest so the drug regimens wouldn't erode his skin. While I was trying to make friends, Ben was in a hospital bed with a meteorology textbook between his knobby knees. That's all he wanted to talk about. Whenever he called or I visited, Ben would lecture me over the phone about ionization and electromagnetic radiation, and he always sounded thrilled. The magic of the weather sustained my brother, and he sustained me until he was gone.

Then there was Johnny. He was a tall and mean-looking boy from my high school who wore black shirts and slam-danced by himself in his car. One day I was waiting for the bus after school, and when a shower started up, I couldn't bring myself to go outside. My father and brother had moved to live near the Mayo Clinic in Jacksonville where my brother could get experimental treatments, and with Ben miles away, I felt lightning bolts hanging in the clouds above me, waiting to drop. I froze in the doorway that day, people thumping past me with their backpacks. I waited in the vestibule while the rain fell, watching the last of the buses pull away, and then I saw Johnny walking toward me with his keys in his fist.

"Hey," he said. "It looks like shit outside. Want a ride?"

What I loved about Johnny was that he refused to let fear or anything else stop him from doing what he wanted, even if it was me that was afraid. Whenever I was worried about my brother, we'd go on an "adventure," where he'd pick me up in his car, point it in one direction, and drive until we ran out of road, listening to Johnny's CD collection.

It made me comfortable enough to talk about about my brother, and Johnny let me. I told him about the hospital visits, the stuff my brother was learning. Sometimes I complained about my dad and how protective he was of Ben and how distant he was toward me, and Johnny just drove, with his eyes set ahead on the road. I was never sure if he was listening, but he never interrupted me or seemed uncomfortable, even when I ended up crying. I could talk until I had voiced every worry, and when I was empty, Johnny would reach into the backseat, grab his binder of CDs and put it in my lap.

"Pick something," he'd say, and I loved him a little.

The first time I let Johnny touch me—really touch me, more than fumbling over the gearshift in his Toyota—was in church.

Mom's boyfriend was raised Lutheran and took us to every council meeting and choir practice and potluck dinner, and I started bringing Johnny just so I wouldn't feel so outnumbered. We wandered all over the building, rifling through drawers in the empty offices and scrunched ourselves onto the tiny plastic chairs in the nursery with its colored pictures of Jesus and the twelve disciples looking like they were in a death metal band, but mostly we made out. In stairwells, in the library, and one time, during a Saturday night choir rehearsal, Johnny dragged me into the janitor's closet.

It was cramped and dark, and smelled like ammonia and lemon air freshener. The door opened in, so Johnny pushed me up against it. I had my hands in his hair, he had his fingers hooked in my belt loops, and everything was hasty and unplanned, how he liked it. I was starting to get lightheaded, and not the good kind.

"Can we go somewhere else?" I panted.

"Why?" He'd started in on my neck and it felt like he was chewing on me.

"It stinks in here. Let's go somewhere else."

Johnny pushed up my shirt, and the door was cold against my back. "It's not so bad in here," he said. "You smell fuckin' great."

I caught his fingers and shook my head. I tried to smile, but I felt dizzy. "How about we go back to your car?"

He grinned and pulled at my belt buckle, which clacked open without protest. "Too long of a walk. And we fool around there all the time. Come on, we've been wanting to do this forever."

Swallowing felt thick, like a mouthful of glue. I was trying to catch my breath through the chemical haze, sweating nervously, and Johnny must have taken that as encouragement. His fingers were cold as he pulled open my jeans. I tried to think of it as exciting. We were fooling around in church, while outside the door and across the hall, my mom and her bald boyfriend were singing "A Mighty Fortress is Our God" in warbling voices. Johnny was always getting me to do things I didn't think I'd like—climbing fences into graveyards, driving out to the middle of nowhere to see a punk show in an abandoned barn—and this had to be no different. Johnny was just getting me to open up and stop worrying so much. As his cold fingers blundered into me, I heard through the door the choir singing another chorus of a different song.

"Hearts unfold like flowers before thee, opening to the sun above."

A week later, we were in Johnny's crawlspace. If the basement was its guts, pumping heat and water through ducts and pipes, this was its hidden heart and I had gotten inside. It smelled like sawdust, and dried-out pine needles from the boxes of Christmas ornaments stacked under the stairs. There was a crib and a high chair packed against the wall with rolls of spare carpet and a battered vacuum cleaner, but the box I wanted to break open, to raid and steal away was in the far corner next to where Johnny sat. His arm was propped up on it.

"What's in there?" I asked, but already knew. It was marked on the side, "Photo Albums." I had maneuvered Johnny there, I had planned this deliberately, to ask him for a tour of his house on a weekend while his parents were away. In that box was the childhood Johnny never told me about, only tidbits here and there, when he wasn't paying attention enough to censor himself. Johnny had been inside me and now I wanted to see the inside of him.

"It's just crap," he said, lifting the flap of the box, "old pictures from when I was a kid."

"Can I see?" He shrugged.

I slid over next to him, pressing my hip against his as Johnny lifted a leather-bound album out of the box and opened it across both our laps. Here were his baby pictures, his mother with creases around her mouth, tired behind the eyes but happy, his bearded father propping him up toward the TV. I flipped the page, looking for the great secret that would explain Johnny's reluctance and solitude—a lost twin, or a missing father, but my expectations had been too high. They seemed like average pictures of Johnny at the beach, riding his first bike, and playing with a girl in the lawn of a house I didn't recognize.

"Is this your first house?" I said.

"Yeah." Johnny glanced at it and turned the page for me. I flipped it back to get a better look at it: a squat little brick one-story with a small yard. In most of these pictures, Johnny was playing with a group of kids, clustered around him in a sandbox or following him pulling a wagon. But in all of the pictures I recognized of Johnny's new house, the one we were hidden inside, he was alone. In the pictures, he sat on his bike or the seat of a swing and glared at the camera like the sun was in his eyes, or posed stiffly with his parents, standing slightly aside. There in glossy print was evidence of what I felt, this strange space around Johnny that pushed people aside.

"This was in Park Ridge," he said. "My parents didn't have a lot of money then, but it was pretty great. Kids in school liked me, and I was cool. All the neighborhood kids followed me around. There was this little girl who lived next door who never left me alone. She'd knock on my door every day and ask my mom if I could come out. I'd play with her for a while, doctor or house or whatever, but then I'd get bored and tell her I was going inside to watch TV. She just waited outside for me, sometimes for hours. My mom yelled at me for leaving her out there, but I guess I didn't care." He laughed. "Everyone just liked me. I'd probably be popular now if I'd stayed in Park Ridge."

I was treading lightly now. "What about here?" Would he have missed not meeting me?

"We moved when I was six," he said, "and I hated it. I just never felt right, like I'd been taken away from my home. I guess that was when I stopped trusting my parents. You know, and people."

I was watching his face. Johnny closed the photo album in his lap and stared out for a moment across the crawlspace into the corner with his baby furniture and the rolled-up carpet and the old vacuum cleaner. I waited quietly for him to say that he at least trusted me, but he didn't. He just packed the book back into the box and got up.

The last time I talked to Ben, I was sixteen and he was at the Mayo Clinic in Jacksonville. He'd come down with another infection, and I found out later that fluid had been accumulating in his lungs. I wanted to fly out and see him, but Ben told me to wait.

"Don't skip school to see your older brother get over a cough," he said. His voice was raspy and I said so. "I'll be fine. Come see me this summer, when it's warm," Ben told me. "Florida has an incredible storm season."

With the phone wedged between my ear and my shoulder as I washed dishes, I could see Ben propped up in his hospital bed next to a big picture window looking out over the ocean. His hair would probably be all gone by now, and he'd be thinner, the hospital gown draped over his bones like a shirt on a wire hanger.

"Just be OK," I said, and tried to make him laugh. "It's been raining here a lot and I might need you to turn off a thunderstorm."

"You know I can't do that, Angela. But I finally figured it out." I imagined Ben sitting up in bed and leaning toward the window with the hospital phone.

"I learned the secret to thunderstorms." His voice dropped to a whisper. "Telluric currents."

"What?"

"The Earth is like a generator," Ben said. "The tectonic plates and the oceans move through the Earth's magnetic field and charge the planet with electricity, The whole world is conductive, Angela. It's happening under our feet. Energy travels through the water and the ground through telluric currents—like invisible power lines right underneath us. The charge builds up wherever they merge and turns clouds into thunderstorms."

Ben was thrilled, but the thought made my toes curl in my shoes. I imagined an electric current snaking below me, chasing my footsteps wherever I went, and twisting the clouds into black thunderheads.

"Can you avoid them?" I said, "Or stop them? How do you get away?"

"They're everywhere," Ben said. "It's just part of nature. You can't run from the worst storms, so you have to find shelter and wait it out. Or maybe you take the risk and chase the storm down just to look it in the eye. You're more likely to die of cancer than lightning," he said with a laugh.

"Is that what made you the Thunder God?"

"No," he said, "Storms are still dangerous. I'm just not afraid."

A month went by and I hadn't heard from Ben. The chemo cycles made him weak and lethargic, but he hadn't told me that he was scheduled for another regimen like he usually did. I was spending most of my time with Johnny or studying, but my thoughts had been drifting to Ben. I tried calling his room, but the nurse told me he'd been moved to another hospital. I left voicemails at the house, and even tried calling my dad, but no one would get back to me. I couldn't concentrate on school, and Johnny was becoming more distant and avoiding me, because I wouldn't stop worrying about my brother and it was starting to annoy him.

The call came on a Saturday night when I was holed up in my room with an earth science textbook. It was raining outside and I was rewriting my notes on cloud formations. Copying down those names and drawings was mindless and mechanical and made sense. When my phone rang, I thought it was Johnny wanting to go for a night drive and fool around, but it was my dad's voice.

"Where's Ben?" I asked him. "Can I talk to him? Where are you right now?"

"I'm at the house, Angela. Listen—"

"Well, is he with you, or is he at the hospital? No one at the hospital will tell me anything."

"Angela, Ben died yesterday. Pneumonia."

When someone you love dies, before the tears, before you collapse, before you scream and try to disbelieve it, there's a calm that surrounds you. It's like being lifted up on a cloud, up from the phone in your hand, up out of your room and your house, up above time, just light breezes and stillness. This is the place where memories live. I remembered my brother and the last time I saw him as he really was, with messy blond hair and his own clothes, carrying a jacket and a radio slung over his arm before a thunderstorm. The ground was still dry, and Ben was trying to put on his jacket and tune to a weather report at the same time. I was watching from his bedroom window, not supposed to tell Mom and Dad that Ben had snuck out. With his back to me, his neck lifted up as he listened to the throaty thunder, my brother looked invincible.

I don't know what I expected Johnny to do, since I never could be sure—and that was probably what I loved about him—but trespassing, broke, sitting on a stranger's deck hundreds of miles from home while the fury of a thunderstorm glared down on us, that was not what I wanted. I wanted to see the clinic where my brother died, and now I wanted to go home.

The first raindrop hit me on the earlobe and the rest hurried after it, splattering the deck with dark spots. We ran to the patio door, as the spots expanded and engulfed each other until the whole slab of concrete was dark and shiny slick. Inside, the house was cavernous up to the vaulted ceiling, with sharp shadows and bare walls. The two of us dripped onto the carpet, clothes clinging to our skin.

"We'll camp out upstairs," Johnny said, heading toward them.

"Wait," I said. "Can we just leave?"

The rain was falling in a torrent now, like someone had torn the belly of the clouds with a knife. It poured off the roof tiles and splashed onto the deck, ran down the sides of the drained pool, rising until the empty beer cans started to float.

Johnny gripped the stair railing and looked at me like I'd just peed my pants, like I was his idiot little sister making another mess. Like it was the stupidest thing I'd ever said so far.

"We just got here. You dragged me down to Florida and now you want to leave?"

"I didn't ask you to break into someone's house for me! I just wanted to see—"

"To see your brother," he said. "To see the place where he lived in a hospital for years, and what, get a memento? A bedpan? A puke bucket? He's gone, and you never learned how to be alone."

Johnny disappeared up the stairs and into the darkness at the top of the house, and I stepped out onto the patio.

This time I closed my eyes and listened for the seams of the storm, for the secret sounds my brother used to hear. We played as kids, and we both knew Ben was the Thunder God to be a power for me to believe in, but I wanted to imagine what Ben felt back when he was my hero. I listened and I waited.

Gusts of wind heaved off the ocean and slapped against the house, the palms flailed their leaves, and when I heard a lightning bolt burst nearby, I cried out for Ben. If only he could say the words, the storm would pass, and Johnny could take me and the car and drive as far and as fast as we could get from here, until everything was still and quiet and right again.

The sounds of the waves were like traffic, the steady rush of the highway leading home. The spray hissed into the air like the flicker of a match lighting the cigarettes Johnny and I smoked in his car. Raindrops fell faster and the winds began to separate: the flap of palm leaves were the streamers at my sixth birthday party, the hush of grass blades were Ben's fingers brushing my cheek. The layers of the storm were falling away. I could hear the clouds as they crawled toward shore, the air moaning as the pressure dropped, and then, in the depths of the storm I heard a voice.

It was a faint whisper, pollen floating in the summer air as I drove with Johnny along the rural roads of Illinois. The voice sung louder, clearer, growing strong and vibrating, crackling like leaves underfoot as Ben and I ran through the woods behind our house. The hum swelled and the snaps merged until I could hear the clouds glittering with electricity. I felt a shape forming, long and jagged, and I reached my hand out to grasp it. The hairs on my body bristled, my arms rose up with the trance, and I brought my palms together to clap the world awake.

A blade of blue-white lightning drowned the yard in light and the triumphant bellow of thunder.

When I opened my eyes, a purple gash floated across my vision and a palm tree loomed over the house, skewered by lightning and groaning as it fell, splintering wood and shattering the skylight, pouring rain and broken glass into the house and onto Johnny.

I wanted to scrunch myself into a ball, to crawl under a picnic table and wait for rescue, as if holding completely still could keep the house from crumbling.

The roof sagged under the weight of the tree, crushing the second floor where Johnny must have been. I was afraid in that moment, choking on black terror, but I was moving, running through the rain falling into the living room and up the stairs, where the body of the tree had torn open the roof.

My voice echoed through the empty house calling Johnny's name above the wind and rain. At the end of the hall I saw a light in bathroom door, where the roof beams had buckled and split.

I imagined Johnny, crushed by the trunk of some storm-cursed tree, with a cracked skull, bleeding out onto the bathroom floor. I imagined Ben, how he must have looked when he died –thin and pale, struggling to breathe against the fluid in his lungs, knowing that if this infection didn't kill him, it would be the next one, or the one after that. Had he been afraid? If there had been a thunderstorm that night, would I have called him? Would he have held on a little longer?

In the bathroom, I found Johnny propped up against the bathtub, bleeding from his scalp, but conscious. A chunk of plaster had fallen loose and caught him on the temple. The wind swallowed the sound of my voice, but when I knelt down, Johnny wrapped his arms around my neck and whispered, "Don't leave me."

Later in the emergency room, while a nurse bandaged his head, Johnny would deny saying anything, and I let him.

But under the open roof of that empty house, as I held Johnny and listened for the sound of sirens though the rain, I imagined a coil tying us together, an underground wire leading back home, to my bedroom and Johnny's crawlspace, to Ben's hospital bed and the window in his old room, along the roads from Florida to Illinois and branching out in all directions like the telluric currents carrying the electricity of the world—deep and invisible beneath the land and ocean, gathering charge where drifting clouds could explode into thunderstorms.

Last Big Breath

Padraic O'Reilly

WHEN ALL OF THE METAL HAD COME TO A REST AND HARVEY'S BIG FORD Crestliner took its last big breath, the death knell rattling somewhere between the tree and the engine block that was wrapped around it, and all of the automobile shrapnel finally settling into the grass, the evening truly became terminal for the only two people whom Harvey truly loved.

The car, outside of Lee's view, was well illuminated. The yellow head-lights shined off the naked wood of the tree, underneath where the bark had all been smashed away with the impact. Heavy smoke poured out from underneath the hood and swirled along the cool windshield glass. It was mostly calm now, mostly still.

Lee was smashed up into the backseat of the car, his torso folded at the abdomen like he was slouched way down in the seat. He could smell Harvey intensely in the dark; he couldn't see anything. Harvey's seat was pressed way back, his legs felt wet and warm, and he worried that he might have wet himself or worse, left something heavy.

Luanna, Lee's mother, was pitched forward in the car, but her body was not pressed up against the dashboard nor was she relaxed and resting in the seat; she hovered somewhere in between, her head slung low and retreating inward towards her solar plexus. She was frozen in time between impact and aftermath, and if you looked a little closer, you could watch her body sway as if she were a punch-drunk boxer only moments from feeling the ropes, or maybe it was the other way around: the ropes were behind her, growing farther away as she pushed her body, through sheer will, back into the ring.

Then she started in with a wet scream that reached crescendo at a gutteral purr. If you cupped your hands against the window and looked inside, it might be bright enough to see Luanne's craniofacial region blossoming like an unnaturally red hibiscus. Oh, it was horrible. A blessing that Lee was trapped under Harvey's seat so that he couldn't see anything, but backhanded that he had to endure her howls while Harvey didn't even seem to stir a bit. Lee couldn't even reach his ears to cover them, to paw at them.

Luanne fought to lift her head, rolling her shoulders back. Ahead of her on the windshield was a quarter-size divot, only a few inches above the dashboard. The glass around the dimple was spiderwebbing out in every direction; some of the crack was slithering across and jumping back and forth at hard angles. That was where Luanne had hit her head, pinching her face down in between the glass and the dashboard, which snapped her jaw in half right at her chin and drove it straight up, around her nose, swallowing most of her face.

Her jaw hung there, two big flaps. Three with her tongue.

As they eventually carried Lee away, he watched his mother in the front seat, her head turned towards him. He reached out for her as she got smaller and smaller in the distance until she was a pale and languid spot in the decimated evening.

Playing with "Roman Fever"

Kaitlyn Wightman

SETTING

A Roman terrace, 1930s.

(*At rise, MRS. SLADE and MRS. ANSLEY, holding scripts, are leaning on the parapet looking at the view.*)

MRS. ANSLEY
(*reading*)
"The new system has certainly given us a good deal of time to kill, and sometimes I just get tired just looking—even at this."

MRS. SLADE
(*smacking script on parapet*)
This is outrageous!

(*PLAYWRIGHT enters.*)

PLAYWRIGHT
That's not your line.

MRS. SLADE

This isn't the proper way for the scene to go!

PLAYWRIGHT

(*patting MRS. SLADE's script*)

How I wrote it is how it goes.

MRS. SLADE

This is NOT "Roman Fever." This is NOT Edith Wharton's story.

PLAYWRIGHT

It's an adaptation. MY adaptation.

MRS. ANSLEY

Of Wharton's short story.

PLAYWRIGHT

You're the characters; I'm the writer.

MRS. ANSLEY

You mean that we are the actresses and you are the playwright.

PLAYWRIGHT

That still makes me the boss.

(*PLAYWRIGHT starts to walk off-stage.*)

Take it from the top.

MRS. SLADE

Why should we? You certainly didn't.

PLAYWRIGHT

(*returning to them*)

You're acting as if you don't want to be here.

MRS. ANSLEY

She's trying to make this right. That's who she is.

MRS. SLADE

This is my character. If you want me to be mild and non-opinionated, then rewrite me.

PLAYWRIGHT

Speak away, but I'll be sure to put you in your place. Feel free to join in, Mrs. Ansley. Do the Wharton twist.

MRS. SLADE
(*reading*)
"Setting: A Roman terrace, 1930s." That's all?

PLAYWRIGHT

Don't worry about anything before the dialogue.

MRS. ANSLEY

You mean, before our lines.

MRS. SLADE

A Roman terrace? It's supposed to be "the lofty terrace of the Roman restaurant."

PLAYWRIGHT

"The lofty terrace of the Roman restaurant" is too wordy. Playwriting is concise.

MRS. ANSLEY

We only know prose.

PLAYWRIGHT

Didn't the set designer make this terrace look lofty enough for you?

MRS. ANSLEY

It isn't Rome.

MRS. SLADE

You didn't even mention the restaurant.

PLAYWRIGHT
(*pointing*)
There's the table. It's set. You sit at it later. Seems pretty self-explanatory to me.

MRS. SLADE
Where is the view "of the vast Memento Mori"? I want my eyes to be "fixed on the golden slope of the Palace of the Caesars."

PLAYWRIGHT
What will it show, you looking at this golden slope?

MRS. SLADE
Contemplation.

PLAYWRIGHT
Contemplation?

MRS. SLADE
Of the past. But that's all I'll tell you. For now.

MRS. ANSLEY
I would be contemplating too, but after I "fidget with my bag." We wouldn't be in contemplation at the same time, you know.

PLAYWRIGHT
Unless you two are communicating telepathically with the audience, they're not going to know what's going on. They just need to see you two standing on a Roman terrace.

MRS. ANSLEY
But our contemplations are how the audience understands what's going on. Our thoughts reveal where Mrs. Slade and I stand with each other in thought and in society.

MRS. SLADE
How will they know that we had "run across each other in Rome, at the same hotel"? That we "had been intimate since childhood" yet we still

barely know each other? That we "had lived opposite each other—actually as well as figuratively—for years"? Of our lives as wives while our husbands were still living? That our husbands died "not many months apart"?

PLAYWRIGHT

Wharton wrote the background information outside of the quotes—

MRS. ANSLEY

Intentionally.

PLAYWRIGHT

—and I wrote it within the quotes. Let's start over, with Mrs. Ansley's line: "The new way has given us—"

MRS. ANSLEY

"The new system has certainly given us—"

MRS. SLADE

That's not where the scene begins. Our daughters have the first lines.

PLAYWRIGHT

I cut them.

(*MRS. SLADE and MRS. ANSLEY gasp.*)

They're still in the play. They're just not onstage.

MRS. SLADE

Our daughters' conversation is how Mrs. Ansley and I start talking. For us to notice the scenery.

PLAYWRIGHT

Not the scenery again.

MRS. ANSLEY

It's how the story is triggered.

PLAYWRIGHT

I'm not paying two girls to speak a handful of lines, even if their lines are read offstage.

MRS. SLADE

They're supposed to go down the stairs.

(*She looks around.*)

Where are the stairs?

PLAYWRIGHT

Stairs going through the stage? I don't think so.

MRS. SLADE

You want us to start the scene by wanting to talk to each other? But we wouldn't want do that at first. Don't you remember that we barely know each other? People that barely know each other really don't have any-thing to say to each other, let alone be willing to jump into a relaxed con-versation with each other.

PLAYWRIGHT

I wrote it with you two talking to each other because that's how plays are written: with character dialogue and interaction. No one wants to witness awkwardness for ten unneeded minutes.

(*walking off-stage*)

Start the scene, Mrs. Ansley.

MRS. ANSLEY
(*reading*)
"The new system has certainly given us a good deal of time to kill, and sometimes I just get tired just looking—even at this."

MRS. SLADE
(*not looking at script*)
"Well, I don't see why we shouldn't just stay here."

(*sitting at table*)

"After all, it's still the most beautiful view in the world."

MRS. ANSLEY
(*joining MRS. SLADE at table*)
"It always will be, to ME."

(*MRS. SLADE makes an assortment of faces at MRS. ANSLEY.*)

PLAYWRIGHT
(*O.S.*)
Just say your line, Mrs. Slade.

MRS. SLADE
I'm contemplating.

PLAYWRIGHT
(*entering stage*)
I don't pay you to contemplate.

MRS. SLADE
I'm supposed to be thinking that Mrs. Ansley put too much stress on her "ME," and that she "was always old-fashioned."

MRS. ANSLEY
(*rather surprised*)
And I wasn't supposed to know these thoughts.

MRS. SLADE
You sure that you can't afford telepathy?

MRS. ANSLEY
There are several points of view in this scene. You've written in the overall vantage point but have forgotten my point of view and Mrs. Slade's point of view. Without our viewpoints, the audience knows less about us. The audience won't be affected by our later conversation

without these contemplations.

PLAYWRIGHT

Then act out the contemplations. Mrs. Slade, try out your contemplations as a monologue.

(MRS. SLADE steps downstage. Stage lights dim on all except MRS. SLADE.)

MRS. SLADE

The "stress on the 'me'; was that merely accidental, like the random underlinings of old-fashioned letter-writers? Grace Ansley was always old-fashioned."

(Stage is fully lit again and MRS. SLADE rejoins the group.)

PLAYWRIGHT

Is that a good compromise?

MRS. SLADE

Only if I can do it again later. I have more thoughts about Mrs. Ansley.

PLAYWRIGHT

Just say them now. You can have one big monologue.

MRS. SLADE

It's later when I think about Mrs. Ansley in detail. If you care to know, it would go like this:

(MRS. SLADE steps downstage. Stage lights dim on all except MRS. SLADE.)

"[I] would have told [my]self, or any one who asked [me], that Mrs. Horace Ansley, twenty-five years ago, had been exquisitely lovely—no, you wouldn't believe it, would you? . . . Though, of course, still charming, distinguished . . . .Well, as a girl she had been exquisite; far more beautiful than her daughter Barbara, though certainly Babs, according to the new standards at any rate, was more effective—had more edge, as they say.

Funny where she got it, with those two nullities as parents. Yes; Horace Ansley was—well, just the duplicate of his wife. Museum specimens of old New York. Good looking, irreproachable, exemplary. [I] and Mrs. Ansley had lived opposite each other—actually as well as figuratively—for years. When [her] drawing-room curtains . . . were renewed, I . . . was always aware of it. And of all the movings, buyings, travels, anniversaries, illnesses—the tame chronicle of an estimable pair. Little of it escaped [me]. But [I] had grown bored with it by the time [my] husband made his big coup in Wall Street, and when [we] bought in upper Park Avenue [I] had already begun to think: 'I'd rather live opposite a speakeasy for a change; at least one might see it raided.' The idea of seeing Grace raided was so amusing that (before the move) [I] launched it at a woman's lunch; it made a hit, and went the rounds—[I] sometimes wondered if it had crossed the street, and reached Mrs. Ansley. [I] hoped not, but didn't much mind."

(*The stage starts to be lit again. MRS. SLADE dramatically coughs and the monologue spotlight resumes.*)

"It was a big drop from being the wife of Delphin Slade to being his widow. [I] had always regarded [my]self (with a certain conjugal pride) as his equal in social gifts, as contributing [my] full share to the making of the exceptional couple [we] were: but the difference after his death was irremediable. As the wife of the famous corporation lawyer, always with an international case or two at hand, every day brought its exciting and unexpected obligation: the impromptu entertaining of eminent colleagues from abroad, the hurried dashes on legal business to London, Paris or Rome, where the entertaining was so handsomely reciprocated; the amusement of hearing in [my] wake: 'What, that handsome woman with the good clothes and the eyes is Mrs. Slade—the Slade's wife? Really? Generally the wives of celebrities are such frumps.' Yes, being the Slade's widow was a dullish business after that. In living up to such a husband all [my] faculties had been engaged; now [I] had only [my] daughter to live up to, for the son who seemed to have inherited his father's gifts died suddenly in boyhood. [I] had fought through that agony because [my] husband was there, to be helped and to help; now, after the father's death, the thought of the boy had become unbearable. There was nothing left but to mother [my] daughter; and dear Jenny was such a perfect daughter that she needed no excessive mothering. Now with Babs Ansley I don't know that I should be so quiet. Jenny . . . was that rare accident, an extremely pretty girl who somehow made youth and prettiness seem as safe as their absence. It was all perplexing . . . and a little boring. [I] wished that Jenny would fall in love—with the wrong man, even; that she might have to be watched, out-manoeuvred, rescued. And instead, it was Jenny who watched [me], kept [me] out of draughts, made sure that [I] had taken [my] tonic . . ."

(Stage is fully lit again and MRS. SLADE rejoins the group.)

PLAYWRIGHT

Is that all?

MRS. SLADE

For now.

PLAYWRIGHT
(to MRS. ANSLEY)

Care to compete with Mrs. Slade?

MRS. ANSLEY

A few words come to mind.

(MRS. ANSLEY steps downstage. Stage lights dim on all except MRS. ANSLEY.)

"Alida Slade's awfully brilliant; but not as brilliant as she thinks . . . . [But] Mrs. Slade had been an extremely dashing girl; much more so than her daughter, who was pretty, of course, and clever in a way, but had none of her mother's—well, 'vividness' . . . . No; Jenny was not like her mother. [It seems to me that] Mrs. Slade was disappointed; on the whole she had a sad life. Full of failures and mistakes; [I] had always been rather sorry for her."

(Stage is fully lit again and MRS. ANSLEY rejoins the group.)

PLAYWRIGHT

Seems like Mrs. Ansley could teach you a lesson in concise thinking, Mrs. Slade.

MRS. SLADE

I don't know what you're talking about. I couldn't hear what she was thinking.

MRS. ANSLEY
(to PLAYWRIGHT)

Rather, Mrs. Slade could teach you a lesson. What did her thoughts reveal?

PLAYWRIGHT

What were you doing while she was "thinking"?

MRS. ANSLEY

I was kept in the dark.

PLAYWRIGHT

I heard what she said, and she said everything: about her past, her thoughts about you, her thoughts about her husband, her thoughts about her daughter, her thoughts about her son—

MRS. ANSLEY

So she gave the audience all the information they need to know about her side of the story as I have just given my side of the story. The audience needs to know this before our heated conversation in Part II begins so when it is revealed that—

MRS. SLADE

Don't say it! I can only bear to learn it once!

PLAYWRIGHT

All this information in both of your monologues is slipped in the dialogue later. The audience will learn it eventually. Pausing the action for long speeches will bore the audience because there is no action, no present.

MRS. ANSLEY

But they need to know it now before we begin our debate. It's the past that makes the present.

PLAYWRIGHT
(*starting to exit*)

Just continue the scene, Mrs. Slade.

MRS. SLADE

"I'll cure him of wondering."

PLAYWRIGHT
(*returning to them*)

You're supposed to say: "There's no knowing, I suppose, when [our daughters] will be back. Do you even know back from <u>where</u>? I don't!"

MRS. SLADE

I will worry about our daughters' whereabouts later. But right now I'm supposed to say, "I'll cure him of wandering" and call the waiter over.

PLAYWRIGHT

There's no waiter.

MRS. ANSLEY

But the waiter has an important role in the story. The waiter shows that we have privacy. That's why we are so personal later on.

PLAYWRIGHT

You're alone onstage. You're alone in the restaurant. The waiter means that you're not alone.

MRS. SLADE

My buying him off means that we're alone. And I need to show my money.

PLAYWRIGHT

I'm not paying someone to walk onstage, accept fake money, and walk off.

MRS. SLADE

My money isn't fake!

MRS. ANSLEY

Then what's the need of this table? Of these chairs?

PLAYWRIGHT

They're props. Use them to emphasize your lines. Toss them, pound on them, stand on them if that's what you need to do.

MRS. SLADE

But these "props" are supposed to be setting up the restaurant scene where I present my wealth to Mrs. Ansley with my money.

PLAYWRIGHT

Didn't I spend enough on wardrobe to make you look wealthy?

MRS. SLADE

I need to SHOW her my money.

MRS. ANSLEY

That's just the beginning.

MRS. SLADE
(*flipping through script*)
And why isn't there anything spoken about my physical appearance?

MRS. ANSLEY

About our physical appearance.

PLAYWRIGHT

What of it?

MRS. SLADE

You need to say that I am "fuller, and higher in color, with a small determined nose supported by vigorous black eyebrows." And you need to say that Mrs. Ansley is "the smaller and paler one."

PLAYWRIGHT

Are you fuller and higher in color?

MRS. SLADE

Yes.

PLAYWRIGHT

And do you have a small nose and black eyebrows?

MRS. SLADE

A determined nose and vigorous eyebrows.

PLAYWRIGHT

And does Mrs. Ansley look smaller and paler than you?

MRS. SLADE

It should be said.

PLAYWRIGHT

You both look the part. That's all I need. You underestimate what the audience will pick up.

MRS. SLADE

It needs to be said.

PLAYWRIGHT

Your looks will have to do.

MRS. ANSLEY

She needs it to be said.

(*PLAYWRIGHT and MRS. SLADE look at MRS. ANSLEY.*)

Mrs. Slade needs to look tougher than me. She wants to appear tougher than me. In the end, appearing tough is all that she has because she doesn't have her husband, her son, or control of her daughter. And she doesn't want anyone to pity her, even though I have all along.

MRS. SLADE

You do?

MRS. ANSLEY

I said so in my monologue, but you wouldn't have learned this until the end of the story.

PLAYWRIGHT

You can't tell me your wants and what needs to be done. I wrote this!

MRS. ANSLEY

You adapted this.

PLAYWRIGHT

This is my story!

MRS. ANSLEY

This is Wharton's story.

PLAYWRIGHT

I'm going to tell it my way!

MRS. ANSLEY

Why are you making this story into a play?

PLAYWRIGHT

Part II has so much dialogue! And character movement! And it all happens in one location. And the twist of an ending! It's a goldmine for any playwright.

MRS. ANSLEY

But what about Part I?

PLAYWRIGHT

I made some changes. It didn't have the same pacing.

MRS. ANSLEY

Part II needs Part I.

PLAYWRIGHT

Part I can all be dialogue. It can be changed. It needs to be changed.

MRS. ANSLEY

You're trying to forget that this is a short story. Short stories have dialogue, but they also have descriptions of place, explanations of history, inclusion of characters with minor roles or roles existing in the past, and different points of view. Even you can't forget that this is a short story.

PLAYWRIGHT

THIS is a play.

MRS. ANSLEY

You've been referencing it all along as a short story.

PLAYWRIGHT

I wrote a play.

MRS. ANSLEY

You wrote this conversation.

(PLAYWRIGHT snatches MRS. ANSLEY's script and flips wildly through it.)

PLAYWRIGHT

Where's my play? Where's my "Roman Fever" adaptation?

MRS. ANSLEY

You never wrote it because it can't be done.

PLAYWRIGHT

But I spent so much time—

MRS. ANSLEY

This is what you've created.

PLAYWRIGHT

How do I end this?

MRS. SLADE
(*tossing her script*)
We return to the short story. Wharton's story.

MRS. ANSLEY
(*handing her script to PLAYWRIGHT*)
But this discovery becomes your own.

BLACKOUT

Raz-Jan

Susan Hope Lanier

A QUIET SORT OF TEENAGER, THE GREATEST COMFORT ALWAYS CAME TO HIM when those around him were happy, which may account for why Baraz did not feel very well when he pulled into the drive. The silhouette of a tall man with broad but lean shoulders and a book in one hand paced back and forth behind the glowing, blind-drawn window on the first floor of the small two-story, brick and vinyl house. Pedar stopped in the middle of the window frame and scratched the back of his neck while peering down into the open book in his palms; something about the way his spine arched into a question mark made Baraz feel his father's sadness.

Baraz knew this sight well.

Pedar had spent his whole life with his big flat nose in the pages of a book. He would tell Baraz to read Faulkner, and Baraz would read Faulkner. He'd tell him to read Woolf and Baldwin, and Baraz read Woolf and Baldwin. He even gave his son that Chicano shit he grew up on in Los Angeles, and Baraz read that, too. It did not matter what it was. "You'll find your answers here," he'd say to his son, and his son would read it all.

Why? Because if Baraz did not read those books, there'd be nothing. It's a sad thing to have nothing between you and your father but a bunch of someone else's words. How do you speak to a man who loves English, who loves language, so much? Baraz couldn't. Everything out of his mouth felt like a disappointment. No matter what he did, Baraz could not please the man, and so without much hesitation, Baraz backed out of the driveway though he knew he'd get shit for skipping out on taco night.

Ever Lorning. Now that was someone he could please.

In contrast to his quiet disposition, Baraz made an unusual amount of noise during sex. With Ever, he sounded like a whale echoing for miles underwater. He liked fucking her with his chest up against the back of her thighs and his forehead pressed against the wall of his Trans Am's back seat. Ever kept her hands on the small of his back, and he liked when she pushed him down into her, as if he was the only thing to keep her from floating to the car's thin ceiling. When it was all over, she swiped his dark hair out of his eyes and pulled her white T-shirt down over her small boobs, the pits completely soaked through with sweat.

"What does your name mean?" she asked.

It was a question she had asked before on multiple occasions, but Baraz never felt obliged to answer her. It was the kind of question—in combination with the cut-off jean shorts she always wore, her round face and pigtails—that made her seem so young and naïve, though at sixteen she was only a year younger than him. He knew she found his tan skin, his delicate, almond lips, and his thick, dark brows exotic because once she had said he smelled like licorice. How cliché, he thought, to say a brown boy's skin smells like a candy most people hate the taste of.

When she asked these kinds of questions—what does your name mean?—he never wanted to indulge her by giving answers about his culture. Besides, what did he know about being Iranian? But now, the way she looked up at him, only her white T-shirt and a layer of sweat between them, biting her bottom lip as if recognizing her own simplemindedness, Baraz couldn't help himself. He wanted to tell her things—things he'd never said to anyone else.

"It means 'exalted' in Persian. It means my dad wants me to be better than what I am," he said, sitting up onto his knees and tying a knot in the end of the used condom.

He leaned over her to roll down the passenger-side window.

"I'm pregnant," Ever said when he tossed the condom onto the sidewalk in front of her parents' house.

He was struck by the bluntness of the statement. A hard lump swelled in his esophagus. The car suddenly felt small and dirty. She felt small and dirty under him. He scrambled to get off of her and search for his jeans.

"Baraz?" She pulled on her shorts, too.

He said nothing. They sat on the brown leather bench seat in silence. Outside, the streetlights glistened against the hard cement. A freight train whistled somewhere past the trees across the street, beyond an abandoned parking lot just before the gentle hum of night traffic of the Beltway. Just a little further was his own house where his father was probably already eating tacos, not yet knowing the full extent to which he could be disappointed in his son. Everything felt eerily still, his entire childhood frozen, as if in a distant, fading snapshot.

How could this happen? They always used a condom. They only had a problem once, when one slipped off and Ever went fishing for it. Baraz used some of the cash his father had given him for a new car muffler and paid for the morning-after pill himself.

"I'm pregnant," Ever said again.

"I heard you the first time."

"I'm sorry." Something about the way she said it, passively—I'm sorry—as if it were the only thing to fill the empty space between them, tightened the lump in his throat. She sounded like he did whenever he said, "I'm sorry," to his father.

He didn't want to turn into his pedar.

He rubbed a hand on her pale, sticky, lightly-haired thigh and said, "I'm sorry too," hoping like hell it sounded as though he really meant it.

"I don't have any money."

Of course she couldn't keep it. She couldn't raise a kid. He couldn't raise a kid either, and anyway, he didn't love her. At least, he didn't think he loved her.

Not knowing what else to do, he kissed her; she tasted like salt and honeysuckle.

When she slipped out of the Trans Am, a half smile in her blond eyelashes, she said, "We'll figure it out," but the words never burrowed themselves into his skull.

Baraz drove down Ravensworth, purposefully missing the turn onto Heritage Drive. He couldn't go home yet. He needed to think. The pregnancy formed a hollowness in him. It was now his problem. She didn't even have to say it. He had to get the money to pay for the abortion. His weekly allowance was only enough to pay for gas and buy a shitty pink-tray lunch at school. No matter, he'd get the cash any way he knew how.

What Hadi Elahi remembered most about his first day in America, at ten years of age, was the smell of the Pacific Ocean when he climbed out of his uncle's van. The sweet and salty air of sand and Mexican food made his nostrils tingle. He always associated that smell with Los Angeles, with home. Though his wife, Ashleigh, hated Mexican food, her potato tacos with refried beans and sugared plantains would overwhelm the house every Sunday night, without fail. It made living in Virginia just a little more bearable.

He hadn't wanted to leave California but a job was a job, and teaching English literature at George Washington University was more than that. It meant opportunity. You do not pass up opportunity, at least that's what he tried to tell Baraz—what he even had trouble believing himself—when he explained why they had to move across the country to the suburbs of Washington, DC.

Truth be told, Baraz felt distant even before the relocation, but Hadi liked to blame his son's rebellious streak on their change in environment. Why wouldn't a son hate his father for moving him away from his only life? Hadi thought Baraz might come around to living here, but lately he had resigned himself to the fact that his son hated him. He had practically given up on parenting all together.

"I don't even care anymore," he said to his wife. "I really don't. He doesn't want to come? Fine."

"Maybe that's why he doesn't. Because he thinks you don't care?" Ashleigh said, placing a tray of tacos between his large stacks of papers and books on the kitchen table. She laid a white plate meant for Baraz at the empty seat across from him. Hadi tried to picture her without her long, dirty-blond hair, parted perfectly in the middle and framing her narrow, perpendicular features. Every part of her face pointed upwards—the slope of her nose, the top of her chin—everything but her diamond-shaped eyes.

Hadi frowned. "I never pissed off my parents so much when I was young."

"No, just when you married me."

"That was different."

"How?"

Hadi didn't know the answer to this question. Maybe it was just rhetorical.

Ashleigh raised a skinny eyebrow. She shoveled two tacos onto his plate. "He loves you, you know," she said finally. "He's just scared of you."

She removed a salad from the fridge and took her meal to the back of the house without another word. Hadi cringed when he heard the television in the living room click on. He took a bite of rice, knowing how she sat there with the bowl on her lap and her dirty sneakers up on the teak coffee table, no worries in the world. It bothered him how easily she managed, not giving anything a second thought, as if going purely on instinct, and how those instincts were almost always right. He knew he just had to talk to his son and set some boundaries, but really, there was nothing he could do about it now. Baraz showed no signs of coming home tonight.

Baraz drove all the way to Lake Barcroft, circling the small lake three times before finally parking his car by a wooden dock. He needed to think. Across the lake, a couple in their teens wearing glowing orange life jackets pushed a paddleboat into the black water. The moonlight caught in the girl's blond hair. Baraz suddenly didn't feel so alone. He imagined these two lying in beds, unable to bear being home, staring at their dark ceilings before deciding to sneak out. He imagined them giggling in hushed whispers to one another as they paddled, happy to thieve what very well might be their neighbor's boat, happy to get away at least for one night. Then, as the couple disappeared under a low wooden bridge in the distance, it hit him.

Steal it.

Steal the money.

The thought of stealing from strangers felt all too terrifying, but from Ever's parents? It could be easy. He knew that the window by their red front door was broken. He just had to crawl around the oversized pine bush and push the window pane in. His left arm would be long enough to reach the front door's lock. He'd seen Ever do it once when she forgot her house keys.

The plan, in the end, came about simply as a matter of convenience, and by two a.m. that night, Baraz found himself in front of their perfectly white house. All the lights were off. There were just a few things he hadn't quite worked out: What happened once he got inside? Would he find anything of value? Would someone wake up? What if he were caught? Baraz had no way of knowing that just as he reached a hand through the window, Mr. Lorning sat up in his bed craving a glass of milk.

Mr. Lorning was creeping downstairs wearing only his tightie-whities when, from the living-room landing looking down the six steps into the dining room, he saw a dark, hazy shape grab something off the dining-room table. The figure stopped, silhouetted by the open front door, and though everything looked blurry, Mr. Lorning thought he could see the figure's white teeth grimace dumbly up at him.

"Stop, or I'll call the police," his voice called out.

Baraz, with Mrs. Lorning's purse under one arm, froze still in his spot.

The door behind him pooled a faint light across the hardwood floor that stopped at the base of the stairs. Baraz looked up into the darkness. Though he could just barely make out Mr. Lorning's massive frame, he recognized the voice instantly.

Baraz's whole body grew numb.

He suddenly felt dumb for stealing from people who knew him, who knew where he lived and how to find him.

God, he should have at least worn a mask. There was no point in running now. Surely Mr. Lorning had recognized Baraz as his daughter's boyfriend.

Mr. Lorning's big, round shadow of a beer belly swayed to one side when he took a step down the stairs. He held the hint of a hand out in front of him and said, "You don't want to do this, son."

"Son?" Baraz whispered to himself. The image of Ever growing a belly to match her father's came to mind. He was a son. He could not imagine having one of his own.

Baraz hugged the heavy, brown leather bag to his chest and wondered what Ever would say when she found out about this, if she'd even talk to him again.

Oh, what a horrible mistake he'd made.

"Please, just put that down."

Mr. Lorning stepped closer, his right hand turning from charcoal to a ghostly white as it emerged from the shadow of the stairwell into the pale light.

"Please," Mr. Horning said again, his voice quivering. His hand shook just a little.

He was scared, but why? Couldn't he see that Baraz didn't have anything to threaten him with? Besides, Mr. Lorning was a huge hulk of a man. He could easily beat Baraz if it came to a fight.

Mr. Lorning took the last stair and came entirely out into the light of the dining room. Baraz's long, skinny shadow fell onto Mr. Lorning's big frame. Mr. Lorning had thick, stocky legs and a chest full of curly-wire hair. His underwear looked a size too small. Baraz lingered momentarily on the spot where the shadow of his skull hit Mr. Lorning's scruffy Adam's apple before reluctantly looking into his squinty snow-blue eyes.

How strange. They didn't seem to look at him, but straight through him, past the door, out to the front lawn. Baraz wondered if Mr. Lorning knew about the condom he'd thrown out there on the sidewalk earlier that night.

"We can figure this out," Mr. Lorning said, sliding one bare foot forward over the hardwood floor and twisting his outstretched arm so his palm faced upward. "Just give it to me," he said.

Baraz loosened his grip around the purse, and held it out by its long, skinny strap. The dining-room walls shrunk in towards the bag's weight, as if gravity had shifted ever so slightly. Mr. Lorning reached out towards the purse. Baraz held his breath, waiting for his life to collapse in on itself.

"What's your name, son?"

His name? Mr. Lorning couldn't remember his name?

Baraz looked to the purse, then back into Mr. Lorning's eyes. He pulled the purse to his chest, suddenly recognizing the strangeness in those eyes.

Mr. Lorning wasn't wearing his glasses. Mr. Lorning could not see him clearly. The brave man had confronted a stranger, a thief, while virtually blind. He had no idea it was his daughter's boyfriend staring him straight in the face.

Relieved, Baraz turned on the spot and ran through the door behind him, still clutching the stolen property. Baraz felt exhilarated, but soon these positive feelings waned. He was out of control, doing things he never believed himself capable of. By the time he pulled into his parents' driveway, the guilt felt so overwhelming that he thought he might cry.

The hard taco shells had turned well past soggy by the time Baraz sauntered into the kitchen, hands dug into his wrinkled jeans' pockets, a scowl deepening across his sweaty forehead. He'd hidden the stolen purse in his black backpack, which hung from one shoulder—a dead mass weighing him down.

"It's late," Pedar said. He stood at the kitchen counter, pushing a bag of tea into his mug with the back of a spoon. He looked so old sipping tea like that, with cream that turned the drink gray, like his short, dead hair.

"Zan is already sleeping," he said.

Baraz hated how his father called Mom wife in Persian. Zan is asleep. Zan cooks what I like. Zan always listens. It sounded so archaic, particularly coming from a man who married a white woman.

"Mom hates tacos," Baraz said, spotting the cold tray of food on the kitchen table. He wiped the sweat from his forehead with the nook of his elbow, then slid his hand back into his pocket.

"Still, she made them," Pedar said, but all Baraz heard was: Zan does what I ask her to do. Why don't you?

"It's three a.m." His father pulled out his chair at the kitchen table and sat, nodding at the empty plate across from him.

Baraz slid his backpack off his shoulder and made sure to place it between his feet when he sat down. Pedar felt so far away, behind his books and papers set neatly out in front of him, the stack of papers on the left covered in red pen, the stack on the right, clean. Pedar's reading glasses lay over the essay he had been in the middle of grading.

"You didn't mow the lawn." Meaning: Where were you?

"I forgot," Baraz said.

"You forgot your father?" What was so important that you'd forget your pedar? He rubbed his temples. The lines of his crow's-feet stretched out, then reformed a little further from the corner of his eyes.

This simple gesture struck a nerve in Baraz—his father's sadness made the piled papers look less white, the books more worn and tattered, even the leftover tacos seemed sad—and it was all he could do to say, "I'm sorry," and, "I'll do it tomorrow." Feeling the lump of his backpack at his feet, Baraz half-wanted to ask about being paid to mow the lawn.

"There are leftovers," Pedar said.

"I'm not hungry." Baraz pushed back his chair, the legs making a quick, chirping whine as they dragged across the linoleum floor. Baraz leaned over to pick up his backpack from under the chair.

"Raz-jan?"

Baraz rose to his father saying the distant but familiar nickname. He hadn't heard it in so long.

Raz.

No, he hadn't heard that name, not since he was a little kid running across the hot sand in California. He couldn't remember when or why his father stopped calling him that—"Raz." He thought of Ever and wondered what nickname he'd give his son, if it were a son; that is, if they were to actually keep it, which they weren't. Hearing this nickname for the first time in so long, Baraz almost dared himself to speak these secrets and tell Pedar everything.

"Raz? Do you hate me?" his father asked.

"I do not hate you," Baraz said.

What he wanted to say: I don't know how to tell you anything about my life. I don't know how to love you.

Pedar turned from him, dumping his tea into the kitchen sink. He said nothing. The steam rose up, and Baraz climbed the stairs to his bedroom.

Hadi went back to his papers, but after getting halfway through one essay, his mind went west to California.

They used to sit on the edge of the boardwalk wearing matching sneaker sandals—Raz's feet a smaller version of his own—that swung back and forth over the sand as they played their game.

Hadi told long tales that his son ate up and when he stopped mid-sentence, usually on a noun, Raz would smush Hadi's face delicately with little fingertips, contorting his lips into strange, unfamiliar shapes. Then a sound deep in Hadi's throat creaked up through his mouth, revealing a word that would change the course of whatever tale he spun.

Raz would giggle the softest laugh. Then, "More, Father. More, please!"

This, Hadi thought, was the last time either of them had been truly happy together. How he wished his son would still say, "More, Father, more, please," whenever he handed him a new book to read, but Baraz didn't, not anymore.

This, he thought, as his head slowly drooped forward, he would never have again. His left cheek pushed flat against the stack of graded papers on the kitchen table. His eyes closed to the California shore slammed with waves, the water inching towards the boardwalk, and Raz giggling, "More, Father. Please. More!" without sound.

A gust of wind runs through their thick, black hair, but the child doesn't notice a thing. The water moves up to Hadi's feet. One of Raz's sandals slips off, splashes in the water, and floats away, an orange fleck of color in the distance until the undertow sucks it down, and it disappears in the crash of the next onslaught.

The water collects, heavier, colder, and faster than before. Soon the waves are up to Hadi's chest and Raz's neck. Still, his son mouths the words: More, Father. More! And then, in an instant, Baraz is completely submerged.

Panic lurches through Hadi's bones. Without thinking, he inhales a gulp of air and dives under for his boy. The water stings his nostrils. He closes his eyes to keep out the cold, then reluctantly opens them again.

Everything is calm.

The entire beach is underwater. It's as if he is looking out through a pair of blue-tinted glasses. No one else has noticed the phenomenon, least of all Raz, who mouths, "More, Father. More stories," and claps twice, four air bubbles floating from his lips up towards the sky.

Hadi wants his son to notice what is happening to the world.

"Look! Look!" he screams, but his voice comes out as sludge.

Raz puts his index finger to Hadi's face and begins swirling around his cheeks.

"No. Look what has happened."

He grabs Raz by the wrists and shakes him. He feels his eyes cry and wonders if tears look different from oceans, if anyone could distinguish the two.

"Look! We're underwater! We aren't even breathing," he screams.

He squeezes both of his son's shoulders and shakes him even more violently. Raz's face is a single, blank stare of bewilderment; his features, just like his mother's, pointing up towards the watery sky.

Minutes after falling asleep, Hadi Elahi woke to a puddle of drool collecting at the corner of his mouth. He washed his hands and flicked off the kitchen light before going to bed.

Upstairs, he stopped at his son's bedroom. Light leaked onto the maroon hall carpet from under the door. He hoped Baraz was reading. He knocked and heard no response. He waited a moment before opening the door.

A lamp sitting on a wooden desk pushed up against the window of the far wall gave everything in the small room a warm, yellow tinge. Posters of old cars hung from the wall opposite a twin bed. Baraz sat at the foot of the bed, a brown leather purse in his lap, his eyes wide and guilty.

Baraz turned to hide the purse behind him, but he was caught.

My son, a thief? No, Hadi thought. He would not steal from his mother. There had to be some explanation.

"Knock, why don't you?" his son said.

He had knocked. Why was Baraz always so angry? "If you have something to hide, why didn't you lock the door?" He knew Baraz wasn't stupid.

"I shouldn't have to." Baraz sucked his bottom lip, exposing his wide, white teeth.

"Don't be a smart-ass."

"I'm sorry," said his son.

"Are you sorry for being a smart-ass or for stealing your mother's purse?"

Baraz pushed the bag farther behind him on the bed.

"Don't be stupid."

Baraz's oval face grew blank. He looked so much like his mother. Hadi saw nothing of himself there.

"Sorry," Zan's son said.

"Sorry you got caught?"

"Sorry for everything."

Hadi sat next to Baraz. He didn't know how to reach out to him. Hadi had tried to share his work with Baraz, but evidently that wasn't enough.

"Do you need money?"

Baraz looked down at his knees and shook his head.

"Is it money?" Hadi asked again.

This time Baraz nodded.

"Are you in trouble?"

"No."

"Why do you feel you need to steal, then?"

"Um," Baraz hesitated. "It's for the car."

"How much do you need?"

Baraz shrugged.

"One hundred dollars?"

He shrugged again.

"How much?"

"A hundred. Yeah."

Hadi stood up, removed his wallet from his back pocket, and pulled out five twenties. He knew this wasn't the right thing to do. He knew he should take his son's car away. He knew he should ground him, at the very least, but he couldn't stand that sour look. He couldn't stand Baraz hating him any more than he already did. At least, this way, he could help him.

Baraz reached for the cash and Hadi pulled his hand away.

"You can't do this," Hadi said.

"I know."

"If I give you this money, you have to apologize to your mother."

"I know."

"You have to see that disappointed look on her face when you give her back her purse—"

"OK."

"You have to tell her what you did."

"OK."

He handed Baraz the five crisp bills.

Baraz looked up at him with a sad, sullen expression similar to that of a wild animal begging for food, and Hadi knew, or thought he knew, that Baraz really was sorry.

"Don't wake your mother. You can talk to her in the morning," Hadi said, before closing the bedroom door behind him.

Baraz had felt the tension in his neck and jaw, even on the roof of his mouth, the center of him aching, wanting some sort of relief. When his father closed the door, Baraz couldn't hold onto it any longer. Hot tears streamed down his face, and he sobbed.

Pedar had called him stupid, and that was exactly how he felt.

Stupid.

The sobs stopped as quickly as they started. He wiped the snot from his nose, then counted the cash in Mrs. Lorning's purse again. Sixty-eight dollars. Not much. Not even close to being enough, but it was better than nothing.

In the morning, Baraz stuffed the money into an envelope, folded it in half and slid it into his back pocket. He left before his parents woke. He could talk to his mom later. His plan: ditch the purse, give Ever the buck-sixty, then wash his hands of the whole ordeal, but when Ever slid into the passenger seat, Baraz reaching for her hand and knowing by the way she yanked her own hand away that it was all over between them, this plan suddenly didn't seem so good. No, this plan was lousy. Now all he wanted, more than anything, was to keep her there, in his car, for just a while longer, even if it meant lying.

"What do you have to say for yourself?" Ever crossed her arms. Today her hair was down and swept over one shoulder. Baraz wanted to be that shoulder, to feel her soft split ends.

Baraz's new plan: feign ignorance.

"I'm sorry for the way I reacted," he said.

"What?"

"I'm sorry. I didn't know what to say."

"I thought maybe you—" she paused. Her eyes scanned his, and Baraz tried to look confused, dumb even.

"I what?"

"Forget it."

"Ever, I'll do whatever you want. What do you want?" he asked.

"Maybe I'll keep it."

"Keep it?"

He wanted to tell her everything he had gone through the night before, all for nothing.

"I don't know." Ever bounced her knees up and down. She always did this to keep her thighs from sticking to his leather car seat. He felt so grateful for the familiar gesture. Baraz reached for her hand, and this time she took it.

Baraz started the car, and they drove to school in silence.

Finally, at a red light, Ever said, "You'll never guess what happened last night."

"What happened?" he asked, leaning over to kiss her warmly on the cheek, his weight rolling onto the wad of cash in his back pocket.

Sweet Dreams

Ed Scherrer

I DREAMT OF MAKING PEACE ON EARTH AND DISTRIBUTING MY MASON JARS OF maple syrup to destitute children. The dream continued to include Nana and Poppa blasting a stick figure you could see from space into Mount Everest's face to symbolize humanity. I feel a caveman with modern weaponry would bomb the earth in pictures far away from people. I wanted to live my dreams, but I was from the country where no one can hear you because nature refuses to speak English.

"I want decibels," I told two chickens. "Do you agree that the voice of reason needs more decibels?" Horses nodded, but it was actually a reflex. "You are much like the others." I pointed at the noisy orange barn cat born without ears: "You make adorable noises but you don't listen properly." She smashed her messy face into my boot. "Pussy cat, I like you, but I have dreams and to live them I must be heard and I must have influence."

"Hello," I announced to my family in my sky-blue farmhouse after they sang me happy birthday. "My entire life I've searched for decibel deposits in our sugar bushes and beneath our manure piles so very unsuccessfully." My mother froze with a knife halfway into the devil's food cake, and my father stopped his scotch halfway to his open mouth. "But they are being mined like a precious metal by millions in the city: the ore of influence. The decibels are in the loudest places on earth." Twenty-one candles burned below my gaze while my aunts and uncles and my little cousins all had their plates ready for cake below their mystified faces. I blew out my candles and ran out the door. I didn't stay and open presents because I hate receiving gifts. I want to give them.

On June number 1, I ran from my cake and flew on my very first airplane (a tiny craft called an American Eagle) over big Lake Michigan. My body was ripe with intensity. *You close the bedroom door for some privacy with someone special*. I flew southwest to Chicago and felt just like that: Little sailboats were splashing in the blue water and the city stood on the shore like stone drill bits and flint. Rooftops and trees went off as far as my eyes could see and sunshine turned my plane window to gold. The plane's metal wing fell and I snuggled against the fuselage like I was in bed looking into the gold face (the porthole) of my bare-ass soulmate: a sandy crystal ball with a city inside.

I put my hands against the hot glass to say, "Zachariah Shoemaker has come here to live his dreams." The city teemed with cars and trains; I had the power of weightlessness. "I am Zachariah Shoemaker."

I tried to live vertically, but I just drank and slept and walked the streets in disrepair. My steel-toed boots and undershirt, my workpants and suspenders raised eyebrows. I was five foot ten, standing beside buildings over one thousand feet tall. The trains that banged around on wooden rails over my head startled me every time.

I lost my balance and tripped over African men banging on plastic buckets with drumsticks; I stumbled and stepped on a little blind girl's cane and snapped it in half.

A foal gorged on fermented apples, got lost, and then toppled down a grassy knoll. The foal cartwheeled off a cliff and its horseshoes flew off as it reached terminal velocity—I was that foal, and the knoll and the cliff are metaphors for train platforms and barstools; the cartwheel is a metaphor for my indifference towards self-destruction. On the city's waterfront I eyeballed the skyline the way a boy glues his eyes to a supermodel inhaling a cigarette on a balcony—oh, how I dreamed of making her mine—to live with Chicago (with any city) and live my dreams while not terrorizing people with my country gait. Why couldn't the ore of influence course inside hardwood trees or conceal itself under a brown pile of shit? I could have got my taps & buckets and my snow shovel, respectively.

But it is now August number 31, and I'm lost in the sugar bushes inside me—I'm manure! I've plummeted down internal mineshafts. No one wants to discuss with me the ore of influence, and I am beginning to think there will be no syrup for the children. My new dreams are selfish and I'm drinking gin: *glug glug.*

Grant Park, full of grass and trees, faces the lake while megastructures and hotels loom behind it. Between the lake and the city is the park's epicenter: a vast patio of pink brick that circles a colossal cake-like fountain made of two dirty-pink slabs of stone sitting on each other like different layers with stale crusts. A stone bowl is set on red columns and crowns Buckingham Fountain. The fountain sits in a great big pond.

I was just there watching airplanes dot a dark blue void on the lake like gnats with dysfunctional flashlights, and then they were dragonflies in the pink sky when I had my head hung back. The dragonflies became silver angels that went off to war against a big red sun that floated up on Chicago's façade in the purple-red air; and the sun's powerful glow made the planes white hot, and the angels turned into small comets that crashlanded the runways of O'Hare and Midway. *Glug glug* I salute them.

With my feet temporarily on the bedroom floor, to test the cold waters of reality, I decide to fall back asleep at 12: 01 P.M.

"I can't live my—*glug glug*—dreams but maybe I—*glug glug*—can . . . *zzz zzz zzz.*"

Honey

The dusk is royal blue with fat black clouds, and the supermodel puts her hands apart on the railing: A naked woman wears a man's dress shirt, and her icy blonde hair looks like it was cut with a scythe. When she touches the arms of her black sunglasses smoke shoots through her red lipstick like an icicle before she smiles. Down below in the bleeding hearts and pussy willow, *I'm a boy again* and spring up with dirt on my face and leaves in my hair.

"Make me the special one!" Little Zachariah says.

"In your dreams, *honey*," she answers, as a shirtless man with an executioner's hood passes through white curtains behind her, grabs her by the waist, and flings the ecstatic woman back into a secretive bedroom. The sunglasses land in the soil at the boy's feet. He puts on the sunglasses, and the plants in the garden turn to seaweed; the clouds turn to herds of humpback whales that move across a sparkling sky of sapphire and make noises like creaking doors.

I wake up and am drenched with seawater—oh—it's grain alcohol. A cigarette smokes in my left hand! That could be dangerous. A wiry one hundred and fifty pound man with big brown eyes and long brown hair lives in my mirror. My skin was once red and my muscles brick-like from using a wheelbarrow, but now I'm pale and weak and my lips look blue.

My metamorphosis has been so dramatic that the Mexican grocer I buy my alcohol from demands my identification because he doesn't recognize me. With concern in his green eyes, he asks if I'm OK, and when he passes me my plastic bags I say, "I'm better than OK. I'm living my dreams."

Glug glug glug . . . zzz zzz zzz.

Devil's Food Cake

It sure is hot out. The four amphibious horses that thrash in the fountain's big pond are made of green bronze and hide water cannons in their throats. These horses, half submerged in metal bulrushes, are as large as any I've ever fed an apple to, but each has a face like the creature that lurks in the curtains of Fuseli's *Nightmare*. A warm wind ripples the jade pond below the pink sky, and it ripples my white T-shirt; the wind is scented with the exhaust of cars, each cruising leisurely along the scenic highway below the teal chop of the oceanic lake. I puff on a smoke and watch hundreds of multicolored bodies move on the patio; they remind me of recess on a playground. Birds chirp in big trees that make a ring around most of the patio.

A character with buzzed red hair and pallid skin stands fifteen feet away from me with the lake behind him, and night crashes in on his weak shoulders. He has a filthy white undershirt tight to his ribs. A circle of children are fishing around in his pockets and he speaks to them with a nasty sinus infection. He smiles with his white arms up in the air: "Whoever gets the most wins," he says with amusement.

The children take wads of green cash and run off smiling to their parents who kiss around the patio because the hotels and the nearby lake, the canned-salmon sky and the water pouring over the big stone cake is inspiring romance. This malnourished man, who is walking at me, might be thirty years old and he definitely sleeps outside.

He says, "I'm going to sit and smoke with you."

His denim jeans have been burned off at the knees. The leather sandals on his feet scrape grains of sand against the brick as he squats, and we smoke against wickets that circle the grass and the pond. Each of the man's arms keep one horrified seagull trapped under the skin. They are so large, so lifelike, these tattoos up his veiny limbs.

A hoarse voice calls out, "Hey pervert!"

A hairy man with khaki shorts, silver aviators and a fishing cap laced in a black beard moves across the busy patio. We see the lake—and he sees the fountain and the city's façade behind us. He is livid like he is getting bit by a horsefly.

"You." He points down at the man with the rusty scalp.

—Who checks over his shoulders and then dramatically plunges two fingers on his heart.

"*Moi?*" he says preposterously, with bruised, puppy-dog eyes.

"Yes, you. Why does my boy have your money?" He holds out a few hundred-dollar bills. His aviators suddenly glance up and mirror the pink sky and a noisy helicopter which resembles an insect flitting across a pair of tulips on his face. "Why does my boy say you told him to stick his hands in your pockets?" he shouts, and my acquaintance, who I believe has a broken nose, grabs the money and crouches back down.

"—Like you won't need it to pay for your triple bypass next year. Your child reached into my pockets because, as you can see," he holds up his white hands to reveal that they're skinned and that blood leaks from slits in his palms, "I fell off my unicycle. I needed someone to reach in my pockets to get my bus fare, and naturally I felt a reward was in order. Should I have touched your child with bloody hands?"

The bearded man takes a quick step back—"You monster," he says, as a woman's light voice arrives with a warm breeze to summon her husband.

"Papa Bear! Oh, Papa Bear!"

A girl in a yellow sundress and with yellow hair moves a baby carriage and leads a small boy across the pink expanse to a bench. Papa Bear touches his black beard—distracted, and then furious once more—he points at me.

"You're in bad company." He jogs across the patio towards the benches.

Blood fills the cupped hands of the stranger like a bowl, and he says, "Zachariah, I need to wash up."

He steps over the wickets onto the grass and walks towards the foaming pond. I too go over the wickets. Cameras snap pictures of the fountain, and bicycles and skateboards make a lazy slalom course out of the people holding them. Night moves over the highway and slips its purple fingers into the pink sky to touch the face of the city.

"How do you know my name?" I ask, as he sinks his sliced hands into the pool, forcing the blood to cloud in the water; it then quickly congeals into the bodies of two trout that swim off. My back straightens and my head nearly pops off with amazement.

An authoritative voice seems to come down from the sky. "Get off the grass!" A helmeted police officer perches on a Segway where we had just smoked.

The stranger thrusts his sliced hands below my nose, and I see that the wounds have closed. He smiles with crooked teeth: "God loveth the clean."

"Get off the grass!"

"I'll handle this." The bony man struts, leaning his shoulders back and letting his gangly arms dangle. We step back over the wickets where the policeman idles seven feet tall on his apparatus.

The policeman says, "The green wickets mean well. This fountain is city property and not for you to dance on."

"Fuck your mother," says the troublemaker in a high pitched voice.

Cameras drop below faces to watch us while the policeman thinks aloud, "My mother?"

The man in the undershirt speaks curtly, "She burns in hell."

The cop looks dazed and his lips move, but no words come out. It's like his mother just died last week.

The freckled skeleton then becomes very interested in the Segway. "That is a marvelous chariot you ride, *lawman*." The strange rebel caresses the handles of the machine so the policeman jolts it away from us.

His face burns very red. "A citation," he stammers, with a tear in his eye and a hand on his gun. "I am writing you each a citation," he proclaims, but his Segway suddenly lurches forward and then backwards.

A look of surprise twists his face as my acquaintance continues, "I wonder what speeds it is capable of?"

Suddenly the Segway takes off as though it is being pulled by galloping horses. It moves in a straight line, and people dive out of its path as the officer jets towards the lake. He disappears down a gradual set of wide stone steps—screaming, while children on benches stand on the wood to watch him go. Down below on Lake Shore Drive, tires scream and horns honk as the chariot crosses the highway and smashes into the median. The tiny officer and his pedestal flip over the barrier and are carried two hundred feet out onto the smoky lake where he splashes like a pebble. Hundreds of shoes slap on the bricks and run to the top of the steps. I rush to join them, as I curse with astonishment, but I hear the nasally voice say my name.

"Zachariah." I turn and see a seagull at the skinny man's sandals and another one on the wickets behind him that stretches its wings and cracks a yellow beak. His veiny arms are now bare. "Stay focused."

The pink sky is sucked into the city, and a starry night floats on top of us. The volcanic fountain lights up like pyrite while strands of cream-colored water shoot from the seahorses' gaping mouths. Other strands dance from the stone and the bloody trout (or are they carp?) throw themselves from the pond and climb up the pound cakes as if to spawn in the bowl on top. White water spouts enormously from this cupola in the form of a lily. Its gigantism is defined by its pistil—a one hundred and fifty foot geyser which streams into the stratosphere and mists below the Big Dipper.

The bird on the wicket hops down and whispers something to the other bird, and they run at me on their quick yellow feet and screech! They flap their wings and jump on me. My arms become a little heavier when they become tattoos under my skin. I swat the white ink and run off.

"Jesus *god*—get these shit-hawks off me!"

"You can't go to sleep with those gulls on you! Boy!" Below the fountain the freak picks pink gum from the bottom of his sandal. "Or you'll wake up without eyes or a tongue—your *mentula*,"—he laughs and grabs his crotch— "will be gone! There's no disparity between the dead and heavy sleepers." He picks the rest of the gum off his sandal and chews it. "Or so the birds have told me." He blows a pink helium balloon and lets it float away.

Students standing by more wickets watch the balloon go up to the stars; they smoke grass and examine the screens of their iPods. Geezers in jean jackets stand in the middle of the patio drinking beer. One of them imitates the cop by hopping around in circles and then by pretending the Segway has exploded like it is full of gasoline. People skip away from him when he smashes his bottle on the bricks.

"My friend," the man in the undershirt calls me closer to the fountain, which he points at. "Mansart's in Versailles was smaller, but he didn't mind us bathing in it. '*City property?*' Huh!" He snorts. "I told the scooter to sodomize that man. It's happening on the bottom of the lake." He takes a deep breath and swells with pride. "I am the Devil. I'm very influential." His arm moves like a pit viper and snatches my bicep. "You still want to change the world?" I become stiff as a board and a cold breath squeaks out of my throat. His tongue is the color of eggplant and matches the shiners under his eyes.

"Please no," I say.

"Balderdash."

"Man—" Two wet hands coil around my neck and squeeze like snakes. Water comes from my eyes and falls down my cheeks.

"If you call me 'man,' I will kill you with something that doesn't exist."

"Help!"

"Oh, stop your bitching."

He releases me and shoals of endorphins shoot into my veins after confusing his embrace with intercourse; my knees shake; the seagulls hop from my arms and onto the bricks and untie my shoelaces with their beaks. The full moon turns the pink bricks to a silver stage, which shadows explore like troops of ancient humans covered with dark fur, and the beast continues, somewhat lightheartedly and desperate like a child at the front door.

"Will Zachariah come out to play?"

"I've got a lot of homework."

His lips pout. "Pretty pweeze?"

"Stop that," I spit.

"*Pretty pweeze*, with a cherry, w*ith a chair-we?*"

"You have to stop talking like that."

"*Pretty pretty pweeze* with a chair-we?" His voice becomes monstrous. "With god's severed head on top of a hot fudge sundae?" He points a finger. "You want to know my secret?"

"What?"

"*Persistence* . . . with sprinkles."

"Persistence?"

"That's right. For example, I am immortal—*so influential.*" He presents me with a business card: *Lucifer: Party Planner, Immortal, and Literary Device.* "I can make you the first two."

"Well," I stroke my chin, "I was thinking of becoming more selfish."

"Your other dreams were strange: give starving children diabetes and blow shit up? Get serious."

"Are you saying there's more to life than what I see?"

"The Devil's in the details." He spits purple. "Let's do this." He grabs me by the wrist and leads me into the middle of the patio and to the men in denim. "Pardon me, sirs—may I borrow this?" He picks a piece of glass off the bricks. "Everyone gather around; this is a performance piece." The students with skirts or beards flick their roaches and wander from the fountain. "Don't be shy." Papa Bear comes from the benches with his wife and boy—who pushes the baby stroller. Tall Frenchmen and Asian girls fill out the group, and so beneath the Big Dipper, we have a circle around us. "My assistant is fully qualified." The Devil slashes at my open palm with the glass like he would with a letter opener. The audience's reaction is predictable as he cuts my hand open in front of them and I don't bleed. He flaps my open hand around in front of their faces while they cover their mouths. He opens my skin like an envelope to show them my finger bones. "Would anyone like to guess where this young man's blood has gone?" He guts my arm and opens my skin like it is a husk of corn to show them my arm bone. "Hmm?" he contemplates with a finger on his lips. The Asian girls shriek, and a six-foot-six Frenchmen faints in such a heap that he cracks his head on his own knee. The bricks at our feet vibrate, and the jets of the fountain stop shooting water—they clog, and gurgle like a person with mouthwash while the Devil's eyebrows arch and his eyes enlarge. With his long nail he points at the fountain that is larger than a house. "What do we have here?" Bricks eject themselves from the patio.

I hear exclamations in Chinese before a voice says, "*Earthquake*."

And Papa Bear ponders, "Did the concierge mention this?" He asks his pretty wife, "Mama Bear?" just as a hot wind steals his fishing cap and makes trash and sand swirl about on the patio.

People squat in the windstorm. The fountain makes the noise of a giant balloon popping, which echoes out on the lake as the stone bowl that grew the lily shatters. The fountain roars and a crimson beam gushes from its center and jumps up to the stars like a beanstalk. There are seconds of silence before blood blobs like medicine balls crash down from space and shatter windshields on the highway, knock branches off trees and people unconscious. When the baby carriage is demolished, the young mother squeals, "Fuck!" while the Devil grabs his shaved head and laughs at the panic-stricken faces. The essence of my being comes straight from the horses' mouths.

I wake up naked with a case of beer. Empty bottles ornament my mattress, and my sheets have knotted around my neck to cut off my air supply. I crash out of my bedroom into the pitch-black kitchen. The fridge light bursts into my face and evaporates my eye fluid; I feel like a nocturnal monkey who has pranced across the railroad tracks for the last time.

I call home for the first time since I left my cake on the table.

"Zachariah!" I hear my mother scream, and I'm sure it is the clock on her nightstand that breaks on the floor.

My father cries, "Son! Your mother was beginning to believe you had died!" And so I casually explain that this is impossible because the blood in the fountain is mine.

My mother blurts out, "What does he mean—"

"I have no idea," says my father.

"What is he searching for?" My mother sounds like she has her hands in the air and is begging the ceiling for an answer.

My father's voice crackles, "My son, speak to me."

I say, "Perhaps I shall live forever." I light a smoke. I grab a *glug zzz glug glug zzz.*

Pie in the Sky

In the crystal ball I see that Lake Michigan has flooded Chicago with twenty feet of water. The little sailboats float in the streets between the stone drill bits and the elevated trains that move along the blue surface like robotic water snakes. My seat-belt light dings.

I stand and realize I'm the only one inside the sunlit fuselage of the American Eagle. The laughter of a man and woman calls me from the cockpit, and I open the door.

I see sunglasses and lipstick, and my pilot shows off her creamy legs below the dress shirt and smokes a cigarette with a very long ash.

White clouds are whipping below the nose of the plane as the city is replaced by open water. The bare-chested white man with the hood copilots and rests a pie box on his dress pants.

"You want some pie?" a deep voice asks emphatically from behind the mask.

"We baked this pie just for you, Zachariah," the lady says, and kicks back to fly the plane with her toes that have red nail polish.

There is an empty bottle of red wine jammed into a broken cup holder. The hooded man puts three pieces of pie on paper plates; the pie's filling is black and yellow.

"It's peach-blackberry," he says, passing me a fork and then extending his hand. "My name's Julius." He removes his hood to reveal that he has the head of a black man.

"And I am Zachariah Shoemaker." We climb ever higher until the thick sheet of clouds and water resembles the Arctic Circle. "And I came to the city to live my dreams. So where exactly are we going?" I put a forkful of pie in my mouth, and the flaky pastry, the peaches, and goopy blackberry filling fuses together. "This is the best goddamn thing I have ever tasted," I say, and Julius smiles and nods, also eating some pie. The border of black and white skin that traces his collarbone is the border between America and Canada.

"It's sweet as wine," he says, with an aura of jubilation. He ducks out of his seat and motions that I should sit down next to the woman, who has fallen asleep. Julius rocks her shoulder. "Wake up, city woman." She is unresponsive. "Veda!" Her body flinches.

"Oh, sorry." Her fingers climb under the black lenses to rub her eyes. "The sky bores me." I see my young reflection in her dark lenses and she grins, showing me rows of gold teeth. "You love me," she teases.

Julius laughs. "A country boy falls in love with the city; my goodness, isn't that a new one."

They laugh but I interject, "Take me to Chicago. Take me to the Himalayas!" There is only the sound of air hissing. The couple doesn't eat their pie. They only watch the white and blue void ahead of us. "Where do you think you are taking me?" I say, but I am ignored. "For the love of God, tell me where we are going!"

"They are flying you home," says the voice with a sinus infection. The Devil is standing in the cockpit door. "Tell me what smells so fruity," he says, and Julius offers him some pie, which he accepts. He whispers something in Julius's ear and both men crouch and smile. Veda touches my arm and points out the windshield.

"Look where we are."

The clouds below evaporate to reveal the organic circuit board of rural Earth: miles of farmland and forests divided into squares of brown and gold, their borders traced by thin roads and overlapped with irregular patches of woodlots and small lakes. The plane moves up and down as though we are skipping across a mattress.

"Say it ain't so." My voice is weak. Veda once more flies the plane with her bare feet, and it begins to rain. Julius eats peaches with his hands. The Devil offers up a flask.

"What's in it?" Julius asks, with peaches falling out of his mouth.

"I call it Christ on a Cross—it's gin, dirt, and mercury."

Julius drinks some. "It's not bad, and such a refreshing name."

"Right?"

"But I prefer wine."

"You and your wine."

"What is happening?" I interrupt the men.

"Here, let me try that." Veda throws some of the cocktail into the back of her mouth and looks at me. "You want some?"

"What is happening? Why are you taking me home?" There is a grave silence and a dark fog hangs on the horizon of the brown, green, and gold earth. Once more I am inside Veda's sunglasses. Her voice is condescending and a bit robotic.

"Uh, because you are killing yourself; you have become subhuman, hilarious and sad."

"Uh, wrong, I am tremendous and immortal." I answer and Julius and Satan roll their eyes.

"You've lost it, young man. I'm rescuing you because I love you." Veda sits forward in her seat and takes off her sunglasses. The beauty and compassion in her face is destroyed by the sadness in her ocean-blue eyes. I would guess that she has been crying her entire life. "Drink the drink."

Julius places his hand on my shoulder and also says, "Drink the drink, for the love of Jesus."

I drink the drink. It tastes like juniper, but also like I'm sucking on grimy coins taken from the bottom of a fountain. All of a sudden I feel as though I have a slush pile in my diaphragm, which melts into something warm that crawls into my arms and legs. I become woozy and cold. I start wheezing and lean over the controls to peer out the front window at the pastoral wilderness below.

Blue and red farmhouses and barns sparsely occupy the circuit board of farmland like three or four colored houseflies spaced apart on a table.

"Home," I drool. Veda's hand creeps under my shirt and begins to scratch and soothe my back with her nails.

"This is called 'a visit,' honey. I can make you special, but I can't let you forget who you are."

"There's no such thing as the ore of influence," says Julius, and I turn and he nods at me.

And the Devil agrees, "Yes, that is positively insane."

I'm breaking out in a cold sweat as the plane continues to float up and down like we are part of a merry-go-round.

"Listen to me," Veda says as she pulls her hand out from underneath my shirt, stands me up, and plops me down in the pilot's seat. She sits on my right-hand side and gestures to the territory rolling beneath us as hamlets come and go. "Stand up and stop worshipping yourself."

"Oh, *please*," scoffs the Devil, but Julius quickly pokes him in the eyes.

"Pain!" he yelps, as he covers his face with his hands.

His vascular arms are bare, and my voice slurs when I observe, "You have no seagulls…"

He wipes his bloodshot eyes and looks surprised at each of his arms, "That's weird, I—"

His eyes leap out the windshield, and he smiles and points. "Oh wait, there they are."

Two ashen specks dot the dark fuzz ahead, and like white feathered bullets they sail with alarming velocity into the engine on the left wing, making it explode. The plane rocks back and forth violently as black smoke spews out of the turbine (the wing of the American Eagle has been broken by a couple of seagulls). The controls of the plane beep and go haywire as the cockpit vibrates.

"Sorry," mutters the Devil.

"I forgive you," replies Julius. "You must forgive every man that kills you"— he has a moment of reflection, blinks and decides —"although, the next man who kills shall receive no forgiveness."

"What do you call this place?" Veda points out of the windshield and I recognize big squares of green, big squares of brown, and a square of gold where a light blue housefly is my farmhouse on the circuit board, on this table of Earth set in the country.

"Macton," I garble. "Ontario," I say.

"A Canadian! How irrelevant! But then surely you've heard of *The Wild Hunt*, or *La Chasse-galerie—The Flying Canoe*?" questions the Devil. "You lost soul. Let us sing to your return!" He chants, "My paddle's keen and bright—it's *flashing* with silver! We follow the wild goose flight—*dip dip* and swing." Wilderness flows beneath us; Julius offers up his baritone. "*Dip dip* and swing her back—it's *flashing* with silver! Be swift as the wild goose flies—*dip dip* and swing." Veda puts on her sunglasses and the cockpit rings with their three voices. "Blue lake and rocky shore! The boy has returned once more! Boom-diddy-ah-da, boom-diddy-ah-da, boo-ooo-oom." The Devil and Julius dance into the fuselage and their duet trails off. "High on a rocky ledge—we'll build our wigwam."

I watch them leave and ask Veda if she is dating Julius. She grabs my head and kisses me on the mouth. She offers me a cigarette which I take while water spatters against the windshield. My heartbeat is slow but my voice is even slower.

"There will still be peace on Earth. There will still be maple sugar."

Veda shakes her head and sighs quietly, "Dream on, Zachariah." The plane shakes harder and the controls buzz, but I grip the yoke tightly with blue hands and smoke the cigarette. I look over the territory and fall from the sky like the beads of sweat that stream from my forehead—and descend onto the squares of empty dirt fields. I glide over deep-green sugar bushes while Veda breathes down the back of my neck, and I bring the plane low enough to burn the treetops with the flaming wing. Holstein cows flee up a green field towards my farmhouse, which stands a mile away in a castle of yellow light as I sweep into the eye of the rainstorm. "Tell them how you feel," Veda says, as I bear down on my house. I fly over top of the crisp golden cornfields and scorch them at four hundred miles per hour.

My aunts and uncles and my little cousins are in the tall grass with big smiles; they wave dessert plates high in the air. My mother and father stand on the porch at the open door, holding a chocolate cake with twenty-one candles. A deformed cat sits at their feet, and I aim the nose of the plane at the cat's face. "For my family and friends, I speak to you with all of my decibels, and I tell you that I love you. You have made me the special one."

When I crash the plane my bed bursts into flames.

Wrong Cast

Mad Candy

WE ENTER IN THE LOBBY. HE PRESSES 47, AND THE OTHERWISE EMPTY ELEVATOR starts to rise. He pushes me into a corner. My face looks back at me in the polished doors, over his shoulder, his bangs falling in my eyes. My blazer's pulled open; his hands slide up, then down my waist, over, then under the buttons of my shirt.

The lights are warm.

The whole elevator is warm.

Golden, elegant, deliciously pretentious.

I grip the handrails and lean back slowly.

He whispers, licks.

This should be good.

The mirrored ceiling brightens that warmth. He whispers and whispers, his hands getting braver and braver. I rest my head back and let him wander, let the charm of his words twitch the corners of my mouth into a lazy smile. On and on he goes like this, the elevator always rising, fingers roving and lips hissing and kissing, brushing and biting, until—

It all quite suddenly feels like a script.

My mind drifts with a cringe. I know I want satisfaction, but *not from him*. His words: so cliché. His actions: predictable. It's all last night and the night before. Last boy and the boy before.

"This is nothing new," the elevator says.

"This is nothing dangerous," the lights scream louder.

"This is not what you want," breathes my own reflection in the door.

I want . . .

Hips: sweet, sharp, soft, and hard.

I want nails: polished, clean, cutting, and cut.

I want legs: smooth, lean, lengthy, and shapely.

I want curves: contoured, slithering, weaving, and sleek.

I want hair: delicious, tangled, flying, and stroking.

I want perfume: intoxicating, luscious, and expensive.

I want *tits*: full, supple, unbound, and perked.

I want dresses off, her under me, legs spread, knees bent, music blaring, lipstick smearing, clits throbbing, fingers clawing, tongues sucking—

Give me a bitch; make me a bitch.

I want a woman. Give me a girl. And get out.

No, you don't get to stay and watch.

Why? A gorgeous man wants me here and now, the hand squeezing my breast and the tongue on my neck assures me of that. Turn me on.

Turn me on.

The elevator passes 13. No one has stopped it. Passes 22 and we're still alone, save for the cameras. *Think of the girl, think of the girl.* 27 . . . 29 . . . *Don't waste this high . . .*

I grab, I breathe, I graze, and I falter. Where are the breasts? I want to trace curves with the tip of my tongue. I want legs wrapped around *me*. Full lips, tight thighs, mascara, and liner. But here is sex! Satisfaction *begging* for me, right there in his capable hands and the bulge between his legs.

But fuck, it almost disgusts me. That stupid appendage, ugly and selfish. It revolts me tonight, and I don't think I could handle him undressing and utilizing it. The thought of a naked man, even one as delectable as this one, sickens me and spits on my fire.

At 36, the walls purr, "This isn't what you need right now."

Around 42, the mirror above says, "You won't be satisfied."

And by 47, my reflection all around me is nothing but jaded, tired of this chore.

It's over—all of this—before it's even begun.

Jerry Beauty, from
The Beauties (forthcoming)

Lauryn Allison Lewis

THE ULTIMATE IRONY: TO BE A MAN NAMED BEAUTY AMID THE ATROCITIES OF war. Jerry Beauty can take no solace in the name. It does not color his memories—all he's seen since leaving home six months ago—in a soft or brighter way. It does not shield him from the futility of sanctioned killing, the American farce of this second world war. It does not shield him from the taunts of other soldiers looking to tap an easy anger, the easy jab: Beauty, so feminine, stitched across the right breast of Jerry's starched wool uniform. He lets them have the joke. The name means nothing to him, the way a mole on one's arm or the color of one's hair means nothing. He was born to it, did not ask for or choose it, and so the name is meaningless except for those times when others point out its significance. It was his father's name, and his father's father before him, and Beautys though they may be, none ever adapted their nature to fit it. They were men who spent their lifetimes outdoors doing hard work. They noted the weather without acknowledging the splendor of sunrise. They turned over rows of black earth covered in wildflowers, and not once ever thought, *now there is a pretty sight.* They cut across fields and woods the way men of other professions clicked down long corridors.

In three hours Jerry Beauty, one of the last in his town to be drafted, will rejoin a small rank of other men also dispatched on weekend leave. A cargo plane will carry them twelve hours over the black ocean and summarily return each to the blight, the blood, the bombed-out structures looking even more gruesome for the little time spent away from them. It will seem to the men as though nothing has changed in the hours they were away, and each will vow never to leave and return like this until their tours have officially ended. But for now, Jerry leans over the marble banister of Union Station in Washington, D.C. and studies the civilians passing by beneath him, or else stares up at the patinaed ceiling, the skewed and golden constellations, because when he closes his eyes he sees the war still raging, and if not the war, then Henry, Jerry's youngest brother whose funeral he is returning from.

Henry was just eleven, a birthday Jerry had missed within days of leaving for his first tour. The boy's mother had given her youngest a small, woven basket and sent him out to the field just beyond their town's eastern edge to pick the wild blueberries that grew there and along the railroad tracks that cut a stapled gash through the dry Minnesota prairie. When the morning train was a mile off from tearing across the field and he could feel its vibrations under his bare feet, Henry decided to jump it, seeing as his basket was still rather empty and the large swath of wild blueberry bramble he was standing in picked clean, first by deer and then by his own careful hands. But the train was moving too fast, and Henry lost his footing or else timed his jump poorly, and when the engineer felt the jolt, looked out his window and down and behind and saw what was left of Henry's body caught under the train, he decided to forge ahead until the next scheduled stop, believing mistakenly that Henry was a bum, a grown man trying to steal a lift.

There was hardly anything left of the boy to bury. And it was Jerry who finally went back to the field, found the basket and Henry's pocket knife farther up the tracks, and hid both where he knew his mother would never find them, his father's tool shed. Jerry's father had given his four sons their ramrod statures, tensile and sinewy, their way of walking—a long, loose stride—of manipulating held objects, carefully but confidently. Their mother gave her boys their coloring, fair with tinges of red and gold, freckles just shades darker than the warm, oaky-brown of their almond-shaped eyes. They were wavy-haired boys. Boys with hearty appetites and kind smiles. Boys who bruised easily but mended just as quickly. Henry was always more outspoken than the rest. He had a tendency toward a type of good-natured honesty and was forthright to the point of bluntness. He couldn't help but make others laugh at themselves, or at him, because he loved to laugh at his own fallibility, and was usually the first to acknowledge it. And so Jerry Beauty keeps to what is there to see below him because he cannot bear the phantom of his youngest brother running one last time through a dry field just behind his shuttered eyes.

He mistakes Opal Portico for a child when he first sees her clicking her way across the rose-quartz granite floor of the station's lobby, until she adjusts her bag under her arm the way only a woman can. Her hair is remarkable, bright red and fully animated, swinging around her face and down the back of her green coat. Her coat is the color of new tulip leaves, and though the season is bending toward winter, Jerry sees her as something preserved and held over from spring. In a certain way, this initial impression of her will never leave him. In later years, when Opal becomes sick, often tired, when her faculties fail and her memory begins to shift and slip, Jerry will feel blindsided, just as one feels when autumn finally betrays summer, incredulous at her blatant mortality.

But for now he feels he must meet her. It means losing sight of her momentarily behind the massive columns flanking the mezzanine, and the possibility of losing her causes him to panic, which means he must meet her all the more. The station is in a state of restful quiet, having expelled its morning throngs hours earlier, and there will not be another bout of frenzied activity until later in the afternoon, so it should be easy for Jerry to keep Opal in his sights, but still, he reaches ground level and does not see her. And suddenly the tears he wasn't able to shed at Henry's funeral, or during those nights in the bunker with shells exploding all around his head, threaten to rise and pour out of him, and he knows he will either find the young woman with her hair like poppy petals or dissolve into a heaping, sobbing mass of uselessness right there in the lobby of Union Station. If he loses her, if he loses her before he's had the chance to know her, Jerry Beauty will attach all of the anger from the recent events of his life to this moment. And somewhere deep within he understands that finding her means so much more than finding a beautiful woman, it means a chance to live with hope for eventual happiness, a chance to wager on the certainty of happier times to come.

He stops just long enough to shake out a crease in his pant leg, stops his shaking breath, and wipes the filmy sweat of panic from his forehead. And there she is. She's pushing through the doors of the station and he sees the wind catch the edges of her coat and throw it open. It lifts the back of her gauzy yellow dress, not suited for the snapping season, and then she turns left and vanishes. The people milling about in the space between Jerry and Opal move out of his way as he runs because he is a man in uniform running through the lobby of Union Station, and he looks as though he is running toward an emergency. They watch him with reverence, their hands covering their mouths; they turn toward each other after he's passed and say things like, "What do you think could be the matter?" And, "I hope everything's all right."

Out on the street, Jerry glimpses Opal heading toward an inner-town trolley waiting with its door open, and he is at a loss as to how he is going to catch her without coming upon her at a dead run. He knows he looks like a crazed man and that any woman would be right to cry out, clutch her purse to her chest, and claw at the eyes of anyone who approached her in such a way. She hasn't taken the time to fasten her coat closed; its tails continue to flutter in the wind, and Jerry wants so much to wrap it more tightly around her body, or better, take all of her under his own coat and button them in together. She is reaching to hand her bag to the trolley driver—who is leaning from the door to take it—and Jerry Beauty knows that he is watching the chance he has at happiness depart.

He screams, "Miss! Miss! Miss, you dropped your—you dropped something!" Every woman on the street turns to look, first at the young soldier and then at their handbags, each taking account of her personal effects. Opal is one of these; it slows her pace for a moment but she does not stop. "Miss! Excuse me! In the green coat! Miss you dropped your—" He has no plan. In the span of ten paces he will be standing face to face with her and he has nothing to say once he gets there. He is panting and sweating and she blinks rapidly, sees the intensity of his gaze, looks away, to the side, to the driver whose face has become a smirking question, and then back at the soldier.

"You dropped your, you dropped this. I think, I think," Jerry rummages through his left pocket for something, anything, and pulls out the telegram containing his orders for the day. "I think this belong to you?" Opal looks down at the scrap of paper in Jerry's shaking hands without reaching for it. By its shape she can tell it is a telegram, and no one has ever sent her one.

"I'm sorry, you're mistaken. That's not mine. I'm sorry."

"Miss?" asks the driver. "Are you coming along, then?"

"No, wait." Jerry steps between Opal and the trolley door. It is the move of an aggressor and so he smiles as he does it. "Are you sure? I saw it slip out of your things as you were walking toward the station."

"I'm sure it's not mine," Opal says, clutching her coat to her chest. Now that she's stopped moving she can feel how cold it's gotten just since this morning. The driver turns from the open door and takes his place behind the wheel. Opal raises her arm in an effort to hold the driver, but he sighs and shakes his head and pulls back on the lever that closes the door. And so she is left standing there, shivering, before a man whose eyes look lost and more than a little wild. Both watch the trolley round the corner before turning back to face each other.

"I'm sorry to have held you up." But the words ring false to both of them. And then Jerry's arms are out, reaching for Opal's coat and before she can swat him away he pushes the bone buttons through the buttonholes, and she blushes but smiles and takes the telegram she knows is not meant for her, and waits until Jerry lifts her case from the sidewalk and leads her into a smoky cafe across the street.

At the crosswalk Jerry rests his hand gently on the small of Opal's back, signaling for her to stop and wait for the traffic to clear before crossing. He glances at her profile and watches, captivated, as she lifts the back of her gloved finger to her face, just below her right eye, and wipes away a rogue snowflake that's settled and melted there. Oh, she is so beautiful. The cafe is called Bluebird's, and the moment they enter, Jerry regrets having chosen this place so hastily. Tinny dancehall music chirps and sputters from a record player positioned near an antiquated brass register and several ser- vicemen in their olive drabs smoke and hover over two young women trying to enjoy their coffee at the counter. By their slouching, slinking, slurred bravado, Jerry intuits that the men have been drinking, and though he cannot blame them, he also sees plainly that the women are uncomfortable; they volley panicked glances while twittering benignly, they touch their hat- pins, their jewelry, compulsively. He guides Opal toward a booth for two near the back wall of the cafe, choosing the seat that will allow him to mon- itor the situation at the counter by gazing over Opal's right shoulder.

"You're distracted it seems; perhaps I should go." Opal has been trying to get a solid hold on Jerry's eyes from the moment he approached her, a difficult undertaking as he's not stopped moving from the first. By way of reply Jerry nods over Opal's shoulder, and Opal turns in her seat and watches the scene at the counter until she understands fully what is tran- spiring there. "Do they need help, do you think? Should we help them somehow?"

"I'd rather just keep an eye on it for the time being. I didn't know what kind of place this was when I brought you. I'm sorry. Should we go somewhere else?" Jerry removes his hat and wipes the hair back from his forehead as he says it.

"Oh, no. This is a fine place. At the moment I'm just grateful for anywhere warm to sit and rest."

"Well, then . . . ," Jerry clears his throat while Opal shrugs out of her jacket. She leans forward in her seat to do it, exposing her collarbone, the milky skin just beneath it. Jerry sits back in his seat and wipes his forehead again. After her coat she pulls off her gloves, finger by finger, and lays them beside her coffee cup on the small, square table. A glass shatters behind the cafe's swinging kitchen door, causing Jerry to startle and knock his spoon and napkin to the floor.

"It's all right. I think the cook dropped a glass. Just a glass. It's all right." Jerry's eyes are on the kitchen door, the spoon on the floor, the men at the bar, everywhere but Opal's face and she has the sudden urge to reach out and steady him, cup his face in her hands.

"No, it's just . . . gosh . . . I haven't even asked you your name yet."

"Your mother would be horrified," says Opal, lifting her menu just for something to do. The comment jars Private Beauty. He sits up straight as a hatpin in his seat.

"Do you know my mother?"

"It was a joke. No. Forgive me, I'm nervous. Just making a joke."

"Oh."

"My name is Opal. Opal Portico. And you?"

"Jerry Beauty." Jerry's voice slopes down at his surname. He circles the rim of his empty mug with one finger and waits for her reaction; everyone has one. Always.

"You have a lovely name, Jerry Beauty. Will you eat?" Opal opens her clutch and reads the telegram Jerry had handed her earlier in the street. "You're supposed to meet your train at 3:45. It's 2:30 now. Is there time?"

"I'm really not very hungry." An hour ago this would have been a lie, but sitting here now, across from this woman in her off-season clothing over delicate bones, her tendrilous fingers plucking the top button of her dress, Jerry feels full-up, near busting, and the thought of eating seems ludicrous. "But please, order whatever you'd like."

She orders walnut pie and coffee for them both. Their waiter is a graying man, and as he turns from their table one of the servicemen calls out, "Hey, fella! How 'bout some gin for the ladies!"

"There's a war on, pal, don't you know?" remarks the waiter. He's seen their kind before, this is plain. "No gin. Besides, it's early. You want gin, why don't cha take your friends over to Lennox and Hill."

The soldier jumps from his stool, wavers, and makes for the waiter. Opal leans in toward the wall, away from the impending conflict, and Jerry shoots up from his seat, pointing frantically toward the door. "Your commander, Private! He's waving for you!"

"Where?" says the soldier.

"Right this way," says Jerry. He steps between the soldier and the waiter, takes the soldier by the shoulder of his coat and leads him to the door. "What did you say your commander's name was?"

"Commander Samuel Marshall," says the soldier.

"Exactly," Jerry winks. "He's right over there, see? Across the street and down a ways. He waved for you to follow him. See? Just down there?"

"Oh, yeah," says the soldier, though he is obviously confused. "Fellas! Fellas! We gotta get! C'mon!"

Opal has joined the women at the counter, Jerry sees. They are quietly buttoning their coats and gathering their things. Opal gently pushes them through the doors of the kitchen and mouths something to the waiter that Jerry can't make out.

"Does your kitchen have a back door?"

"Yeah, of course," says the waiter.

"See these ladies out and point them toward their street, please?"

"Sure. All right." The waiter smiles covertly before the swinging kitchen door closes, separating the women from their hoppy, war-ravaged and drunken pursuers.

The men file out through the front behind the leading soldier, each throwing money on the counter before straightening his hat. They struggle to regain their composure, believing they are about to face a commander who, in truth, sleeps fitfully in Amsterdam.

By the time the issue's been settled, it's 3:30 and the coffee in both Opal and Jerry's cups has gone cold. Opal checks her wristwatch. "You should go."

"But—" Jerry starts. What was he expecting? That this woman—this stranger—and he could slip away, fall off the far end of the Earth never to be seen again, and ride out the war hibernating like bear cubs in each other's embrace? There is so much to say, so much to tell her, to ask, and never, never, never enough time.

"Orders are orders, Private." Opal is reaching for her coat.

"No. No, Opal. Just wait. Just wait a second, OK? I don't care if I'm late. Let them leave without me. Just. Just, hold on a second."

"All right, Jerry. What is it?"

"Opal, I didn't know how this would go, but I thought . . . well, better than this. Different. Opal, I think, well, it's just . . . You're just so gosh-darn pretty. And, well, what I'm wondering is. What I'm wondering, Opal, is— will you write to me? Can you write me while I'm away? And do you think, do you think when I get back, I could see you again? I'd sure love to see you again, Opal Portico."

She gets his eyes then, his full sincerity, all his youth and grief and good intentions. He delivers his gaze unblinking, and her breath catches in her throat. "I'm going to nursing school," Opal starts. It was not the right way to begin, and so she grasps the reins of their dialogue and pulls it around, back toward where it started. "I didn't know until a few days ago that I'd be going to nursing school. I'll probably be very busy at first, but I can write you every chance I get." Except for the grocer on the corner, the druggist she'd talk with while picking up Mena's pills, Opal has never had an extended conversation like this with another man, and especially not with a man her own age. She passes her bag between her hands. She leads him outside.

"That would mean the world to me, Opal, really. It gets hard over there. A letter from you sure would go a long way toward easing the burden." Jerry notices the double cowlick in her gently curling hair and takes it as a confirmation of her uniqueness. It's beginning to snow harder, though it seems too early, not even December yet. Snowflakes catch and shimmer in her hair.

"Well then," Jerry takes her by her shoulders. "Can I have one good look at you? If I were blind I'd still know you were beautiful, Opal. I'd just like to look for a minute, with the snow in your hair the way it is now, and the city all around us. But you're like something from home, something bright and sweet and natural. I knew I had to meet you when I saw you in the station. I'm so glad. I'm so glad I did." He encounters a dizzying parallax, trying to stare into both her green eyes at once. There is an iridescent quality to her skin that causes him to feel run clean through by something bright white, diamond sharp.

"I'm glad too," Opal agrees, and then they do something unseemly for the time, something women and men rarely did in public then—they embrace. Opal presses her face against the scratchy fabric of Jerry's uniform, and he holds her there, one hand cupping the back of her head and the other under her arm and around her back. An eagle, wings spread open, is embossed upon the brass buttons of Jerry Beauty's uniform, and as it presses into Opal's cheek, she hears it whisper: *I'm coming loose. Take me.* They pull apart just enough for the wind to whip between them, and when Opal takes a gentle hold of the button, it falls into her palm. "Will you get into trouble if I keep this?" she asks.

"I don't care if I do. Please," he says, closing her hand around the shiny button. Just then they hear the trolley's whistle and Opal untangles herself and steps toward it. "Good-bye, Opal. I'll be looking for your letter!" The falling snow absorbs some of Jerry's voice, so it sounds as if they are already very far from one another.

"Good-bye, Jerry Beauty. I'll write to you." And then Opal is aboard the trolley, clearing condensation from her window so that he will see her wave and smile as she passes.

A Man Holding a Spoon and his Wife Who Is Really Quite Upset

Micah Ariel James

(Lights up. Charlotte is alone. There is also a suitcase.)

CHARLOTTE

Johnnie? There's a suitcase here.

JOHNNIE
(offstage)

Yes?

CHARLOTTE

Why?

(Johnnie enters.)

JOHNNIE

I packed it for you.

CHARLOTTE

A suitcase?

JOHNNIE

It's what you asked for.

CHARLOTTE

I asked for what?

JOHNNIE

You don't remember? You said, "I want to move." And I said, "What would you want to do that for, Charlotte?" And you said, "I want to move to the city." "The city?" I said. "I want an apple tree," you said. You said, "There isn't enough space here. Too much green." And I said, "What's the city like, Charlotte?" And you said, "Empty. Nothing but buildings for miles and miles." And I said, "You could have two apple trees! We could—" "Pack my bag, would you?"

CHARLOTTE

I don't remember.

JOHNNIE

Hm.

(*Johnnie extends a wooden spoon to Charlotte.*)

JOHNNIE

I almost forgot.

(*Charlotte takes it.*)

CHARLOTTE

What's this?

JOHNNIE

Go on.

CHARLOTTE

I'm not going anywhere.

JOHNNIE

It's starting to get dark.

(Johnnie kisses her cheek.)

CHARLOTTE

John—

JOHNNIE

I'm not breaking your heart, am I, Charlotte?

CHARLOTTE

What's the matter with you?

JOHNNIE

Your trousers are on the top because I know how you hate to wear them for more than a day without a wash.

CHARLOTTE

I don't—

JOHNNIE

Write me, would you, from the city? Send me a photograph of your apple trees?

CHARLOTTE

I'm not going to the city.

(Johnnie stops and looks at her.)

JOHNNIE

You've cut your hair.

CHARLOTTE

Just a little.

JOHNNIE

You look like a child.

CHARLOTTE

A child?

JOHNNIE

Like a tiny, little, four-year-old—girl. Gosh, that's odd.

(*Charlotte extends the spoon to Johnnie.*)

CHARLOTTE

Open your hand.

JOHNNIE

My hand?

CHARLOTTE

I need you to take this.

JOHNNIE

Don't be silly, Charlotte. You'll need it in the city. You'll have to cook. You'll have to eat. You can only survive on apples for so long before—

CHARLOTTE

You can't—

JOHNNIE

I'm sorry if this upsets you.

CHARLOTTE

I never said anything about apples. You're not helping anybody by—pretending. You're not—proving anything to anybody or anything.

JOHNNIE

I'm not proving anything. I'm letting you go.

CHARLOTTE

I'm not going anywhere.

JOHNNIE

Go, Charlotte.

CHARLOTTE

Don't tell me what to do.

JOHNNIE

You're a child.

CHARLOTTE

Why? Why am I a child?

JOHNNIE

Because you always ask why. That's why.

CHARLOTTE

You're an idiot.

JOHNNIE

And you're a child. A sick child. A dying child. Poor. With no mother to hold her. Go now.

CHARLOTTE

You want me to leave?

(*Charlotte grabs the suitcase, hands Johnnie the spoon, and starts to exit.*)

JOHNNIE

Take it, please.

CHARLOTTE

It's yours, Johnnie. I gave it to you. It belongs to you.

JOHNNIE

I don't want it.

CHARLOTTE

I gave it to you.

JOHNNIE

I'm giving it back.

CHARLOTTE

I can't take it back. It doesn't belong to me. It belongs here, with you, where it's always been.

(Johnnie pauses before walking away from her.)

JOHNNIE

You always make all of the rules. Why is that?

CHARLOTTE

What is this, Johnnie?

JOHNNIE

You never listen to anything I say.

CHARLOTTE

I listen.

JOHNNIE

When I beg, Charlotte. I have to beg.

CHARLOTTE

You've never had to beg.

JOHNNIE

I'm asking you for one thing.

CHARLOTTE

You're asking me to leave.

JOHNNIE

You asked *me* to leave! You want to go; I'm letting you go. What *I'm* asking is for you to take this with you. For me.

CHARLOTTE

I don't understand.

JOHNNIE

For my sanity.

CHARLOTTE

I'm going, Johnnie. For your sanity or mine. But I won't take this. It's important to me that this stays here. Do you understand? I need this.

                    JOHNNIE
I don't care.

                    CHARLOTTE
You do, Johnnie. You care. You've always cared. Anyone can see that.
Right there. In your—eyes. Anyone can see.

        (*Charlotte lingers incredibly close to Johnnie's face for a moment. She*
        kisses his nose and she pushes him away. She takes the spoon from him
        and walks away. She turns the spoon in her hands.)

                    CHARLOTTE
Do you know where this came from?

                    JOHNNIE
The city.

                    CHARLOTTE
Yes, but—

                    JOHNNIE
The airport. The little gift shop next to the—bookshop.

                    CHARLOTTE
Wine shop.

                    JOHNNIE
You met a man.

                    CHARLOTTE
Yes, and—

                    JOHNNIE
Thomas. And he asked you if you'd ever been in love and you said, "No.
Never." But he didn't believe you.

CHARLOTTE

No. He smiled—

JOHNNIE

He smiled and said, "I'm going to tell you about yourself."

CHARLOTTE

And he did.

JOHNNIE

And he did. And when he was finished, he said, "Do you know what's missing, Charlotte?" And you said, "From what, Thomas?" And he said, "That's the question, isn't it?" And then he reached into his pack and out comes this most magnificent specimen. And he said, "Take this." And you said, "What for?" And he said, "For when you figure out what's missing." And you took it.

CHARLOTTE

That's very good.

JOHNNIE

I'm not an idiot.

CHARLOTTE

You are. But that was very good.

JOHNNIE

I wish you'd die, Charlotte.

CHARLOTTE

". . . find whatever's missing," he said. And then I found you.

JOHNNIE

You didn't find me then, Charlotte. You just remembered I was there.

CHARLOTTE

I'm trying to tell you something.

JOHNNIE

Besides, it'll look better inside something new. This house is old. It never quite fit here, did it? You can—put it up against the wall between that photograph of the moon and that painting of the chef slaughtering the fish you like so much.

CHARLOTTE

Listen to me.

JOHNNIE

Or in the bathroom, above the toilet, above that creepy basket full of tiny ceramic clowns you find so inspiring.

CHARLOTTE

Do you hear me?

JOHNNIE

Put it in the bedroom, Charlotte. Nail it to the center of your very first godforsaken citified wall. Maybe it'll add a little perspective. That'd be nice, wouldn't it?

CHARLOTTE

What I need is for you to be reasonable.

JOHNNIE

I don't know what that means.

CHARLOTTE

It means you hear me out. I need for you to hear me out.

JOHNNIE

Stick it to the front door—

CHARLOTTE

If you don't listen to me—

JOHNNIE

Then what?

CHARLOTTE

If I have to kill you, Johnnie, I swear to god, I will. And I'll have you buried with a bowl of chili and this *thing* taped across your stiff, cold chest.

JOHNNIE

That wasn't very nice, Charlotte.
(*Silence.*)

CHARLOTTE

Mother was right, you know? She always said strangers have no business discussing philosophy.

JOHNNIE

Why do you say that?

CHARLOTTE

Thomas was a liar—

JOHNNIE

It's getting dark.

CHARLOTTE

—and a stranger. We had no business discussing philosophy.

JOHNNIE

Should I call a car?

CHARLOTTE

You're not a stranger, Johnnie.

JOHNNIE

Come, Charlotte.

(*Johnnie goes to her, puts his arms around her, and holds her tightly.*)

JOHNNIE

I'm letting you go. Don't you see?

CHARLOTTE

I don't want to go.

JOHNNIE

It's all right to cry.

CHARLOTTE

How much to pretend this means something, Johnnie?

JOHNNIE

I can't pretend.

CHARLOTTE

I have money.

(*She pulls herself away from him.*)

CHARLOTTE

I have—

JOHNNIE

I don't want your money. I just want you to go and be happy.

CHARLOTTE

It was in the hall first, hanging on the wall. Do you remember that? Then the kitchen. You liked to look at it. It made you smile. It made us smile. We used to look at it and smile, Johnnie. It's the only gift I ever gave you.

JOHNNIE

I never liked it.

CHARLOTTE

How much to pretend?

JOHNNIE

A hundred dollars.

(*Charlotte takes out a hundred dollars and puts the spoon and the money in Johnnie's hand. She grabs her suitcase once again and starts to leave.)*

JOHNNIE

A million!

(She stops.)

JOHNNIE

A million dollars, Charlotte. Nothing less.

CHARLOTTE

You know I don't have a million dollars.

JOHNNIE

That's what it's worth.

CHARLOTTE

It isn't worth a penny and you know it.

JOHNNIE

It's what I want.

(Charlotte drops her bag on the floor.)

CHARLOTTE

Do you know what you do to me?

JOHNNIE

What, Charlotte?

CHARLOTTE

You make me want to stab myself in the spleen.

(Johnnie offers the spoon to Charlotte.)

JOHNNIE

All right.

CHARLOTTE

I see your face and I want to drown myself at the bottom of some famous lake. Do you see? I see you and I just want to break every bone in my body. I want to jump from the highest bridge in Texas—and live. Do you understand? You make me physically ill.

JOHNNIE

Your spleen, Charlotte.

(*Charlotte takes the spoon and drops to her knees. She begins to slam the spoon on the floor. Her movements are wild, child-like. She struggles a bit longer before she stops to take a breath, dropping the spoon at her side. Johnnie goes to her. He lifts her head and stares into her eyes.*)

CHARLOTTE

The most beautiful man in the entire world.

JOHNNIE

Who is?

(*Charlotte stands and begins composing herself.*)

CHARLOTTE

Thomas told me a joke, Johnnie. Do you want to hear it?

JOHNNIE

Go on.

CHARLOTTE

"The funniest thing about tears is that they rarely feel cold." Do you think that's funny?

JOHNNIE

I guess.

CHARLOTTE

But you didn't laugh.

                        JOHNNIE
No.

                        CHARLOTTE
And you didn't cry.

                        JOHNNIE
No.

                        CHARLOTTE
That's the joke, isn't it?

                        JOHNNIE
What is?

                        CHARLOTTE
And pretty soon, we'll all be saying it. "Do you know what's funny about
tears?" And we'll all have a good laugh.

                        JOHNNIE
The sun's gone now.

                        CHARLOTTE
You don't laugh, Johnnie. You don't smile.

                        JOHNNIE
You're smiling.

                        CHARLOTTE
Do you know why?

                        JOHNNIE
Because you're happy?

                        CHARLOTTE
Because there's a suitcase with my name on it.

JOHNNIE

That makes you happy?

CHARLOTTE

Why?

JOHNNIE

That's all I want.

CHARLOTTE

Thomas said, "It's only human to be happy with other people's sadness."

(*Charlotte picks up the spoon.*)

CHARLOTTE

You've never felt more human in your life, have you?

JOHNNIE

I'm not happy, Charlotte. I'm hurt. This hurts me.

CHARLOTTE

The city? Is that what I said?

JOHNNIE

Yes.

CHARLOTTE

Apple trees?

JOHNNIE

What do you want from me?

CHARLOTTE

Nothing. I'm not sad, Johnnie. I'm smiling, see?

JOHNNIE

Yes, I see that.

CHARLOTTE

Would you like to move on?

JOHNNIE

I want you to move on.

CHARLOTTE

It's already tomorrow.

JOHNNIE

What happens then?

CHARLOTTE

That's the question. Isn't it?

(*Pause.*)

CHARLOTTE

Now then, we've just discussed philosophy.

(*Charlotte starts to exit.*)

JOHNNIE

Charlotte?

(*She stops. He takes the spoon from her.*)

JOHNNIE

Put it in the kitchen, would you? In the drawer between the rolling pin and the ladle?

(*She takes the spoon back.*)

CHARLOTTE

It's already tomorrow, Johnnie.

(*Charlotte exits. Lights fade.*)

The Most Dangerous Woman in the World

Dorothy Schultz

1

YOU DON'T BECOME "THE MOST DANGEROUS WOMAN IN THE WORLD" FOR
nothing. I mean, think about it. Even "Toughest Chick in School" would be
hard to come by. You'd have to have a pretty bad-ass reputation. Maybe
bully a few cheerleaders or talk smack to the lunch ladies with the clear skin
and baby blue eyelids. Or smoke cigarettes on school property and flick off
security guards. You'd be a tomboy in baggy jeans, an oversized jacket, your
greasy hair pulled back in a low pony-tail. No makeup, no softness, no pay-
ment for the Pace bus.

But "The Most Dangerous Woman in the World"? That's taking
"Toughest Chick" and adding fifteen years in federal prison, a featured spot
on *America's Most Wanted*, and an increase in airport security from yellow
to orange. It's serious shit. But there's a woman, a 5'6" welterweight from
Holland, who's claimed that title. Lucia Rijker. She is the "Queen of
Lightning," "Lady Ali," "The Dutch Destroyer." She is "The Most
Dangerous Woman in the World."

In October of 1994, at the age of 25, Lucia had 36 kickboxing wins under
her belt. Thirty-six wins and no losses. Twenty-five of those were first-round

knockouts. She defeated the American champion, Lilly Rodriguez, in 30 seconds: 30 seconds of leg kicks so powerful, sharp shin against fleshy thigh, that Rodriguez had to throw in the towel. A champion bowing to a 17-year-old newcomer. A year later, Lucia went up against Cheryl Wheeler, then the world-titleholder. That bout ended in a broken nose and an early retirement for Wheeler. Lucia fought other champions, too. She defeated Nancy Joseph in 3 rounds, Ann Holmes in 30 seconds, and Daniëlle Rocard in 15 seconds. After 8 years and 36 defeats, Lucia was looking for a new challenge.

And so she fought a man.

2

I sat Indian style on the beaten-in sectional couch in the sunroom and sifted through Sunday's newspaper. The columns and advertisements were sprawled out on the ottoman in front of me, the morning sun spilling over them through the blinds. *X-Men* played on the TV, and occasionally, I'd look up to catch glimpses of Rogue. When I did, when I saw her pale, pathetic face looking as blank and innocent as wrapping paper, I'd roll my eyes and scowl.

The Rogue in the comics is nothing like the Rogue in the *X-Men* movies. The Rogue in the comics is sexy, fiery, flirtatious. She doesn't *whine*; her face isn't wrinkled like cabbage. She's a Southern belle with a sailor's tongue, not a timid orphan who's as rebellious as a suckling kitten. I don't hope she dies like I do when I see the movie Rogue plague the TV screen. The only thing I can do at that point is let Walgreens or JC Penney entertain me, their semi-annual sales offering more entertainment.

While I tore out coupons for tampons and soup, something in the newspaper caught my eye. It was a front-page article with the heading "Crystal Lake Man on Trial for Deadly Punch." I suppose *deadly punch* could have referred to a poisoned ginger ale concoction, but that didn't cross my mind. I pictured a fist instead. A single clenched fist. It wasn't scarred or bleeding from the knuckles, no scab wounds of any kind. It was white and belonged to a man. Nails cropped, cuticles neat.

I placed the coupons on my knee and picked up the newspaper. I cradled it in my lap, rereading the heading. Beneath it was a picture. It showed a white, middle-aged man with dark features. A Rhett Butler type, but with a nicer smile. The picture wasn't a mug shot; it was something taken by a girlfriend or wife, something outdoors with natural light and trees in the background.

I scanned the article. Rhett Butler was married and had children. After leaving a Crystal Lake bar one evening, he exchanged words with another man, also a husband and a father. What was said is up for grabs. How things went down was he said, she said. Perhaps they were arguing about baseball. Whatever the case, something triggered Rhett Butler. Something triggered him and he sent a punch into the other man's face. One punch. One single punch to the face. The man fell to the ground and died two hours later. And Rhett Butler was arrested in his home while his kids slept in their tiny twin beds.

When I finished the article, I read it again. Then I looked up from my lap and stared at the television screen. The X-Men were fighting Magneto in some final battle, but I couldn't focus on them. I saw past them, into my own reflection on the screen. I saw my oval-shaped face, the slight crookedness in my nose, my thin, chapped lips. Around my face were explosions. Huge, fiery explosions. Orange and yellow flames, ballooning out across the screen and whipping my cheeks. Sparks igniting from the dark crevices of my mirrored eyes. Clouds of smoke, black and hot as coal, puffing out across my hairline.

I looked away from the battle and back down to the newspaper in my lap. I looked at Rhett Butler's face and thought about the man he killed, the man whose brain swelled inside his own head. And somewhere, somewhere deep inside me, I couldn't help but think it was *cool*, that a fatal punch was something impressive, like a trick in a video game, and that feeling, the feeling of being impressed and in awe of something, exploded within me and made me smile, my thin lips stretched out like rubber bands.

3

The posters read: Luci Rijker vecht tegen een man! Behind the bolded font was a young Lucia, wearing a baggy white T-shirt that hid the rise and fall of her chest. The sleeves were cut off, baring Lucia's caramel-colored skin. Her bronzed arms and face, dark eyes, dark hair, and full lips made her look Hispanic. Like a Hispanic male, actually, the way her hair was cropped short and box-like on top of her head, and the way her nose flared. She seemed alive in the picture, breathing slowly through her nose, staring intensely at the camera.

She wore red satin Thai shorts with white detailing. Around her waist was a thick belt, the colors of the German flag, thick stripes of black, gold and red. In the middle, a large silver medallion in the shape of a diamond. Two gold figures were facing off in the middle of the medallion, their little fists painted red.

Lucia's own fists were at the center of the poster. They were bare, her nails clean and cut short. She didn't clench her fists, just as she didn't clench her jaw, but yet, they still seemed strong, infallible. A steel jaw, some might say. Indestructible fists, others would say.

The poster's image was the same used for the cover of *Het Martial Arts Magazine.* On the side of the magazine's cover, in a large white font, was the phrase "Fighting Spirit." The following headlines were also featured on the magazine's cover: "World Games: Karate and Taekwondo," "Ninjutsu Without Mysteries," and "Farewell to 'Big' George Foreman." Lucia's fight was the lead story.

It was October, 1994.

4

"Losing weight sucks," I told Ania. "It's like Dante's motherfuckin' trip through hell." We were in Orlando, Florida, sitting side by side in a sauna, hunched over with our elbows pressing into our thighs. Little white towels cocooned our legs and bodies and were draped over our heads. We used our hotel key cards to scrape away excess sweat from our bare arms. Weigh-ins were in two hours and we still had a few pounds to lose.

"For starters," I began, "you've got that pre-losing-weight limbo stage, that time about a week before the fight when you know you have to lose weight, but since you still have seven days to drop, you're not too concerned about it." I ducked my head between my legs and spit, but my mouth was so dry that the saliva stuck to my lower lip and hung like a piece of melted cheese. With two fingers, I pinched the drool from where it collected on my lip and wiped it on a towel. "That's the blissful stage," I said, "the time when you're conscious of but not physically affected by this shit."

"Oh, how I miss that stage," Ania said, unwrapping her leg for a moment in order to scrape off the beads of sweat forming on her thighs and calves. Ania's the only other female fighter at our gym. When we're not talking about fighting, we're talking about food. In saunas, we talk about how we suffer when we're *not* eating food.

"Then there's that lust stage," I continued, "when you start to cut off all food from your diet and, simultaneously, start craving every single thing you lay your eyes on." I spat again and this time it cleared my lips, shooting down to the pile collecting between my callused feet. I used to get pedicures every once in a while, treat my feet to a salt bath or something, but whenever I did that, my calluses were shaved off or they hung loose from the balls of my feet like little white pockets, forcing me to peel them away. But that would leave my feet too tender for the gym. They would blister up immediately, quarter-sized bubbles filled with clear pus. And if I let my nails grow too long, they'd catch on heavy bags and split down the middle. So pedicures became a rarity. I'd rather have ugly feet than sore feet.

"I know what you mean," Ania said. "I can never stop eating pizza. I love pizza."

I laughed and looked at her, nodding in agreement. Her face was pale and wet. It looked as though she had applied one of those skin-clarifying face masks, the type you peel off when they dry, the type that look as glossy as clear nail polish.

"Pizza is just the beginning," I said, looking down again and spitting. "Then you start craving weird things like sweet pickles and deviled eggs. Even Tic Tacs look like tiny pieces of heaven."

"I once had a craving for gravy," Ania said, "the kind they have at Old Country Buffet. It's their country sausage flavor, I think. I could eat bowls of that."

"Exactly," I said, "weird shit like that. Completely random and off-the-wall. And all those cravings make you the biggest glutton-to-be. I'll be at work, and while shooting off e-mails to managers or clients, I'll also make lists of things to buy at the grocery store once the fight's over. I could empty out a Dominick's with the things on my list. I become a goddamned food slut."

Ania choked out a laugh, the sounds catching on the inside of her dry throat. "There was one time," she said, "when I played the alphabet game by naming foods I wanted to eat. A is for applesauce, B is for bologna, shit like that. I went through about seven times."

"I swear," I said, "fasting for a couple days makes you crazy. You're a glutton one day, a hoarder the next. My roommate bought some chocolate Moose Tracks ice cream the other day and I was so concerned it would be gone by the time this fight was over that I hid it in the back of our freezer, behind a stash of frozen peas. I hoard left and right."

Another sheet of sweat had sprouted from our legs, so we took our key cards to our bodies and scraped. When we reached our ankles, we flicked the cards, shooting teaspoons of sweat to the floor. The sauna felt hotter than it did only five minutes before. I felt as though I were wrapped in flannel sheets fresh from the dryer, wrapped and wrapped in about sixteen layers, and then stuffed into a broken elevator shaft in a high-rise in Arizona, a building without ventilation or AC of any kind, a building standing tall in the middle of the day beneath the blazing sun. And with every minute that passed, the elevator got smaller and smaller and the flannel sheets wound tighter across my body.

"And today we're total sloths," I said, gliding the key card slowly over my knee as if it were a razor blade. "I just feel so slow today. Slug-like. I went to the bathroom this morning and just standing up from the toilet made my heart race."

Ania nodded, adding, "Peeing takes too much effort. It's like you have to squeeze it out, like the last bits of toothpaste from a flattened tube. I never thought I could be so dry."

"I know," I agreed. "I almost requested a wheelchair from the hotel concierge desk, but then I thought that pumping the wheels with my arms would be way too much work." I looked down at my arms. They looked thin and flushed.

"And this," Ania said, indicating the sauna, "is hell. If I had to imagine hell, this would be it."

"Oh, it's *all* hell," I said, "but this part, this sitting and wasting away in the god-forsaken heat, is our flaming tomb."

"I really do feel like I'm melting alive, like I'm on a slow-cooker spinning around and around," Ania said. She wiped her face with the towel draped over her head. I mimicked her. The towel was moist and smelled like oak. It was just as wet and stiff as I felt.

I nodded towards the door of the sauna. "The things I would do for a swim in the pool out there." The hotel we were staying at was the largest Marriott in the world, its pool area rivaling a Six Flags water park. There were about six separate pools, all connected with lazy rivers or water slides or floating kiosks where they served piña coladas in pineapples. We had walked past it all on our way to the sauna, which was buried deep inside the women's locker room. From inside the sauna, we couldn't see anybody, but we heard little girls, the pitter-patter of their feet as they ran in, probably in their sagging two-piece swimsuits with the ruffles, their hands tucked under their crotches, holding in the pressing pee.

Ania looked at the door, probably imagining the same thing. "I'd kill just for a breath of fresh air," she said. "Breathing in here feels like I'm sucking on wood."

"Yeah," I agreed, "my tongue feels like a pinecone."

"Let's just give this a few more minutes and then leave."

"Done." I took a deep breath as if to prepare myself for our last few minutes. It was a marathon, really, this sitting around and melting.

"I wish we could just weigh in after this," I said, a slight whine creeping up in my voice, "'cause you know the lines are going to be out the door and everything's going to be disorganized as shit. We'll probably have to stand around for at least an hour. The hell will continue."

"Shut up," Ania said. "Don't remind me."

"I hate those lines," I said. "I hate them to death. If I stand, I can't hold myself up for too long, and I'm forced to sit. If I sit, I feel nauseous. And then other fighters let their friends join them in line, inevitably making me wait longer, and that is not cool. At that point, I would kill for food."

Ania nodded and the movement in her face caused a bead of sweat to drip from her eyebrow. "Nothing beats a little violence *before* the fight," she said.

"I may not have strength now," I said, "but I can muster enough anger when it comes to weighing in. Or at the buffet table after weigh-ins. Now *that's* a mess, too."

"How so?" Ania asked. "That's typically the best part of my life. Eating again. It's so wonderful."

"Because," I explained, "we're so bewitched by food and our cravings that we would trample our own—willingly, knowingly—in order to get the first plate. You better believe that if you and I were in line and there was only one deviled egg left, I'd get Tonya Harding on you. Take a bat to your knees. Slash your face with a skate. You get the idea." I pretended to make a slashing motion, but my arm felt heavy, making it look like I was slowly painting a wall or something else similarly nonthreatening.

"Wow," Ania said. She paused for a moment, stood, and let all the towels but the one tucked around her chest drop to the floor. They fell with a heavy thud, like washcloths dropping in a tub. "But I guess you have a point," she said. "I'd back-stab you in a moment if it meant I could get some OCB gravy."

I laughed, imagining the gravy that looked like clumpy clam chowder, and hung my head back, letting the towel fall from my head. I stood up, too, next to Ania and gestured towards the door.

"After you, ma'am."

"Why, thank you," she said. She turned towards the sauna door and leaned her body against it. As it crept open, a flood of cool air hit our faces, and for a moment, however brief, it felt like I had stepped out of hell.

* * *

It was one of the most publicized male versus female fights. There have been others, of course. In 2008 in Phuket, Thailand, Chantal Ughi defeated Kwan Fi in a decision. That same year, but in the Netherlands, Germaine de Randamie knocked out Tom Waes. A picture from the fight shows Waes unconscious in the ring, lying faceup on the blue mat, blood trickling from his broken lip. Sunshine Fettkether, whom Lucia would eventually fight and beat, defeated Randy Pittman with a first-round knockout. German boxing star Regina Halmich beat Stefan Raab by unanimous decision. Regina was 112 pounds at the time of the fight. Stefan was 190.

But none of those were as big as Lucia's Muay Thai fight against a man. Some people remembered his name—Somchai Jaidee—but most referred to him as the Thai guy Lucia fought. Muay Thai, which means "Thai boxing," originated in Thailand, so it's always impressive to say you fought a native. Lucia was going to the heart of the sport, where she could find the best competitors.

But Somchai Jaidee's first name was Adam. And Adam hailed from New Zealand. He trained in Thailand, however, and as is the tradition, took on the name of his gym. He *became* Somchai; he was baptized through the sport. Every day he woke up at 4:00 a.m. and ran across the rural roads in 85-degree weather. After that came an hour of strength training. The gyms in Thailand aren't equipped with ellipticals or machines that target your outer thighs with simple leg pulses. So instead, Somchai would do 300 sit-ups on a bench, his spine hammering into the splintered wood. Or he'd jump and grab a tree branch, lifting himself into 100 pull-ups. Thin, wavering stems of bamboo hung from the gym's wooden frame, allowing Somchai to climb up towards the feathered roof.

He was 21 years old when he faced off against 25-year-old Lucia. He'd had 14 fights in Lumpini Stadium, fights against other Thai fighters, all of them male. He was younger than Lucia, and had fewer fights, but he lived and breathed Muay Thai. He lived *at* his gym, slept on a small cloth cot, and ate soup out of a wooden bowl every day with the other Thai fighters. He spoke Thai, too, the fast-paced clucking assimilating him with the others. They talked about Muay Thai when they weren't training.

So what he lacked in age and experience, he made up for in his training. But despite everything, despite who had more fights or who had the better reputation, there remained one simple fact: Somchai was visibly and physically stronger, his upper body making Lucia's biceps appear almost feminine.

* * *

The gym was in the corner of an L-shaped strip mall. From the outside, it looked like all the other businesses: a door and two large windows with nude-colored blinds that were tightly closed. When I opened the door, the blinds rattled and I was hit with the smell of stagnant sweat and body odor. Bitter like vinegar-drenched spinach, but mildewy like wet towels. The gym was about the size of four boxing rings, small but enough. One floor-standing ring stood in the corner along the windows. The rest of the gym was covered in thick navy wrestling pads. A mural of a bull stretched across the main wall. Bulging with muscles, the bull stood on his hind legs, ready to attack, his eyes yellow with fury. Smoke billowed from his nostrils, puffing out and away in large clouds, slowly forming letters that read *Team Toro*.

It was my first time at Team Toro. Brian, the person who told me to come and check it out, wasn't there yet, so I slinked along the windows towards a small alcove of tiled flooring, where a few chairs and a desk were situated. I took a seat and tucked my gym bag between my feet, my hands still gripping the strap.

A handful of other people were already there, all barefoot, all walking across the mats and shadowboxing, pausing mid-punch to talk to the person nearest them, a quick something followed by a laugh. They wore shiny shorts, a cheap satin perhaps, in bright, bold colors. It was something you'd see on stage, characters dressed in eye-catching materials, costumes sporting fringe or sequins or triangular scraps that appeared like flames from the seats in the audience. Tucked into their shorts were T-shirts, already succumbing to the gym's humidity, hanging heavy with moisture.

I was suddenly conscious of the fact that I was uncomfortably warm, sitting there in front of the window in a gym without fans or AC. Not knowing what to expect, I had worn a T-shirt, a gray one at that, and I hoped I hadn't started to pit. I tried to check. Casually, I rubbed my chin against my shoulder, pretending to scratch it, while also peering down towards my armpit. That vantage point didn't reveal anything. Unsatisfied, I let go of my gym bag's strap and raised my arms and arched my back in a fake stretch, keeping my eyes lowered so no one could notice they were targeting my underarms. I was safe: warm, but not pitting. To keep it that way, I rested my elbows on the arms of the chair to allow some air flow into the sleeves of my shirt.

When I looked up, I saw a man walking towards me. He was short and squat, his head completely hairless except for two very thick, black eyebrows that collided with one another. A mole, the color and size of a peanut-butter chip, was wedged between his nose and cheek. I had to actively tell myself not to look at it when he began to talk.

"Hey," he said kind of shyly, "you here for Muay Thai?"

"Yeah, I am. I'm Brian's friend," I said, hoping Brian had mentioned my arrival. If he hadn't, the man didn't seem to care.

"OK, cool. I'm Ricardo. I'm the trainer here."

"I'm Dorothy."

We didn't shake hands, but there was a moment where neither of us knew what to say next. I looked away, careful to avoid the mole, and saw that the shadowboxers—a few guys and a girl—were now occasionally shooting glances over at us, curious, but probably wanting to impress me with how well they could punch the air.

"Well, I'll need you to sign a waiver for the day," Ricardo said, bringing my attention back to him. He turned and took a couple steps towards the desk. Opening a drawer, he rummaged around before withdrawing a wrinkled sheet of paper and a pen. He handed them to me and asked, "You have any fight experience?"

I shrugged, "I hit my brothers all the time."

Ricardo smiled a close-lipped smile and turned towards the others. As he walked away, he reminded me to take off my shoes before getting onto the mats.

I slipped my feet out of my flip-flops. The tiles were surprisingly cold, but I welcomed the cool-down. Pen in hand, paper sprawled across my thigh, I signed the waiver for my first day of training.

7

The video footage appears aged, resembling something from the 1950s, with a male announcer sounding like a character from Old Time Radio. Even the bolded title, "He vs. She," which sprawls across the screen at the beginning of the fight, seems more characteristic of the fifties. The ring is out of focus and gray, making it difficult to distinguish between Lucia and Somchai. The two fighters look almost identical: dark hair, thin legs, similar height. But when you look closely, when you compare their arms, you can see subtle differences in the sharpness and definition.

Somchai's chest and arms are bare, but glazed over with Thai oil. They look stronger because of the shine, the oil sculpting the curves of his biceps. His back is broad and V-shaped. Muscles pop from various areas: above his shoulder blades, under his armpits, near his neck. He wears green Thai shorts with wide yellow script. It says something in Thai, something indiscernible on the video footage. He performs the Ruk Muay, which is the traditional dance done before a Thai fight.

As he kneels down in the middle of the ring, bowing and paying his respects, Lucia paces back and forth in her corner. She wears red shorts and a white cut-off T-shirt. Her lips are pursed together and she keeps her eyes glued to her corner, her back to Somchai. Shuffling from foot to foot, Lucia shadowboxes and stays fresh. She doesn't stop moving. She never looks at her opponent.

Their fight statistics and measurements flash on the screen. We're reminded that Lucia has 36 wins and 12 knockouts. She's a veteran, a veteran who has plowed through past female opponents as if they were amateurs. She has a chance.

8

I slipped out of my robe and stood naked in front of the mirror. It was June, but my skin was still pink and translucent like an earthworm's. My shins were knotted with rotten blood from having been bashed over and over again. I crouched and traced my fingers over them. The skin felt thin, and I imagined it rubbing down so far as to expose my bone. I had heard once that in Thailand boys harden their shins by kicking palm trees. Perhaps the real reason was that they were too poor to afford the luxuries of a heavy bag, so they simply kicked at the next best things: trees, light poles, door frames. Or they'd have a friend hit their shins repeatedly with a broomstick. The idea of it made me go numb. My shins were ugly enough the way they were, from simply smacking leather-bound bags.

I stood and let my eyes drip over the rest of my body. At 143 pounds, I was the lightest I'd been since breaking my jaw freshman year of college and being forced to drink chicken broth from a turkey baster. My current weight was good for my ass, but bad for my breasts, which hung sadly from my chest. If I squinted and ignored the bottom half of my body, then my torso and arms easily resembled those of a teenage boys. I cupped my breasts and pushed them together, seeing if I could get them to touch, but the attempt was futile, because I could only get them within a half inch of each other before they sulked back into place.

Releasing them, I let my arms hang. Beneath my fingertips, my knees swelled like croissants. My sister and I referred to our knees as "Schultz knees" because of how similar they were to our brothers'. We figured they ran in the family. They were quite masculine, and in looking at them in the mirror, they appeared very circular and red, too. Above the kneecap was a thick muscle that hung out like a brow bone. Each of us Schultzes had it; our brothers' were more defined and pronounced, but genetics still hit my sister and me. My knees' only redeeming quality was that they were my secret weapon in the ring; *MMAWeekly* had referred to them as "devastating" in an article summarizing one of my fights. Devastating, but manly.

I shifted my eyes from my knees to my stomach. I liked my abs. Since third grade I'd had a four-pack, a flat, tight stomach edged out in small sections, like an ice tray filled with skin. It was purely genetic; at nine, I wasn't practicing my times tables while doing sit-ups on the living-room floor. But genetics or not, I was proud of my stomach. It was stronger and more developed than it had been in elementary school. Brian once told me, years after seeing me naked for the first time, that he had been jealous of my stomach. I smiled, thinking back to what he had admitted and knowing full well that he'd never acknowledge saying such a thing.

Turning away from the mirror, I walked across my room and climbed into bed. The sheets were cold, forcing me to curl up into fetal position on my side. Under my sheets, in the cool cocoon of my bed, I ran my hand over my thighs and felt them prickle with goosebumps. I rubbed them back and forth, trying to inspire some sort of heat. As I rubbed, I closed my eyes, waiting for warmth, waiting for sleep.

9

The fight begins. Lucia bounds from her corner, hopping and moving from side to side. She seems to float above the mat, never resting or pausing to slow the momentum. She throws two mediocre kicks, probably anxious, probably driven by nerves and simply wanting to appear active. They don't land. Somchai dodges and swats them away. He remains untouched.

Lucia tries again, gearing up for a punch. It lands on Somchai's shoulder. He fires back with a kick that collides with Lucia's liver and a punch that drives her head back against the ropes. She's quick to recover, though. Somchai steps back across the ring and Lucia shuffles after him, looking energized, hyper. She wants revenge. She wants something to land on her opponent. So she kicks. It's a low kick, and as it flies through the air, Somchai slices beneath it and sweeps out Lucia's other leg. She falls on her butt.

She snaps back up and shows the ref she's fine. He grabs her gloves, sees for himself that she's all right, and then motions for the fight to continue. Both fighters kick at the same time. Both fall to the mat. The crowd erupts, eager to see Somchai fall, even if he has tripped over his own feet. The opponents jump back to their feet. Hopping, shuffling, nervous.

The fight's continued and Lucia dives after Somchai. He tries to stifle her forward movement with a punch, but she ducks beneath it and counters with a cross. It lands. Her first punch. She follows it with a head-kick. The combination has potential. It looks solid. But as Lucia's leg winds up into the air, she loses her balance and falls. Her third fall within a matter of thirty seconds. Within the next thirty seconds, Lucia falls twice more. She's losing points every time she hits the mat.

The round is close to over. Somchai delivers a powerful punch that snaps Lucia's head back and forth like a yo-yo. The crowd gasps but loves it. They love it even more when Lucia manages to sweep Somchai to the floor. Her first time knocking him off his feet. As he falls, the crowd rises to their feet, screaming their encouragements to Lucia. The adrenaline is pumping. The fighters are barely letting their feet rest on the mat. They face off, ready for more, but the bell tones. The round is done.

Lucia walks to her corner, rests her arms on the ropes, and exhales deeply. Her trainers offer her water and fan her with towels. She doesn't look too beat up or too tired. She must know, however, that the first round went to Somchai. If she wants to win, she has to win the next two rounds. What she doesn't know is that everything will conclude in the second round. It will all be over within twenty seconds.

10

The dentist office was like any other dentist office: over air-conditioned, walls painted beige and blanketed with framed photos of women with white teeth, and end tables covered with *People* magazines from the entire summer. I sat down in one of the armchairs and leafed through a magazine, looking mindlessly at pictures of celebrities grocery shopping and drinking their Starbucks lattes.

"Coffee?" the receptionist asked. From my chair, all I could see were her bangs, thin and wiry, poofing out like tree branches in the middle of winter, and the frames of her glasses, half hidden by wild eyebrows. Her voice was high pitched and scratchy, like the mom from *Bobby's World*.

"No thanks," I answered, wondering why anyone would want coffee before seeing their dentist. My most thorough teeth cleanings occur before dentist visits. If I made appointments every day, I'd probably have perfect teeth.

My dentist, Dr. Vittori, emerged from a doorway beside the front desk. He wore khaki pants and a button-down collared shirt. Beneath his glasses, his eyes zigzagged. One of them seemed to follow a pattern on the tiled ceiling, while the other looked a little to my left. I sometimes feel that staring at his nose is too obvious, so instead I try to avoid making eye contact altogether.

"Come on in, Dolly," he said, smiling his doctor smile. My dentist calls me Dolly. I'm not sure why. He's either confused Dolly for Dorothy at every single one of my visits, or it's some sort of pet name, which I'd rather not consider. I thought about correcting him once, but he was inside my mouth at the time, and after that missed opportunity, I couldn't bring it up without feeling awkward. So Dolly it is.

I followed him through the doorway and took a seat in the dentist chair. From behind me, a faceless nurse draped a bib over my chest and fastened it behind my neck. Dr. Vittori squatted onto a rolling chair and rolled over to me.

"OK, Dolly, what's this I hear about loose teeth?"

I scrunched up my nose and stuck out my front teeth. I wiggled them back and forth with my thumb.

"They got knocked out of place," I said, after withdrawing my thumb. Dr. Vittori whistled out of the side of his mouth and leaned in to get a closer look. I smelled the rubber glove as it passed by my nose and began prodding my teeth.

"Whew! They sure did get knocked around. Did this happen with that fighting of yours?" Dr. Vittori scooted back in his chair and rested his hands on his thighs.

"Yeah."

"You got hit pretty hard, eh?"

"It was an illegal hit," I said, "but I beat her up for it, so don't worry."

"Well, Dolly, I'm gonna have to take some X-rays to make sure the nerve wasn't pinched or nothing."

"Go for it," I said, and leaned my head back on the chair.

Dr. Vittori stood up from his stool and fumbled around with things on the counter. I stared at the wall in front of me, which was covered with a school of plastic fish.

"So what do your parents think of you fighting?" Dr. Vittori asked, draping a weighted cloak over me.

"They keep wondering when I'm going to start dancing instead."

Dr. Vittori laughed a Santa Claus laugh and told me to open up. He was still chuckling as he slid two braces into my mouth and asked me to pull them out against my cheeks. With my teeth exposed, he stepped out of the room and flicked on the X-ray. Then he returned a moment later and removed the braces from my mouth.

"Now the X-rays will confirm this," Dr. Vittori said, "but I think your teeth will firm right back up in a few days. I don't think any nerves were pinched, but had you been hit harder, that could've happened. Then we'd be in a lot of trouble."

"But they should be fine, right?" I asked.

"Yeah, just don't get hit again."

11

Lucia's trainers must have struck a nerve. When the second round rings, she pounces from the corner. She's mad, perhaps embarrassed. She's never lost before. She marches towards Somchai, throwing combinations in his face, causing him to step backward towards his corner. The seconds tick by with every punch.

Jab. One.

Cross. Two.

Hook. Three.

Lucia keeps throwing them, looking wild, losing some of her technique. The crowd doesn't care, though. They're yelling, "A-hoy!" with every punch she throws, regardless of whether it lands on Somchai or hurts him in any way. They want an upset. They came for an upset.

Hammering away, Lucia has Somchai cornered. But he doesn't remain passive. He cuts her off with a combination of his own. Jab, jab, cross. He pauses before delivering a hook. His timing throws Lucia off. She thinks he's throwing a punch, so she covers. When he doesn't, she lowers her guard. And as she does this, as she lowers her glove, Somchai flings his hook around, his ten-ounce glove slamming into Lucia's jaw. Somchai hurries to follow with another punch, but by this time it's clear that Lucia's out cold. She's still standing, but her arms and head are lifeless, hanging limp like a discarded doll. A second later she falls straight to the mat.

The ref runs to Lucia's side and cradles her head in his arms. Her eyes are probably rolled back. She may be speaking, but she's confused, unaware that she's been hit. Her memory of the last few minutes is vague, maybe gone altogether. Perhaps she thinks she's still fighting. "I'm good, I'm good," she mutters blindly. But she's not. The Most Dangerous Woman in the World has lost.

12

I've lost before. Three times, actually. Once was an exhibition fight, so I don't count it, but it was ultimately a loss. The feeling's awful. Standing in the middle of the ring, defeated, while the announcer takes his time to read the scores. There's a delay before he announces the winner, so for a second you hope the judges saw something that wasn't there; you hope that there's a split decision, at least.

But then the corner's announced. The rrrrrrrrrrrred corner! But you're in the blue corner. You fought out of blue tonight. Your gloves are blue. Hers are red. She's the red corner. She's the winner. The ref raises her hand and her fans cheer. You stare at the mat. In a second she'll come over to you and give you a hug. You hate post-fight hugs. She says something like, "You fought really hard." Gee, thanks.

So I've been there; I've lost fights. But I always remember Lucia. She wasn't famous before or *for* her fight against Somchai. She became The Most Dangerous Woman in the World after her fight against Somchai, after her first loss. It was what she did from there that defined her, made her the person she is known to be today.

About Suicide & Stars

Eliza Fogel

LATE ONE NIGHT LAST WINTER, I WATCHED THE 1987 SUICIDE OF FORMER Pennsylvania Treasurer R. Budd Dwyer. I hadn't set out to watch the startling clip, but I stumbled upon it in my own quiet desperation. I was reeling from my oldest friend's suicide. I'd met Marla when I was nine years old, jumping rope in front of my house, during the earliest days of summer. Isn't that how most childhood friendships are born? With adult-defying intimacy and trust forged over a lollipop and a secret, we had entered the perplexing and curious bond of young girls—we are going to be best friends forever because we'll write it on every passed note and in every yearbook scrawl because we *will* keep in touch.

I hadn't stopped thinking about Marla. Not since I'd received the Facebook message in December 2009: Marla *passed* away. My eyes wanted to skew the words. I've always felt that the eyes are the last part of the body to register permanent loss. Eyes are tricky, fooling you into seeing your ex-boyfriend parking his Passat, into seeing your grandmother at Jo-Ann Fabrics, into seeing your black dog in someone else's backseat. I'd thought about Marla so much, all that grief conjuring her slight frame in the ice cream aisle at Jewel, wedged between Breyer's chocolate chip mint and Edy's vanilla bean. Maybe I turned to the Internet in hopes of discovering the transcendental guide to keeping calm when your dead friend pops up in the grocery store, in the freezer section, pressing her slender, blue fingers up to the frosty glass.

Facebook wouldn't let me forget Marla, either, prompting me to see what my dead friend was up to these days as if we might want to chill later this weekend. (But if you know me, you know I don't chill, and I couldn't give a shit about weekends.) I couldn't help but cower to the request, so I kept checking her wall and reading the newest entries, unable to decide which one was in poorer taste: the quiz to find out her chances of surviving a zombie war, or the message telling Marla to hang in there after she'd already put her head in a slip noose. In this moment, I hated Facebook, the ill-informed Web Beast of social anxiety and popularity contests, that tries to include me, exclude me, poke me, invite me, mock me, unflatteringly photograph me, post up on me, and force me into unwanted seclusion. Facebook, all-knowing monster, how can you not know that Marla is blue in the face with a few strangulation marks from the tight cord she carefully wrapped around her neck—probably the same pattern we'd used to braid our hair—and that she is dressed in a sweet sweater with her hands clasped together and enough makeup to last until the coffin flies set in to do their busywork? You don't know, Facebook, because no one posted a picture?

I'm a big girl when it comes to dead bodies, having put together a thirteen-year-old's pelvic bones as if they were my favorite puzzle and even having crawled into a coffin and shut the lid just to see what it'd be like to wake up dead; yet, when I saw her there, just a hundred-pound weight in a stretch of box, I wanted to run to a corner and whisper primary colors and ABCs to ground myself in a safe childhood memory.

For weeks after the funeral, I continued checking her blog and her Facebook page, waiting for her to communicate to me because it was 2010, and we'd entered a different world. Death was now digitized and our web pages were personalized and our grief was now available for everyone to witness through statuses, posts, and YouTube clips. The desire to see Marla one last time was really what brought me to Budd Dwyer's suicide. I wanted to discover a video of her laughing or dancing. I wanted to see my friend before I went to bed, and maybe, just maybe, if I wrote her a message at 3:28 a.m., when most of the world in our hometown was asleep, her eyes would pop open and she'd touch the top of her coffin and I'd touch my glowing monitor and we'd be kids again. We could go back and save ourselves.

In my desperate search for cyber-Marla, I stumbled into the endless world of the online dead and dying—accidents and videos riddled with sappy songs and flowery fonts and photographs of fathers and children in happier times, before the cancer, before the car crash, before the crib death, abuse, neglect, drowning, mauling, murder, falling, suicide.

Initially, I didn't recognize the name—Budd Dwyer. I was vaguely aware of his connection with the 1995 song "Hey Man, Nice Shot," wherein the lead singer of Filter wishes he could've met the man. And even when the name Dwyer popped up in my search it was tagged alongside "Reaction to Budd Dwyer's Suicide," clips showing people's faces contorting as they watched the footage of Dwyer's shot to the head. His death was an afterthought, a plausible result of a Kardashian world typified by all eyes on me, me, me—Kim, Khloe and Kourtney.

When people post to the Internet they attempt to pull the spotlight back upon themselves, crying out: pay attention; don't forget about me. I think it's because most of us are so profoundly lonely. Back in 1987, we weren't as advanced and didn't have the Internet to give us a million instant friends or overnight stardom as in the case of Antoine Dodson "The Bed Intruder" or Rebecca Black of "Friday" fame or Paul "Bear" Vasquez's "Double Rainbow," or Keenan Cahill's creepy cover of Katy Perry's "Teenage Dream," or Leeroy Jenkins, or Lightning Bolt, or "Peanut Butter Jelly Time," or worse yet—ultimate hell—the evil Rick Roll . . . the list goes on. In 1987, people's stories and antics still came via the newspaper and newscasts and neighborly chats. The fact that Budd Dwyer's suicide aired live on television, rather than as a formal statement or a sound bite, is what makes his public act so remarkable and horrific. The world was yet to call up grizzly death scenes with a few keystrokes in Google, and some might even go as far as saying that society was not as sophisticated or desensitized.

Prior to Dwyer, only one other suicide had taken place live on air, and because of the Sarasota police and the Chubbuck family's forethought—their prescience—the footage does not exist online. On the morning of July 15, 1974, newscaster Christine Chubbuck pulled a .38 revolver from the bag of puppets she'd stored beneath her desk. Having grown tired of the station's sensationalistic coverage, Christine followed up the news report of a shooting at the local Beef and Bottle Restaurant with a story of her own, the now famous words: "In keeping with Channel 40's policy of bringing you the latest in blood and guts, and in living color, you are going to see another first: an attempted suicide." She shot herself behind the right ear as the cameras rolled. Everyone thought it was a joke until her body slumped down and twitched, and the news desk flooded with blood (Quinn 124).

Budd Dwyer's public performance occurred thirteen years later in Harrisburg, Pennsylvania. There was a heavy winter storm brewing on the morning of January 22. Children stayed home enjoying the ever-elusive, often-wished-for snow day. Commuters battled miserable traffic to get to work (Bronner 41). Reporters, cameramen, and photographers made their way to the state capitol building because the treasurer, R. Budd Dwyer, had called for a morning press conference in his office. He'd been found guilty for accepting a bribe, a kickback of approximately $300,000 for awarding a government contract to John Torquato, Jr., without sending the contract out for bid (United States v Dwyer).

That snowy morning was one day before Dwyer was to receive his possible fifty-five-year sentence from Judge John Muir, known as a hangman judge. This is germane to the subsequent events of that morning. For one, as long as Dwyer was still the treasurer (under Pennsylvania law, he was able to stay in office until his sentencing), his family was entitled to his 1.3 million dollar pension. Secondly, Dwyer vehemently denied any wrongdoing and knew that he was going to be used as an example. During the press conference Dwyer stated:

Judge Muir has already told the press that he, quote, "felt invigorated" when we were found guilty, and that he plans to imprison me as a deterrent to other public officials. But it wouldn't be a deterrent because every public official who knows me knows that I am innocent; it wouldn't be a legitimate punishment because I've done nothing wrong (budd-dwyer.com).

Dwyer saw no way out and made his final decision. He wanted to make sure his death occurred while he was still in office so his wife and his two children would receive his pension and not suffer financially. Beyond taking care of his family, he wanted to send a message to the world, to show how far a man would go to prove his innocence.

What we don't see the minutes before the 10:30 a.m. press conference is how Dwyer carefully orchestrated the event (Bronner 42). He arrived early, wearing a dark suit, a pale dress shirt, and a silver tie with diagonal, blood-red stripes, and proceeded to dress the room. He rearranged the furniture and created a physical barrier between him and the reporters. He placed a long mahogany table to separate himself from the crowd, and he positioned a smaller desk behind him, protecting his back.

What we see of the conference, the only portion that seems relevant to viewers today, are the most sensationalistic moments (Documenting Reality, Anonymous). Once the press arrives, Dwyer checks the doorknob to make sure the office door is firmly shut. He places his black briefcase on the table and clicks open the top to reveal a scattered stack of papers and envelopes. He shuffles through, pulls out a select few, and circulates copies of his nineteen-page statement. Men with ties and rolled up sleeves crowd closer in a semicircle, waiting to hear Dwyer announce his resignation. Dwyer, however, does not make the announcement they've been anticipating. Instead, he reads through his prepared speech, choking through tears, his cherubic face flushed with anger.

The cameras keep rolling as he speaks. Six news crews. Four photographers. Paul Vathis is among the gathered men. He's photographing the story for the AP Wire. Twenty-one minutes into Dwyer's speech, Vathis wonders if Dwyer's dramatic resignation will ever come. He's not the only one. Cameramen begin to move around the cherry-paneled room, gathering wires and packing up their gear. Because Dwyer is certain he will go through with his planned act, he warns them, "Those of you who are putting your cameras away, I think you ought to stay because we're not finished yet."

Dwyer senses the crowd's apprehension and his calm is shaken. The sweat on his brow glistens, and he wipes it away with his right hand; the camera shutters click hard and fast, catching his nervous gesture. His eyes scan the room, and he leans back on his heels. There is a man directly on Dwyer's left who is wearing a black suit and tie and taking furtive puffs of his cigarette. This man is standing too close, and Dwyer eyes him momentarily. He skips parts of his speech, moves forward to the end, and looks around for his aides.

"Is Bob Holstey here? Bob?" Dwyer says, looking around for the Treasury Department assistant.

"And where's Greg . . . can you come up here?" Dwyer says, looking for Greg Penny, the Treasury Department's deputy press secretary.

"And where's Don Johnson . . . can you come up, Don?" he says, looking for the deputy treasurer.

One by one, the men elbow their way through the tight crowd. Dwyer leans over the table and hands each of them a white envelope. Bob accepts his first, then Greg approaches, and Don makes it to the front last. Dwyer hurriedly says that the documents are for later and that there's one for Joanne, his wife. He looks around again, with increased anxiety; the smoking man, who is already standing too close, takes Dwyer's attention. Dwyer watches him out of the corner of his left eye. The man is jumpy and leans forward, getting dangerously close to the manila envelope in the brief-case (Bjelić 164). Budd makes a fast move and reaches forward, but the smoking man ignores Budd's hand and proceeds to snuff out his cigarette in an ashtray that is awkwardly near the briefcase. The man gives Budd a curious look. The situation grows worse.

Budd snatches the manila envelope, holding it in his right hand. Eyebrows raise and heads tilt in wonderment. The cameramen zoom in on the envelope and Budd repositions it in his left hand, holding it by the corner, and reaches in with his right hand. In one quick move, he pulls out a shiny, black .357 Magnum revolver. He clasps the gun in his right hand and the hammer instantly cocks. He points the six-and-a-half-inch barrel up to the ceiling, lining it up with the four silver buttons on the cuff of his suit jacket.

The gun is close to his neck. He licks his lips and starts to speak: "When I—and I . . . "

The crowd cries out in horror, pleading with Budd. Voices cry out: "No, no, Budd, don't." He motions for everyone to stay back. He doesn't want to hurt anyone. He puts out his left hand, signaling a strong STOP. He doesn't want anyone to approach him; he also gestures for people to leave, giving them permission and motioning towards the exit.

Budd says, "Please leave the room if this will—" A woman cries out, "Please don't do this." Budd finishes his sentence, " . . . if this will affect you." The crowd's anxiety encroaches, pressing in and around, full of pleas and frantic movements. Dwyer puts the gun closer to his head, on the left side of his face. A person moves towards Dwyer's right side. "No, Budd, No, No." Dwyer warns the man, saying, "Don't." He doesn't want anyone to come any closer. He looks around, left to right, surveying the crowd. He holds the gun with both hands and quickly puts it into his mouth. No one dares approach him. Everyone stays behind the table, uncertain what Dwyer will ultimately do with the gun, fearful that there's still a chance he will turn on them. The second aide, Greg Penny, whom Dwyer had summoned just seconds before, frantically peeks inside his envelope and finds Dwyer's organ donor card. He has a split second to comprehend the meaning before he hears the gunshot.

Pop. One bullet rips through R. Budd Dwyer's skull and exits through the back of his head. The brain is destroyed, but the heart continues to beat for four healthy seconds, pumping a deluge of blood out of his nose and mouth. A small trickle drips out of the top of his head, but the curtain of red running from his nostrils, the waterfall of blood, keeps pouring and pouring down Dwyer's pressed shirt. The streaming flow is steady, drowning his chest. His tie disappears, no longer visible beneath what looks like a thick wash of spilled red paint.

Budd Dwyer's body crumples into the corner created by the wall and the smaller desk behind him. His body slumps slowly, drooping down into his suit as all of his muscles relax and the last of his blood gushes from his gaping wound. He's blown off the top of his peach head and scattered skull fragments and brain matter on the cream and gold tapestry draped on the wall behind him. The cameras keep rolling and moving in for tight close-ups. AP photographer Paul Vathis keeps furiously clicking away, getting far more drama than he had expected.

Duke Horschock, Dwyer's press secretary, runs to Dwyer's side, begging the cameramen to wrap up their gear, insisting they've gotten as much as they are going to get. He looks at Vathis and says, "Paul, please, enough." He stands in front of his friend's body, blocking the cameras, and asks everyone to settle down, begs everyone, for the love of God, for a little decorum.

The audience assumed the press conference would be regular, almost boring. They had no idea they were about to witness a live suicide. The local newscasters interrupted scheduled programs and many of those at-home, snowbound children watched the footage of Dwyer putting the gun barrel into his mouth and pulling the trigger.

Dwyer shocked the world, but he never got in his last words. What he left the world with was his savage cry of innocence. He had every intention of reading his entire suicide script but did not take into account his audience's horrified reaction and how they might try to stop him from completing his final act. The last page of Dwyer's statement contains his last wish:

I am going to die in office in an effort to see if the shameful facts, spread out in all their shame, will not burn through our civic shamelessness and set fire to American pride. Please tell my story on every radio and television station and in every newspaper and magazine in the U.S. (budd-dwyer.com).

His public suicide posed a difficult problem for newspaper editors. The use of the graphic photos presented a dilemma: taste versus news value. The newsroom cliché, "if it bleeds, it leads," was about to be put to the test (Kochersberger 2). Because Paul Vathis kept shooting, about which he said, "From professional experience, I just kept taking pictures," a variety of photographs, frame by frame, were immediately available for the media (Vathis 2A). Vathis's photos landed on the desks of photo editors within an hour after the shooting.

Although AP photographers carried color negative film in their bags, its use was cost prohibitive, so it was only used on the most important assignments. This, after all, was supposed to be a routine press conference. Until Dwyer put the gun in his mouth, his statements that morning did not qualify as a worthy event. For this reason, all of the photographs are in black and white. Dwyer's suicide changed the AP's rules for shooting in black and white. The reason, beyond capturing the truly vivid and gruesome details, was a matter of profit. Color photographs had higher resale value overseas (Gardiner, "Color or BW?").

Dwyer could've taken his life quietly at home or privately in his office but he used the press conference for his grand exit and made it a completely public spectacle. Perhaps, in absolute despair and anger, he wanted to affect not only those in his immediate world, but those well beyond. Of the twenty stations that have regular newscasts in Pennsylvania, only three showed the actual suicide. Most stations ran a sound bite from the news conference followed by the moments of the suicide, stopping the tape as Dwyer pointed the gun upward (Parsons 88). Really, what were the newspapers and televisions supposed to do? It wasn't until 1994 that the government created an outline for how media should treat suicide:

PROVIDING SENSATIONAL COVERAGE OF SUICIDE:
By its nature, news coverage of a suicidal event tends to heighten the general public's preoccupation with suicide. This reaction is also believed to be associated with contagion and the development of suicide clusters. Public officials can help minimize sensationalism by limiting, as much as possible, morbid details in their public discussions of suicide. News media professionals should attempt to decrease the prominence of the news report and avoid the use of dramatic photographs related to the suicide (e.g., photographs of the funeral, the deceased person's bedroom, and the site of the suicide) (MMWR 16).

Clearly, the Internet doesn't play by the same rules. R. Budd Dwyer wanted the media to witness, to document his death, to implicate all of those who didn't believe in his innocence. The bullet mark where he blew his brains to bits still exists. Despite efforts to remove the scar from the office wall, the damage is permanent. Dwyer was a man facing absolute shame and a lengthy prison term. He'd lost all hope and felt that other conspirators had set him up to be the fall guy. Some say that nine-tenths of Harrisburg's system was corrupt and that what happened to Dwyer had little to do with his effort in making any deals and more with the promises being made all around him and behind his back. After all of the supposed discussions over money, Dwyer never received a dime.

Beliefs over suicide vary considerably. Various cultures condone and encourage "altruistic" sacrifice. I suppose, though, that it doesn't really matter what survivors believe. The dead have moved on for their own private reasons that even if spelled out in a letter* or witnessed up until the very last second, are a part of humanity that is beyond our comprehension, maybe something so dark and primitive wrought in a cave with marred pictographs, so far back they came before humanity reflected on existing only once, in this miraculous form. Suicide is a devastation for anyone who has experienced its effects, a loss beyond description.

R. Budd Dwyer could not have foreseen his image endlessly repeating on the Internet, accessed by millions in a split second, or that the masses would begin recording themselves in response to watching his suicide. As he's shown up again and again on various sites, the footage has lost clarity, copied and dubbed so many times that Dwyer resembles a blurred ghost. He probably never would have seen this coming, or maybe he's online right now watching. After all, the only salvageable organs of Dwyer's that could be donated were his corneas (Cusick, *Philadelphia Enquirer*). Imagine: somewhere out there, Dwyer's eyes are gazing at a computer screen, unknowingly watching his death. It is an unforeseeable recursion and a haunting image that sheds light on the fact that we never know what the future holds around that blind corner.

I know it's selfish and doesn't speak to her immeasurable pain, but I'd bring back Marla (and David and sweet Emma Bee). I'd tell each one the

---

* Marla's last words to me: So many secrets only shadows would see. So much shame. So much I could never say because of my cannibalized soul. But my ego is not so big that I can't beg for you to forgive me for anything I have ever said or done that was simply wrong and offensive because believe it or not, your friendship was one of the few lights in my life. In my heart, I always felt our souls were kindred in kind.

truth, plain and simple:

You are worth thousands of stars. You are as precious as wings. You are meant to be here, and if it takes an entire year to convince you, it will be worth every second. I will sit with you on the curb and bring you warm socks and tea, and we can stay right there and cry for the next hundreds of tomorrows if it means I can keep you here on earth with me. We need you more than you know. We need you more than anyone will tell you because it scares us how much we need you in our hearts, in our arms, and if you left us, man, would we hurt. We'd be in the dark. We'd starve like wolves.

Marla: I don't need to see you online to know how much you're missed. You were my first girlfriend, the one all others would be set against. I'll never forget how you showed me to smudge aqua shadow on my eyelids and told me that I'd just know when I was ready to kiss a boy and that I'd make a really good mermaid, and how you didn't laugh when I told you my greatest fear in life was that I'd never be remembered because no one in school ever listened to me like you did.

We'll always be spinning around in leg warmers and ballet shoes, chuckling, listening to Madonna and exchanging black gummy bracelets. Visit me, but not online or in the Jewel, in spaces so publicly naked and porous. Sit in my dreams where we'll have all the time in this world and the next, and all the memories we can remember, and I promise, I won't be scared. I'll have always been waiting for you because that's what BFFs do. We'll skip back long before this good-bye and keep our promise. We'll pinkie swear. This time I won't let you fall. I promise. I swear. Just come back to me, ghost and all, so I can love you all over again.

Works Cited

Bjelić, Dušan I. "Public Suicide as a Deed of Optionless Intimacy." *Symbolic Interaction* 13.2: 161-183. Print.

Bronner, Simon J. "Digitizing and Virtualizing Folklore." *Folklore and the Internet: Vernacular Expression in a Digital World*. Ed. Trevor J. Blank. Logan, Utah: Utah State UP, 2009. 41-56. Print.

Cusick, Frederick, Dan Meyers, Walter F. Roche, Jr., and Russell E. Eshelman, Jr. "Treasurer Dwyer Kills Self Suicide At News Session." *Philadelphia Inquirer* 23 Jan. 1987. Web. Apr. 2010.

Gardiner, Gary. "Color or BW? – The change began in 1987 with "Budd" Dwyer." http://www.newdigitalphoto.gs/technique/color-or-bw-change-began-1987-budd-dwyer/

Kochersberger Jr., Robert C. "Survey of Suicide Photos." *Newspaper Research Journal* Summer 9.4 (1988). Print.

Laurin, Marla. "A Request." Message to the author. 2009. E-mail.

Parsons, Patrick R., and William E. SMith. "R. Budd Dwyer: A Case Study in Newsroom Decision Making." *Journal of Mass Media Ethics* 3.1: 84-94. Print.

Quinn, Sally. "Christine Chubbuck: 29, Good-Looking, Educated. A Television Personality. Dead. Live and in Color." *Washington Post* 4 Aug. 1974: 124. Web.

Stevens, William K. "Official Calls In Press and Kills Himself." *New York Times* 23 Jan. 1987. Retrieved from http://www.budd-dwyer.com.remember.to/.

Vathis, Paul. "...And Just Pulled The Trigger." *Ocala Star-Banner* 23 Jan. 1987. Web. 22 Apr. 2010.

Web. <http://www.budd-dwyer.com.remember.to/>. Dwyer, R. Budd. "R Budd Dwyer's Final moments."

Web. <http://eightyfourfilms.com/Dwyer/USAvsDwyer.pdf>. *United States of America vs. R. Budd Dwyer / Robert B. Asher*. United States District Court for the Middle District of Pennsylvania. 13 May 1986.

Web. <http://www.documentingreality.com/forum/f166/budd-dwyer-commits-suicide-during-news-conference-hi-quality-11738>

Web. <http://www.cdc.gov/mmwr/PDF/rr/rr4306.pdfSuicide> "Contagion and the Reporting of Suicide: Recommendations from a National Workshop," MMWR Vol. 43, NO RR-6, 1994.

Marked

Emily Schultz

I AM IN COLLEGE WAITRESSING IN THE WEST VILLAGE FOR EXTRA CASH AT A funky little Italian joint right off of Union Square. I grumble to myself when I see that a couple has asked to sit outside at one of my tables even though it is a chilly November night and usually the patio is abandoned. I pour two glasses of ice water and balance them on a tray as I make my way outside and set the glasses down in front of them.

Then I look up. And it is when I look up, into the woman's face, that I feel my heart freeze for just a moment with a pause of surprise and recognition. It is her left cheek, stained with a dark purple blotch that stretches around her eye and pours down to her chin. Its color is deep, with a raised surface, small bumps boiling up into a grail, like thick lava on white sand. I catch myself staring.

"Is that a port-wine stain?" I ask timidly. I can't help it. I have only seen a handful of others with a mark like mine.

"Yeah, it is," she says, and turns back to smile and laugh with the man she is with.

"You know, I have one too, right here." I let my hand wave over the right side of my face where a pink birthmark stretches over my skin. I am careful, though, not to let my hand smudge away my makeup, my disguise.

She leans forward and squints, straining to see what I have just revealed, and I wonder if it was right of me to say anything; I wonder if I really want to show her what it is I am hiding.

"I don't see anything," she says, still squinting as if trying to make out something in the distance.

"Well, I wear makeup, you know, to keep it covered." I say this with a shrug of my shoulders and a smile as if it is no big thing, which, of course, could not be farther from the truth. I have spent my whole life hiding from my own skin, trying desperately not to admit it, and this excuse I give her reminds me of how uncomfortable I am with my own self.

"Oh," she says, and it is a long *Ohhh*, her mouth in a big round shape as she sits back comfortably in her seat. Oh. You're one of those girls. You're one of those girls who want so badly to be like everyone else, the kind who will diet rigorously for weeks if they think they are too fat in their size-four jeans, the kind who wear heavy makeup if they think they are not pretty enough. Oh. You're one of those. I see. Well, I'll have a ginger ale please. Thank you.

"I think she is beautiful just the way she is," the man sitting next to her says, and he wraps his arm around her and leans in to plant a kiss on her purple cheek. "I don't want you wearing any makeup, you hear? I love this face." He grabs her chin and shakes it gently, their faces close to one another. She turns away from me, towards him, and they meet at the lips. I walk away and eat my words like sour lemons.

We are so different, this woman and I, and yet we have the same skin. Only three out of every one thousand babies each year will be born with a port-wine stain birthmark, and together, this woman and I make up two out of that three. Port-wine stains are dark, solid blotches that take on shapes of their own, and like globs of paint dripping down a canvas, they leave a layer of noticeable color.

After I was born, the doctor explained to my parents what a port-wine stain is. They were uneasy that something might have gone wrong with their first child and listened carefully to the doctor as she sat with them in the quiet hospital room and answered all their questions.

"The blood vessels in her cheek weren't supplied with enough nerves. This results in the blood vessels in her right cheek being substantially bigger than the ones in the left. It's not that there are extra nerves; it's that they are bigger, wider. This is what causes the stain. Don't worry. It can only cause possible brain damage if the stain stretches onto the forehead, above the eye. Hers doesn't look too bad, but you should consider starting laser therapy as soon as possible."

"Why so soon?" my father asked; the idea of making his daughter endure any kind of pain so young wasn't something he was prepared for.

"The laser will zap her face with an intense light that will burn through the skin and shrink those vessels. It will prevent them from growing, which would cause the mark to thicken in texture and deepen. I'll put you in touch with one of New York's top doctors, Dr. G."

My mother had sat listening to all of this without saying much. She was not surprised when she looked at her little girl for the first time, and as I later found out, she felt like she had known all along that there would be something different about my face.

She told me about it one day after I had come home from college on winter break during my freshman year. We were sitting on the couch, drinking tea and catching up with each other. She is beautiful, my mother, with sparkly hazel eyes, prominent cheek bones, and a slender face. She had saved a newspaper clipping for me about a newscaster who, for the first time, went on camera without any makeup, revealing to the world that her face was almost half covered with a port-wine stain birthmark. My mom had trimmed and neatly folded the paper safely into an envelope, thoughtfully storing it in a desk drawer for me. It was proof that others like me did exist, her way of trying to show me that I wasn't so different after all.

As I sat reading the article, my mother put down her tea and suddenly said, "I knew you would be born with one." I looked up from the paper in my hands, surprised, not knowing at first what she meant.

"Your birthmark. I knew you would be born with it."

"How?" I asked. She had never said anything like this before.

"I had a dream while I was still pregnant. I'll never forget it. I was holding you, and I was scrubbing your face with a rag. I kept scrubbing and scrubbing, but whatever it was I was trying to get off just wouldn't go away. When you were born and I saw you, I realized that I had known all along." She reached out a hand to gently touch my cheek. "I was so worried that you would suffer because of it. But look at you! You have so many friends, you're an A student, you have a handsome boyfriend. It's like you haven't let it bother you one bit." She smiled and I tried to smile back, fighting the urge to tell her how very wrong she was.

* * *

I had my first laser treatment when I was just five months old. Before he started, Dr. G zapped my dad's hand with the laser, a small pen-like device attached by a cord to a boxy machine, so he could know how it felt. Dad held me down between his palms, like a peanut in its shell, as the doctor penetrated the powerful, focused light beam through the skin on my cheek. My father later told me that holding me there while I screamed and cried was one of the hardest things he ever had to do. He had to keep reminding himself that he was doing the right thing, that he was doing it for me.

After a treatment, my cheek swelled so much that my eye became just a slit. The color of my birthmark changed from light salmon pink to a bright, dark purple pigment, like juice from a grape. When I was in elementary school, I would show up the day after having laser with my cheek taped up in bandages. It was almost like I enjoyed the attention, but that quickly changed as I got older. When I reached high school, I couldn't afford to take a whole week off from my social life to recover in complete privacy, where no one could see the embarrassing transformation my face had taken. Nor could I fathom leaving my house without covering up my birthmark as much as I could. I grew to rely on my makeup more than my next meal.

I felt like I was living in the shadow of my own face, constantly battling my own reflection. I believed I would spend my whole life with pores clogged under dense beige cream, forever covering up the thing I could not change.

I was seven years old the first time I ever wore the stuff. I was standing behind the doorway watching my nana as she sat at her vanity, perched on a blue velvet stool in her flowered nightgown. I believed it was magic, the way she could transform herself from an old wrinkled woman with loose skin and wiry gray hair, into someone who smelled like French perfume, who had long black eyelashes and painted lips. She was humming to herself as she got out her tools: wands and powders that knew her secrets and how to hide them. She laid them out on a sheet of Kleenex in a line, like soldiers. Although there was a large mirror in front of her, one that took up almost the entire side of the wall, she preferred to work with a small gold-rimmed magnifying mirror, so she could attack every crevice of skin, every smudge of color, with expertise and skill. I watched her, almost enchanted, as she began to work her spells.

"Oh Emily, I didn't see you there, lovey. Come sit with me while I put on my face," she said, as she looked at me through the reflection from the large mirror. I took a seat on the toilet behind her, still watching. "This is what happens when you get old, my dear. You have to work to make yourself beautiful." She uncapped the long, dark eyeliner stick and began to etch her lids, making her light eyes pop.

My nana was the most elegant woman in the world, and I believed more than anyone that she knew what the word *beautiful* meant. Long, manicured orange nails, and lipstick on until the day she died. Gold bracelets with foreign coins as charms, and stories of Paris: these were the things she knew.

"There," she said, as she dabbed her left cheek with a large puff of cotton stained with rouge. She swiveled to face me and smiled. "Would you like to see how some looks on you?" I nodded without hesitation. She opened a thin black case with cream packed inside its compartment. "Close your eyes," she said, and I did, trying my best to be still as she ran a cool sponge across my right cheek, dabbing under my eye. She didn't bother putting anything on the left side because, after all, that side was perfect; it wasn't stained with the imperfection that marked the right like a stamp. She didn't bother with eye shadow or mascara or lipstick because I was too young to carry the weight of a fully painted face. "All done," she announced, and I opened my eyes with a snap as I stared into the large mirror at a face that seemed different, better.

I looked closer and my eyes grew wide as if I had just witnessed a miracle. "You can barely see it!" I said excitedly with a big grin. My nana watched proudly as I studied my reflection some more. The birthmark was gone. It had disappeared, like magic.

I was careful to resist the urge to run my fingers down my cheek, the way you reach out to touch the images of a 3-D movie, testing what you know is not real. "I look beautiful!" I said, and my nana patted me on the back and nodded that yes, I did. "I'm going to go show Dad!" and I ran out of the bathroom to show my family how Nana had made me look so nice and new.

"Wow, look at you!" my dad said enthusiastically, always there to encourage me. I realized quickly by his reaction that I was right in thinking that the makeup had changed me for the better. For my nana, it dulled the sharp-edged corners of age from showing on her face; for me, it left me looking like every other little girl in my class, pretty and unmarked.

"You can't come in," Joey said, as he stood at the doorway of the clubhouse. It was made of wood and built under the stairs that led out of the school and down to the playground. The large playground had three tire swings, a jungle gym, and a large, fake flowerpot with a plastic flower that would twirl and spray water around the hopscotch court when it was warm out. Joey had peed in the flowerpot the other day during recess, and I had watched, disgusted and appalled, before I ran to get the teacher. Even in kindergarten I knew that boys couldn't just pee anywhere they liked.

"I'm sorry I told on you," I said, thinking that this must be the reason for my clubhouse banishment. I had been welcomed in there before, so I didn't understand Joey's sudden, harsh opposition to my presence.

"That's not it," he spat out between lips that were, like the rest of him, covered in freckles. "You're not allowed in here 'cause you're weird."

"Yeah, you have that stuff on your face," said a boy behind him named Alex, who had a mass of curly blond hair brighter than the sun.

I said nothing back. I was a chubby, shy kid who wanted desperately to be liked and appreciated by others. I understood that even though my face hadn't stopped me from being a clubhouse member before, people's opinions could change, and I didn't question whether they were right or not. That day at recess I sat spinning on the tire-swing alone.

When I got home from school, my dad asked me what was wrong. I lied and said nothing.

"I don't believe you," he said, and I knew that he wasn't going to quit until I gave him some explanation. I have always known myself to be a terrible liar, and even then, I knew my dad could see right through me.

"I wasn't allowed in the clubhouse today," and I continued to tell him why.

"Come on, baby, you know you don't need their stupid clubhouse anyway. Those boys are crazy if they don't see how beautiful you are. Hey, you hear me, kiddo? You're really somethin' else." I sucked at my lower lip and listened to him, not knowing what to think, really. But before I could brood any longer, we were in the backyard building our own fort, our own clubhouse, Dad's shoulder-length hair pulled back in a ponytail just like mine, laughing and playing as if the large green yard was just as wonderful and curious to him as it was to me. Once again, he made me forget the troubles that came along with standing out in a crowd; with him I was always just a simple, smiling little girl.

My father came with me to every one of my laser treatments. We would play board games in the waiting area, and when the nurse called out my name, he would be right behind me as we walked into the doctor's room. I would sit nervously until Dr. G, a stocky man with a thick, dark mustache and hair carefully parted to the side, came through the door. After I had put on the protective goggles, which I always preferred over the optional contacts, and lay down on the crinkly paper, I would grip my father's hand and listen to his husky voice whisper to me that it was all right, that it was almost over. Having my dad there was what I always needed to feel better, safe. I grew up watching him swallow grunts of pain when his knees, which both needed to be replaced, hurt him terribly, and I remember thinking that if he could suffer so gracefully, then so could I.

They were painful, the laser treatments, like hot rubber bands snapping on my skin. I would listen to the rhythmic clunking of the machine, a sound like that of a type-writer carriage being pushed back at the end of a line, only louder, and I tried to focus on something other than the laser zapping at my cheek. Apart from the times when I was a baby, I never cried during treatments. In fact, as I got older, I would tell Dr. G to just do as much as he could, hoping that maybe all of it would disappear.

When I was still very young and required anesthesia to go through with a treatment, my dad would always ask me, "What flavor balloon do you want?" referring to the big plastic mask that would soon knock me out. I always answered cherry. I would breathe in that cherry air as deeply as I could and clutch in one hand my laser doll, a small plastic doll with yellow yarn for hair and big, sad blue eyes that my dad had given to me. With my other hand, I always held his. He would make sure to be there when I woke up, so that the first thing I saw when I opened my eyes was his face.

When I was nine years old, for the first and only time, I went to a new doctor for a laser treatment. My mom had suggested that we try someone new, and even though my dad was the "if it ain't broke, don't fix it" type, it was probably easier for him to give in than to argue with her.

By now I was far past the point of needing anesthesia, and instead, the nurse would usually just apply a layer of thick cream, called topical anesthesia, numbing my cheek to lessen the sting. As I sat in this new doctor's office in the long, leather patient's chair, like the kind you'd find at the dentist, I felt a knot in my stomach begin to grow. On the small table next to me I saw a long silver needle glint under the bright overhead lights, and I knew that needle was for me. The sight of its sharp tip made me shiver. I didn't trust that needle, and when the door swung open and I laid eyes on the nurse, I knew I didn't trust her one bit either.

As she squeezed through the doorway, I immediately saw the huge cone-shaped hat she had strapped to her head, the elastic creased between her double chin. This princess hat was covered in pink sparkles and had yellow, blue, and violet ribbons cascading down from its top. The name tag stuck to her chest had "Cinderella" written across it, and as I watched this nurse brush a few orange crumbs from her chest, approaching me with knees bent inward, ready to collapse under her own weight, I felt that knot in my stomach tighten.

"Hello, hello, hello. How are we today?" she said, as if the words were part of a song.

"Fine," I answered back, but I didn't meet her eyes. Instead, I sat staring at the hat; it was obviously a joke, but for whom? I imagined the nurses coming together at the end of the day saying things like "you should've seen that one girl's face when I walked in. She was shocked! Couldn't believe that I was the nurse!"

Cinderella sat down on a stool, right next to the needle.

"Is this your first time, sweetum-pie? You look so scared! Don't worry, Cinderella won't let anything hurt." She shoved her hands into latex gloves, like sausage meat being squeezed into casings, and let them snap tightly around her fat wrists.

"OK, muffin," Cinderella continued, "I'm going to inject this itty-bitty needle into your cheek, and it'll make you nice and numb so that you won't feel a thing when the doctor gets to work, all right?" I nodded as I sat back in the chair and gulped. I focused on a very peculiar water stain in the corner of the ceiling as she slowly plunged the needle into my right cheek. "What a good girl! What a good girl we have here!" she said in a voice that made me feel like a small puppy about to get a treat.

The doctor was in and out within ten minutes or less, the typical amount of time that the treatment took. But something was wrong, and I knew right away, as a peculiar ache settled into my skin that soon enough began to burn, that this was not the way it was supposed to feel. Perhaps I was being silly, though, and I stayed silent as Cinderella bandaged me up and waved me out the door. But when we reached the parking lot and got into the car, I was near tears from the pain. Usually after a treatment, my face would ache the same way a bad bruise does, but this was much worse, almost like peroxide being poured onto raw skin. The concern in my father's face began to deepen. He carefully removed the bandage, and I heard him suck in his breath.

"What is it?" I asked, scared now that something bad had happened.

"It's all right. It's all right. Those bastards burned your face! Look at this," he said to himself, still inspecting the raw purple skin. "It's practically a black crisp! Stay here," he told me, and I sat in the car and watched him march back into the office to tell that doctor what she had done.

By the time I was in high school, I never left the house without makeup on. Combined with bangs that I brushed over the right side of my face, I hid my birthmark well. Of course, people still made comments—they always did. But by now the comments had evolved from childish jeering to curious questions. I always found it interesting the way people chose their words. "What's wrong with your face?" was the most common remark that I heard. Each time I would answer quickly, "It's a birthmark," practically holding my breath until I could turn and walk away. Other times I was met with sympathetic looks, raised eyebrows, expressions of concern. These people were the ones who asked me in the same voice used to talk to a child, "What happened?" They always tried to ease out of their worried looks when they realized that nothing had happened, that this was just how I was.

My makeup routine soon turned into something as habitual as brushing my teeth. I would first dig out a clump of the condensed, hard cream with a white, plastic tool that resembled a small spatula. Then I would spread it onto the side of my palm to soften it up. I would spend about ten to fifteen minutes applying a thick coat with my finger over my right cheek and spreading some on the rest of my face as well, to even it out. I would use a magnifying mirror just as my nana had, so that I could get every small corner, every speck of stained skin. My face would grow hot from the caked-on cream, and my skin would become so insulated that sometimes I would even start to sweat, meaning I'd have to start all over. Then I would brush on the setting powder, which made my face look even, and finally bronzer, to make it look a bit more natural.

I carried around a makeup bag everywhere I went. I made constant trips to the bathroom to check my face and make sure that none of my makeup had rubbed off. If just the slightest bit had wiped away, I would whip out my trusty bag and the process would repeat itself. Unlike my nana, who had enjoyed her beauty routine, I hated getting ready in the mornings and dreaded the time and energy it took for me to simply leave my house. It became not only a giant part of my day, but a giant part of who I was.

I used to beg my mom to take me on auditions. I wanted to be like her, to be a beautiful actress, to be someone people would die to take a picture of. I would go down into the basement, where she kept her old modeling portfolio, and spend hours looking at pictures of her, enchanted that the person posing in all of them was my mom. My favorite photo was one where she was in a black leotard, her round eyes looking to the side and her red lips making a kiss as she stood among a crowd of marionette puppets, one of their painted clown faces in her hand. She had unusually short hair in the picture; after she had bent down to light our stove by hand, which was always necessary to get it to work, the flame exploded and singed off her long curls. But even with a pixie cut, she still looked amazing. Whenever I would bring up those days, she would always laugh, as if modeling was just a passing phase, as if anyone could do it.

I got a callback once from a big agency in Manhattan that represented young actors and models. When I met with an agent, he told me, "You can be the best actress in the world, but you won't ever make it as a model, not with that birthmark. But don't let it bother you."

I would never be able to be like my mom, and that did bother me. Of course, I hid this reaction and nodded enthusiastically as he gave me the rundown on how their agency worked and the general process of becoming a professional actor. I smiled and shook his hand when he was through, thanked him for his time. When my mom asked me how it went, I told her that it went great, but that I had to think about whether I really wanted to pursue this. I didn't want her to know how bothered I was, how crushed I felt. I didn't want to talk about it, with her or anyone; I was still in hiding.

My senior year in high school, I decided to take a spring break trip with a group of my girlfriends to the Bahamas. As excited as I was, I was equally filled with worry. I envisioned us all on the beach, standing near the shore, with a group of boys approaching. I saw them take notice of my face like a woman takes notice of a juice stain on her white living-room carpet; they suck in their breath and look away.

I told my mother that I had to get some kind of special makeup before I left, something better than the drugstore stuff I'd been using until then. We went to Macy's, straight to the makeup department.

"Can I help you?" the girl behind the counter asked.

"I need some cover-up because I have a birthmark right here and I'm going on vacation and I don't want it to show." I said this all in one breath, quietly and quickly, and I couldn't wait to just get it over with.

"I have the perfect fix." And I admit that I was impressed with the facts she rattled off about this new brand of waterproof concealer, which wouldn't rub or wash off in the pool, or melt under the hot sun. For a total of one hundred and sixty dollars, I began thinking that maybe I would have a good time in the Bahamas after all.

But the makeup didn't fully stop people from taking notice. I was in a record store one day flipping through the jazz section, and a police officer approached me. "You all right there?" he asked, and I looked up for a moment suspiciously, nodded, and then quietly returned to what I was doing. "Somebody get rough with you?" he continued, and it was then that I knew what he was talking about.

I turned around to face him. He had his large belly thrust forward and both hands holding onto his front belt loops. It was common that people assumed that I was hurt, bruised, and injured. Shortly after I was born, a woman marched up to my mother in a coffee shop and told her that she should be ashamed of herself, hurting a newborn in the face like that.

"It's a birthmark," I replied to the officer.

"Oh wow, it looks like a huge bruise! I just wanted to make sure no boyfriend was pushin' you around and makin' you feel bad, you know? Take care, then." And he turned to leave, a job well done.

When I started dating, I would always make sure to tilt my head when giving a hug, so that I didn't rub off any cream on a boyfriend's shirt. When I started having sex, I would retreat to the bathroom immediately afterwards to apply a fresh coat. It was a nonstop, never-ending anxiety: Is my makeup still on? Is my face still covered? Not wearing it was never an option for me, and I hated that more than anything.

One day, while dating Kyle, I was lying in his bed with only a sheet wrapped around me, watching him sketch. He was an artist, and I admired his talent to draw and take photographs in a way that captured a person's features so delicately. He was fascinated with people, their shapes, the way their spines curled to hunch when they sat. He was eight years older than me, and at nineteen, I couldn't help but imagine all the women who had lain where I was now, in his bed, as he studied them like a telescope studies stars.

"Sit up," he said, and he put down his sketch and walked over to the desk. I sat up against the orange wall, still with the sheet held to my chest. "I want to take a picture of you," and fiddled with his big, professional-looking camera.

"OK," I replied, blushing, "what should I do?"

"Just stay like that." He started clicking, steadying the camera with both hands.

When he was through, he asked me if I wanted to see the pictures, which, of course, I did. But when the images of myself appeared on the camera's screen, I cringed and held my breath. The dim light in the room seemed to make the orange walls softly glow in the background, and the one window, with the shade pulled back, revealed the tangle of green leaves that rustled outside. Yet I didn't notice these things, nor did I notice the different angles, the intricacies of a photo well taken. I only noticed my own face; my birthmark, especially in the close-up shots, was all my eyes could see.

"Oh no, no. I don't like them," I said.

"What? Why not?"

"I don't know; I just don't think I look very good. My face."

Kyle put the camera down and sat close to me on the bed. "You're crazy, you know. You're beautiful."

As much as I wanted to, I didn't believe him for a second.

It is after I have moved to Chicago and transferred to a new college, committed to becoming a writer, that I first think about talking about this thing I have so long kept quiet about. While taking a class on censorship, my teacher asks everyone to think about the one thing they have never written about. Other students volunteer their answers: their parents' divorce, their history with eating disorders, their race, their homosexuality, sex, drugs, violence; the list continues. I immediately know what my answer is, but instead I say that I have never written about the death of my grand-mother, which is a lie. I begin to wonder how much longer I can keep this up, this censoring of myself.

Summer has rolled around, and I have just turned twenty-one. My boyfriend, Steve, and I decide to go to a three-day music festival. Unlike all my boyfriends from the past, I don't hide anything from Steve, and I know that this is because I love him in a way that I have never loved anyone else, as if we are necessary parts of each other. He tells me often how much he loves my birthmark, how beautiful and unique he thinks it is, and I believe him. But I do not yet believe that the rest of the world will feel the same way.

We are packing for our trip when I decide to bring up something that has been bothering me for days.

"What about my makeup?" I know that I will have to leave it behind. The only bathrooms at the festival will be the port-a-potties, and there is no way that I plan on spending any more time in there than I have to. Applying makeup in a hot tent is my only other option and one that I am equally opposed to.

"Are you kidding? You're not bringing that stuff," he responds. "No one cares about that kind of thing there." I accept this as the end of our conversation, but I have no idea that it will be the beginning of something else entirely.

For those three days, Steve and I were on our own little musical adventure, forgetting that a world beyond the woods existed, living without a single care or worry. We wandered through large open lawns, going from stage to stage; we knelt under a water spigot to rinse off the brown dust that had dried on our skin, and I let the water pour over my face while a long line of people waited for their turn, never once feeling anxious about my newfound exposure. Pretty soon I forgot to even think about what I looked like to others; I no longer found myself following people's eyes while I talked to them, trying to catch them staring. Three days without makeup? I expected to feel threatened and panic, but instead I felt normal and genuinely happy. I never wanted that feeling to go away.

When we got home, though, I found myself in a bit of a predicament. Should I start back up with my usual makeup routine? I really didn't want to, and when I caked on the cream for the first time since our trip, it felt more unsettling and uncomfortable than it ever had. I didn't want to wear it, but the idea of venturing out into the world without my trusty mask was something that made me nervous. I was safe at the festival, where music was all that mattered, but in the real world, people could be ruthless. I asked Steve what I should do.

"Don't wear it," he said simply. It wasn't the first time someone had suggested this to me, but it was the first time that I ever considered it to be a good idea.

So I haven't worn the stuff since. I realize now how I had expected everyone else to act differently after I decided to ditch the makeup and just stick to the skin, but in truth, I was the only one who had made a change.

Steve calls me his little grape, and I remember when I hated the nickname. But when we went shopping for costumes for this past Halloween, I couldn't help but burst with laughter and snatch up an outfit that just seemed too perfect.

"That's it. You have to get it," Steve said, agreeing that the costume suited me, given my recent revolution of self, just too well.

The costume was an inflatable bodysuit of purple grapes. Big, wonderful, delicious, purple grapes filled with dark juice that can leave such a lovely stain.

It is raining heavily, and I am standing on State Street trying to get my umbrella to work. Unlike before, when I feared that the rain would wipe away the cover-up I had so carefully applied, I find the cold water on my face refreshing.

"Damn, girl, you look like a cartoon character," says a voice coming from my right. I look over, not thinking that this person could possibly be talking to me.

"Yeah, you heard me," says the scraggly man, staring right at me, as he continues to walk past. "Look at that shit on your face, girl. Shit look nasty."

I stand frozen for a few moments, more shocked than anything. The funny thing is that since I stopped wearing makeup and hiding my birthmark, I haven't gotten as many comments as I used to. So I am totally unprepared for this man's remark. He walks away, and I stand there for a few more moments, feeling his words hit me in the stomach like a blow. I am reminded of a feeling I have grown to know so well, one that I decided to reject only recently; the feeling of being out in public and everybody seeing you, judging you, sizing you up with a scowl. I know that I have a choice, a choice to let myself fall back into that feeling, or a choice to believe that although my skin might be different, that does not mean that it is wrong. People will see it and take notice of it the same way they do my hair color, or my eye color, or what earrings I am wearing. I want to be noticed for who I am. I shake this man's words out of my head as I open my umbrella and continue down the street.

* * *

"A Chinese woman once told me this," he says to me from across his shining oak desk. "She had a birthmark not that different from yours, and she told me that in Asia, people with marks like that are believed to be reincarnated versions of someone very great from the past. People hold these individuals in very high esteem. Praise them, almost. So I asked her then, of course...," he pauses, laughs lightly, "why in the world she would want me to remove it?" Dr. Arden leans forward in his leather chair, his eyes twinkling like a mischievous kid. I can tell he loves telling jokes and that he's good at it too. "And she says, 'Because I live in Texas!'"

We both laugh.

The Chicago skyline is to my left, visible through his big office windows. I have not had a laser treatment in eight years, since I was twelve. Even though I am now comfortable with my face, I know there are medical reasons to keep up with the treatments. It is three days before the procedure, and I am having a consultation with Dr. Arden, a small man with a big presence. His story makes me wonder about how "different" is perceived depending on the culture. If I had lived in China, who knows? I might've grown up with some kind of superiority complex.

"Do you wear makeup?" he asks me.

"I used to, until this past summer. Now I don't wear it. Ever."

"Well, the reason I ask is because I can tell just from looking at you that you have a decent amount of natural coloring in your skin. Almost olive. If you want to continue with treatments throughout the year, then your face cannot get tan during the summer. If it does, I won't work on you. We have a new laser that leaves little to no bruising and discoloration afterwards, but it sucks the melanin out of your skin. So if this is the whitest you get, you need to stay that way." It is nineteen degrees today, in the middle of January, so I can safely assure him that I haven't had the chance to get much color lately.

"That's why I asked about the makeup," he continues. "I think it's great, you know, that you've accepted your skin and all that, but from my position as your doctor, I would prefer if you started wearing the makeup again."

I think about this. I don't want to start wearing all that cream and powder again, since my morning routines have become much less stressful. I've spent so many years hating the fact that I couldn't even leave the house without it on, and now that I'm finally free of all that nonsense, I'm being told that I should reconsider. But I also realize that if I did start covering up my face again, I wouldn't be doing it for the same reasons as before.

"It's up to you," he says. "Like I told you, makeup can be very good protection."

I suppose a lot depends on what it's protecting you from.

Knots

Frankie Migacz

ON A BITTER COLD NOVEMBER AFTERNOON IN 2009, I WAS SITTING AT MY kitchen table hunkered over my computer trying to will myself to write when my phone buzzed. I reached across the table and read the quick six-word text message from my sister.

"Andrew Siebenaler killed himself last night."

I read it over twice, and as I did a feeling comparable to failing a test came over me. My stomach churned uncomfortably, my hands became numb and cold, and I started to stare out my kitchen window. All I could respond with was "Oh", my fingers fumbling over the keyboard. Within seconds or maybe minutes, the memories of the deceased began to pour in.

I was in Boy Scouts with Andrew; he was a couple years younger than me, and as an older Scout I had to make sure that he and all the younger Scouts learned the basics of outdoor survival quickly. To me he always seemed like the stereotypical, socially awkward, nerdy kid. He was average height for his age, skinny, pale skinned, a shock of untidy brown hair on his head, and a pair of rectangular glasses that always sat slightly crooked on his long nose.

My phone buzzed again. My sister had more news: his roommate had found him hanging from a water pipe in their Marquette dorm room. My stomach clenched as I realized I was the one who taught him to tie knots. I gave him the tools, the confidence even, to kill himself. You hear stories all the time about people trying to hang themselves but having the rope break or something like that. I know that when Andrew hopped from the top bunk, he knew that his knot was strong and true, that it would hold him there forever if necessary.

I remember teaching him how to tie a bowline knot, relatively simple but unbelievably useful; it is a multipurpose knot used for everything from pulling someone up from a ravine to tying up firewood. I sat down with him, showed him the motions his hands should make with the rope. I corrected him when he made a wrong loop or let the cord tangle. I taught him to pull the rope just right; I told him, "You could tie this to an elephant and drop it off a cliff and it won't break."

As I taught him how to tie it, he didn't speak; he just watched intently. After the first time I showed him, he took the rope from me and performed a perfect bowline. He smiled as I patted him on the back; he undid the knot and tied it again.

He had a knack for learning things quickly; all we had to do was show him how to do it once and he had it mastered, especially knots. It wasn't long before he was the go-to guy in the troop when something needed to be lashed, tied, or fastened. It came naturally to him. There was a time when one of the adults caught him tying a noose. Andrew was thirteen at the time and was squatting on a half-submerged log overlooking the lake that was attached to our campsite, with a rope thicker than his wrists dangling from his hand. Our Scoutmaster, Mr. Jarvis, saw him twirling it around his head and he walked over to him.

"Hey sport, whatcha got there?" Jarvis asked, placing his thick, hairy, sausage-like hands on Andrew's narrow shoulders. Jarvis was a big man, six foot four and at least three hundred pounds. I was intimated by him; I can only imagine how Andrew felt.

"Nothin . . . ," Andrew said, in barely more than a whisper, his voice not quite betraying shame, but still quivering with the nervousness of wrongdoing.

"Nothin', huh?" Jarvis said, plucking the noose from Andrew's trembling fingers. "This doesn't look like nothing. If you ask me, it looks like a noose."

"Yeah," Andrew said, staring into the lake and digging his heels into the log as if he were getting ready to take off in a sprint.

"Now what would a young man like yourself want to do with a nasty thing like a noose?" Jarvis had spun Andrew around by his shoulders so he could look at him.

"I dunno. To see if I could?" Andrew said, avoiding eye contact.

"Well, you can, that's for sure." Jarvis looked the noose up and down. It was perfect. It slid up and down, yet stayed taut, just like the real thing. "You sure that's the only reason, son? Nothing you need to tell me? You know me and the other adults are here for you if you need to talk about anything."

"No, Mr. Jarvis," Andrew said, glancing up for a split second before flicking his eyes back to the lake. "Just for fun."

I believed Andrew then, when Mr. Jarvis told the older Scouts and adults about it later around the campfire, and I still want to believe Andrew now. I truly want to believe that the only intention thirteen-year-old Andrew had was to tie a noose for fun, to see if he could, to test the strengths of what the Boy Scouts had taught him.

I wish I could say this came as a surprise to me, but it really didn't. He always seemed like a sad kid. He only smiled when he was supposed to, and I don't really remember him joking that much. It sucks to say, but if I had to guess that one of the people I knew would kill himself, Andrew's name would've been on top of the list.

One night in 2006, while we were at summer camp, I was ripped from a peaceful slumber by a first-year named Sam.

"Frankie!" Sam squeaked, poking my face with this thin finger.

"Wha?" I mumbled, trying to cling to sleep, irritated at being awakened at such a ridiculous hour. I didn't have a clock, but I could smell the dew forming on the grass.

"Frankie, um . . ." Sam suddenly clammed up as if he had forgotten why he had clambered into my tent and poked me in the face repeatedly.

"Sam, what do you want?" I asked, pushing myself up to a sitting position.

"Oh, uh. I'm sorry to wake you up but, um . . . ." Sam was clearly worried about something; his tiny voice was shaking, and even in the dark without my contacts, I could see his eyes shifting from left to right.

"Sam, I don't have time for this. What do you want?" I said.

"Oh, um, yeah. Well, Andrew can't breathe. I just thought you ought to know."

A chill went down my back, and the grogginess was ripped from my body. "What?!"

"Uh, Andrew started wheezing really bad like an hour ago, and he just started saying, 'I can't breathe, I can't breathe,' over and over again. It was really creepy, so I got you."

I reached down into my duffel bag and threw on a T-shirt and jeans. "Lead me to him," I said, "Have you told his dad?"

"No." Sam said throwing the flap open to the tent, "I didn't want to worry him."

I chuckled in spite of myself; the real Boy Scout motto was, "Don't tell the adults," and followed Sam out of the tent. The air itself seemed asleep; the campsite was completely silent, save the snapping of twigs as we walked and quiet snores coming from the identical canvas tents that stood single file against the treeline. Even though I didn't have my contacts in and the world was nothing more than a giant black blur, I had been coming to this same campsite for five years now, and would have known my way around it blindfolded. The smell of damp grass filled my nose and I could feel my bare feet begin to prune up. Sam and Andrew's tent was on the other side of the site; when we arrived, Sam walked in and plopped down on his sleeping bag.

Sixteen-year-old Andrew was sitting up in his cot. Even in the total incoherence that was my vision I could see his face was pained and very pale. His breathing was labored, sharp gasps paired with an almost melodic wheeze.

"Hey man," I said, sitting down next to him looking him up and down, trying to assess the situation. "Not doing so good, huh?"

Andrew shook his head. "Hhhi . . . c-c-hant b-b-breathe," he managed to get out. He was clutching his chest with his left hand, the other buried in his shock of brown hair. Panic began to flick at me like tongues of fire. Andrew looked like he might keel over at any second, but I knew panic wouldn't help me, or him for that matter, so I took a deep breath and closed my eyes. "I think we should find your dad," I said, trying to map the path to the adult campsite in my head.

"No," Andrew said between wheezes, "J-j-ust . . . l-eave . . . I'll b-b-b-e fine."

"No, man. You're not going to be fine. Look at you." He was starting to bend back and forth at the waist like one of those old-time fire bellows. "Here, I'll tell you what, why don't you just come down to the aid station with me? They'll fix you right up and your dad will never have to know."

Andrew nodded vigorously, and with the effort I've only seen in Ironman competitions, pushed himself off the cot. In retrospect, I should have told his dad. Our campsite, though it was the largest at Camp Mach, also happened to be the farthest point on the map. It was a mile and a half to the aid station, all of which was down an unlighted, loose-gravel hill.

I stepped out into the night once again and breathed in the moist summer air. I put my arm around Andrew and began to lead him away from the campsite. Sharp pains shot up and down my legs and I knew I had reached the path. I looked down at the grayish blur and knew all I had to do was follow this for twenty or so minutes, and I could go back to bed.

It was when the trees started to lean over the path and the moon was blotted out that Andrew began to have problems. He was walking doubled over with his hand still firmly grasping a tuft of hair. With every breath he shot straight up with his head pointed at the sky as if trying to gulp down the oxygen. Without a word, he sat down and curled his knees up to his chest.

"Andrew," I said, squinting to see where he went. "What are you doing? We're nearly there, man, come on."

Andrew said nothing. He hugged his legs closer. His breathing cut against the silence of the wilderness and sent a chill down my spine. "Did you hear me?"

Andrew nodded his head, "J-just . . . go," he said.

"What?"

"Just g-go. L-leave me here. L-let m-me die."

I wonder what he was thinking right before he did it. Maybe of his family or his friends. Was he sad that he was leaving them? Or was he relieved that he wouldn't have to go through the ever-approaching finals? Was he angry with his ex-girlfriend for abandoning him? Chances are he wasn't thinking at all. More than likely his mind was blank and determined—determined to leave a world that had given him so much pain and anguish—perhaps eager for what was awaiting him on the other side.

As I'm writing this I still feel almost nothing, though in the back of my skull I feel anger welling up. Though many would say it takes a tremendous amount of courage to kill oneself in such a brutal fashion, I can't shake the feeling that it was nothing but a cowardly, selfish act.

I can see how it happened. I can see Andrew sitting alone in his dorm room, his small chest heaving with sobs, tears streaming down his face, a smear of salt collecting at the bottom of his lenses as they evaporate. He looks out the window; he hears the crowds of drunk, happy Marquette students stumbling to and from parties, and he feels nothing but pain, nothing but anguish. He looks down at his hands; they are shaking. He forms two fists to make them stop, but the shaking travels up his arms, and soon he is shivering violently, though the heat blares through the vents above him.

He is trying to think, trying to figure out why. Why did she leave him? They had such a great thing. He made her laugh, she made him happy. No one made him happy; to find someone like that, to be able to hold her in his arms, was the best thing that had ever happened to him. But what now? She is gone, probably drunk and flirting with some frat boy.

Nothing. The thought occurs to him suddenly. There is nothing, nothing to look forward to tomorrow. Nothing to look forward to the day after that, or after that. He breaks into another bout of sobbing; he falls from his chair onto the cool tile floor and pulls his knees into his chest. The room seems foggy, not quite focused. He reaches up to straighten his glasses, but they have fallen off, skittered across the floor and under the sink.

He reaches for them, one hand still hugging his knees, grasping at air, at dust mites. His hand connects with something. Not his glasses, but something textured, long, and familiar. He pulls it closer to him: climbing rope. He runs his hand up and down the purple cord. It feels friendly. He remembers packing it, hoping maybe between his studies he could get away, get back to the outdoors, to smell the air and to feel the coarseness of an untouched rock face. But that didn't happen. Of course it didn't happen. It would have brought joy to his life, but Andrew knew that he was not born for joy. He wasn't meant to be happy; he was meant to suffer. He squeezes the rope until his hands begin to throb.

"Do it," a voice says to him.

"Do what?" he responds. His voice is hoarse and shaking. He sounds scared.

"You know. You've always known." The voice is soft and delicate, like a breath of wind. It soothes Andrew and his muscles relax. "It's easy, so very easy."

Andrew sits up and runs his free hand through his hair, "What's easy?"

"Go through the motions," the voice says, and it seems to come from the walls. "You know them, don't you? It won't hurt; in fact it will end the hurt. It will end everything and set you free."

Andrew looks down at the rope. Even as he wonders what the voice means his hands begin to move on their own. They form the loop first, bigger than necessary, of course; there needs to be room to pull tight. Then comes the wrapping, one time, two times around and around until it's thick as his forearm. His hands don't slow down; they don't check their work. They know it's perfect; they pull the free strand through the loops and tighten it just right.

Andrew looks at the noose resting in his arms. The loop is curved, almost smiling at him. "Perfect," the voice says. "Now do it."

"Now?" Andrew asks. A shiver runs down his spine. The moonlight has begun to creep through the window, painting his tiny room silver.

"Yes."

Andrew stands up, breathing in bitter air. His legs shake, but he ignores them. He knows this is it. He knows there is no way out.

His mind goes blank as he clambers up the small wooden ladder that leads to his roommate's bunk. When he reaches the top, Andrew looks out over his room. All the decorations are his roommate's, posters of bikini-clad women touching themselves suggestively line the walls; a tall Seattle Mariner's lamp sits in the corner; and on the shared sink are bottles upon bottles of every kind of liquor cover.

If this is what I'm leaving, Andrew thinks, throwing the noose over an exposed water pipe and tying it off, then I'm glad it's over.

He fits the noose around his neck, savoring the texture against his sensitive skin. He pulls it tight enough so breathing has to become manual.

He looks at the ground and hopes he didn't give himself too much slack. He closes his eyes and bounces his legs off the side of the bunk. The childish gesture makes him smile. He places his feet against the bed frame and pushes off.

The fall is quick, the slack is perfect; a sharp pain rushes down Andrew's neck, and the room goes black.

Now the room is completely still and quiet except for the corpse swaying ever so slightly, and the creaking from the water pipe not used to holding 140 pounds of weight. I can see his body, his feet pointed at the ground, jeans, a polo. I can see the rope wrapped around his broken neck, veins blue and visible even in the darkness. I can see his head cocked to one side, his bulging eyes open and staring off into the world he wanted so desperately to leave. The skin of his face is a pale blue from the lack of oxygen, his tongue lolls out the side of his mouth, useless, dry, and shriveled.

His parents and sister didn't deserve this. Andrew grew up in Clarendon Hills, a perfect place to do so. His father was the Scoutmaster for a number of years, and a nicer guy you couldn't find. He must be wondering right now what he did wrong. Where did he fuck up? Why did his son feel it was necessary to abandon everything he had done for him? His parents must feel worthless, powerless. In the back of their heads, their own thoughts of ending it may be festering. I wonder if that's what Andrew wanted. I wonder if he realized that he left his little sister, who more than likely looked up to the straight-A student. What kind of example has he set for her, to give up when things got hard? To say *fuck you* to everyone who matters because your life is not going the way you wanted it.

And what of his friends? Or people who thought they were his friends? All of them devastated, left in the wake of his decision to end his life. Questions running through their head: "Could I have done something?" "Was I not supportive enough?" "Should I have caught this sooner?" Andrew did more than kill himself; he left a fog of questions and doubts over his entire hometown.

What about the girl who broke up with him? For the rest of her life she will have the weight of his corpse over her. She probably feels like she has blood on her hands, but she doesn't. It's not her fault; it's his fault he couldn't cope. His roommate is scarred, too; how can he sleep at night knowing that in his room a kid he once knew hung himself? From the time the last breath left Andrew's lungs, that room will forever be haunted with his memory. Years from now people will avoid that room; "I hear that some kid hung himself in 309."

"No way, dude."

"No, I'm not lying: some kid hopped from his bunk with a rope tied around his neck and offed himself. I hear it's haunted."

"Fuck you, no way."

"No joke, they say at night if you listen really carefully you can hear the rope swaying and creaking. I swear to God, ask anyone."

Even four months later tears are being shed for him; his family's lives, for all intents and purposes, are changed forever. But he's out and maybe that's all he cares about. If you believe in God, maybe he's in heaven. But if you believe in God, you know he's probably in hell. But more than likely, he's just gone, his short life, strangled away. Leaving behind only a body to rot in the ground.

But I shouldn't judge the dead. I have no idea what plagued Andrew, what skeletons he had in his closet. The switch to college must have been a hard one for him. He grew up in a town that is the epitome of sheltered, where grown men hide out in the back of their garages to smoke cigarettes.

I guess I was lucky when I moved to college. I adapted quickly. I slipped into the late nights, binge drinking, and anti-monogamy mindset like a pair of jeans. I cannot assume that he, or anyone else, could possibly cope as well.

Who am I to say, at the moment of his fateful decision, that death wasn't the only option for Andrew? I hope it was; I really do. I hope that in the last seconds of his life, he smiled to himself and was happy with his choice. I hope that he's in a better place now. But I wish he could see what he left behind.

Andrew's funeral was held two weeks after his death. Mrs. Polus, one of the troop moms, called my house the night before.

"Frankie? This is Barbie Polus, Steve's mom." Her voice was weak; I could tell she had been crying. "It's so good to hear your voice again, I'm just calling about tomorrow. We thought it would be a great show of support for the Siebenalers if all the Scouts would come in uniform. OK? Well, I'll see you tomorrow then."

I had to dig my uniform out of my closet; it was crammed between an old stereo and a trumpet I hadn't picked up since high school. It felt odd putting it on. It barely fit anymore; I must have grown a couple of inches since I stopped Scouting. If I lifted my arms up, the uniform's waistline reached my belly button. The eagle badge on the left pocket was frayed and nearly coming off. But as I fastened the last button, I felt comfortable. More comfortable than I had felt in a long while, as if putting on my old uniform transported me to a time where the only thing I had to worry about was wearing enough bug spray and setting my tent up right.

I drove to the funeral with the radio off. After turning right on Burlington Avenue and crossing the train tracks, it was a straight shot. The funeral home was on the edge of my hometown of Clarendon Hills and the neighboring, more affluent, town of Hinsdale.

I parked across from the funeral home at the train station. I got out of my car and began to walk briskly toward the front lawn. As I approached I saw a large gathering of Scouts mingling. They all wore the same uniform and against the snowy ground they looked like a giant stagnant dust cloud.

Mr. Jarvis was standing on the curb closest to me. He was holding his wife, who was sobbing into his chest. He had lost quite a bit of weight since I last saw him; his uniform hung loose, more like a robe than anything. His curly brown hair had receded a few inches and was now speckled with gray.

I waved to him as I made my way across the street. He squinted as he tried to put a name to the face.

"Wow. Hello, Frankie," he said, holding out a free hand. I shook it. "It's good to see you again. Just wish, well . . ." He sighed deeply and hugged his wife closer. "Just wish, it could have been for . . . for a nicer time."

I nodded at him and patted his shoulder as I headed up the short slope to the congregating Scouts. Most of the kids there I had never seen before, but there were some familiar faces. Sam was there; he still had sleek white blonde hair, but he was taller than me now, and when he said hello I noticed his voice had dropped more than a couple octaves. His uniform was new. I could tell by the intensity of the color and the lack of bloodstains.

By the time Mrs. Polus made her way to the front of the crowd and whistled to grab our attention, the evening's cold had begun to make my bones aches and my fingers numb.

"Hey Scouts!" she said, holding up her arms. "We're going to go in now. I want you guys to line up, oldest up front."

Things don't change in Scouts, no matter how old you are or what event you're attending. So it didn't surprise me that it took about ten minutes to get lined up and in the correct order. I was the oldest Scout there, so I stood in front. Before we walked in, Mrs. Polus whispered into my ear, "We're going to do this, just like a meeting. You remember how to do that?"

I nodded, and waved everyone to follow me. We walked through the front doors in a single file, like a great tan snake. I felt guilty as the warmth of the funeral home thawed my numbed hands; it felt wrong deriving any pleasure from such an event. As we passed though the narrow front corridor, the smell of too many flowers attacked my nose. The smell reminded me of every funeral I had ever been to, sweet to the point of rotten. As if the mourners are trying to overcompensate for the tragic loss of their loved ones.

The parlor was large, but already it was packed with people. They all stared at us as we walked through the aisle of fold-up chairs. Ornate bouquets of flowers took up every inch of nonoccupied space; in the dim lighting of the parlor they looked out of place. Everything else was dark. The carpet was a deep brown, the walls were made of dark cherry wood, the folding chairs were black.

We lined up facing the casket; it was closed, of course. The wood was a dark mahogany and looked smooth to the touch. I tried to imagine Andrew in there, his body too disfigured to show to the public. I clenched my fists. When all the Scouts were lined up properly, I raised my right hand into a three-fingered salute. "Attention!" I said, and all the Scouts' hands mimicked mine.

"Scout Oath," I said. My voice seemed unnaturally loud in the silence that had settled over the room. The troop repeated the oath in unison. A mix of low voices with high-pitched squeaks.

"On my honor I will do my best

To do my duty to God and my country.

To obey the Scout Law;

To help other people at all times;

To keep myself physically strong, mentally awake, and morally straight."

There was silence for a second, coupled with sniffles from the crowd. "Scout Law," I said. I heard my voice crack and my face became very hot.

"A Scout is: Trustworthy, Loyal, Helpful,

Friendly, Courteous, Kind,

Obedient, Cheerful, Thrifty,

Brave, Clean and Reverent."

"To!" I said, and our hands fell to our sides. I stared at the coffin for a while, bathing in the irony of both the oath and law. I was here paying respects to a friend, a fellow Scout, repeating an oath and law that he had heard and said hundreds of times: an oath and law that he had completely ignored by taking his own life. It almost seemed like a mockery to be repeating it. It felt like we were telling him and his family that he disgraced Scouting and himself.

I was deep in these thoughts when Luke, a Scout a year younger than me spoke. "We'll miss you, buddy." Despite my own stoic nature, despite the anger I had felt toward Andrew for abandoning those who cared about him, I felt tears well up in the corners of my eyes. They fell slowly. They itched my skin, but I dared not wipe them away. Without a word to each other, we disbanded into the crowd of people.

I took a seat near the back of the room, just as the reverend, a tall, skinny, black man made his way to the front. Silence settled over the room again and he spoke. His voice was crisp and clean, like a politician's, with the tone of someone who gave the same speech thousands of times.

For the first time, I saw the Siebenalers, sitting together in the first row. Mr. and Mrs. Siebenaler were on either side of their daughter. Mr. Siebenaler looked the same as I remembered him, his son aged thirty years, with a brown, neatly-trimmed beard. Mrs. Siebenaler, who was a runner, was excessively skinny with short blond hair, and their daughter was brown haired and skinny, with big eyes. They held each other close as the reverend spoke.

"We are gathered here today, not to mourn the tragic loss of one of God's flock. No, we are here to celebrate the life of Andrew Siebenaler and to comfort one another in his absence."

The reverend began to pace around the room: he read Psalms and had us pray. The entire time, I couldn't stop looking at the Siebenalers. They hadn't moved. They sat there like a monument, their arms wrapped around one another. They weren't crying; they even chuckled a little when the reverend recounted a story about Andrew when he was a baby. I tried to get into their heads, tried to understand what they were feeling. But I knew I couldn't. I knew all I could do was watch.

After the ceremony, a line formed in front of the Siebenalers. The line stretched from the coffin to the coat checkroom: I got lodged in the middle but I was determined to offer my words of comfort to the family, to try to say something that would make them feel just a little better.

About an hour later, one of Andrew's friends had just stopped sobbing into Mr. Siebenaler's shoulder, and I was next in line.

Mr. Siebenaler shook my hand. "How's life, Frankie?" he asked. A smile broke out over his face. I had to hand it to him; he was stoic, just as he always was. He wouldn't let tears fall even at the funeral of his own son.

"I'm OK," I said, searching for the right words but finding none. "It's terrible."

Mr. Siebenaler nodded and took a big sniff of air. "Well, we'll have to heal each other. Won't we?" He hugged his wife.

Mrs. Siebenaler turned to me and opened her arms in a hug. As her thin arms wrapped around me, I was surprised by the force of her embrace. She held onto me like I was a rock in the middle of the rapids, as if when she let go she would be swept away.

"I'm so sorry," I said, patting the back of her head awkwardly, "He's in a better place now, Andrew is in a better place now."

Mrs. Siebenaler pulled back. Her face was stained with tears, but her eyes had strength to them. "I hope so, Frankie. I really do."

She opened her arms again and I hugged her. "You've always been good at telling stories," Mrs. Siebenaler whispered into my ear. I could feel hot tears rolling down her cheek. "Please, Frankie. Please tell me a story about Andrew. Don't let me forget my son."

When Day Became Night

Ashley Keenan

I FELL ASLEEP THE OTHER NIGHT GRABBING MY CHEST, AS IF MY FINGERS COULD somehow steady my heartbeat. Nothing was wrong, but each time this happens memories stir in my head. Childhood comes back in blanching light as I recall vegetables steaming on my hospital tray, nurses in Mickey Mouse scrubs tickling my feet. I have the very distinct memory of being six years old, waking up to a cloud of surgeons above me wearing blue crisp gowns and face masks taut over their mouths. I remember a bright halo of lights, my arm rising, swinging really, to block the piercing rays from my eyes. I remember the drugged static motion of my tiny fist grazing the surgeon's nose. Then I hear my doctor calling for more anesthesia, nurses swooping in, a great wave of people above me pinning my arms, swabbing for a clean insertion point, and then the gray, slow fade into unconsciousness, the swooning beep of my heart monitor cooing in the background.

When I was a kid, I thought being sick made me special. Some kids took karate, some painted runny watercolor landscapes—egg yolk suns and square boxy houses . . . but me? I was different. I hung out with doctors and old people and had these sweet machines to play with, much to the dismay of my mom. I was a scrawny, hyperactive, little blond creature, unstoppable by all but one. My big brother. I called him "Bear" and acted like his little cub, swinging from his neck and jabbing him in the stomach when he'd pass by.

I asked my boyfriend once to rape me while I was having a seizure. While my body thrashed from limp to tense and limp again he moved inside of me, searching for my presence as I drifted further into my subconscious world. I can't imagine how lonely that must have felt, how real, too real, when my vision shrank—my arms collapsing, shaking, how frightening it must have been to be in the real world all cold and alone, and the terror he must have felt watching me return, limbs growing still, eyes fluttering, adjusting to the light.

I returned, as I often do, with an impeded memory, hazy like dawn in a meadow, the sun not yet breaking the shadow and fog of night. I felt heavy, burdensome, as if returning from a faraway land, supplies in tow, pots jangling from my backpack and sweat-rings encircling my arms, returning to a land that was no longer familiar, no longer home.

He cradled my head at first, lulling me, calming me, but still within me. I did not know who he was. Sensations began to return to my body—in fact they'd never left—but their pathways were unaltered now. My brain was communicating again, speaking the same language rather than intercepting snatches of thought and translating slowly, letter by letter, so that by the time I knew one word, his sentence would be ending, and I could only chase the tails of their meaning.

Then terror hit, swept past the calm of his presence. My pulse whipped faster and faster and I couldn't catch my breath. He knew something was wrong, jumped out and away from my body, grabbing a blanket to cover me. My hands lay idly at my side as the blanket drooped on my pale shoulders, my body like an unfinished sculpture, marble hacked at, identity not yet emerging. I looked at the walls for a clue that this might be a familiar place—photos of a well-groomed lioness were mantled above the windows, paintings and scraps of fabric strewn across the rough red carpet, no thicker than a book covering.

I didn't know this man. I didn't know him or his face or this terribly confining room he'd put me in. The sheets smelled like another girl's sweat. The room was cold and wet feeling, and I felt as if I'd been plopped into someone else's space at a pivotal moment in her life. Maybe my consciousness had just swept into hers, maybe I had died and was now reborn, and this was the lowest tier of karma, being alone and naked and speechless with a strange man.

He came closer, stretching out his fingers, pushing my crinkled forehead smooth, cooing, singing, saying sweet words to the wrong girl. I don't know you, I kept thinking. Sweetness is just posturing, just manipulation, if you don't know me.

"Ashley, it's me. I'm Paul, your boyfriend." His eyes were wet and red like chemicals had just streamed into them.

"Do you know where you are?" He touched my cheek with those soft, officeman fingers.

Then darkness blew in again. I couldn't stand. I was falling. I was being taken. His words got all soppy and saturated and fell even further away. I decided to run, but it was too late. My limbs wouldn't carry me. My head couldn't stay up. I was running to the door, could see the brass knob turning in my mind, my hand turning it, mine or this girl's, but it was too late; the image went blank then, too. I was blank. I was drowning.

By all accounts, I am a living scientific experiment, and not just because I survived a lifetime of wedgies, noogies, and booger wipings. The heart condition I was born with, supraventricular tachycardia, was virtually unstudied when I was born. My mom refused the prospect of open heart surgery, probably saving my life, and opted instead for, well, let's just call it "Experimental Drug of the Month Club." To this day, it'd be a miracle if I could name just one of the numerous medications I guinea pigged as a child. I remember a green liquid in a dropper, little white pills chalky and awful, and an allegedly cherry-flavored syrup, which any expert (or other seven-year-old) could tell you had absolutely no relationship to any actual (and/or pseudo)cherry, berry, or fruit-like flavor.

But I never remember the bad things. I remember my big brother and sister convincing me to play sick so we could skip out on church, the "Dr. Barbie" my friends gave me just before surgery. I remember having enough energy to run one hundred laps around the gym without tiring, slapping my mom's shoulder and shouting my progress each time around. I remember the thrill of pulling an itchy IV out of my arm in the middle of the night while no one was looking.

I had surgery in a brand-new children's hospital, equipped with a huge playroom—video games and play houses and carpets that served as board games, too. I had an invisible illness that let me play and live an almost-normal life. I made awesome nurse friends, roamed hospital corridors at my leisure, and savored the smell of roasting cocoa beans at the chocolate factory just miles away from Hershey's Children's Hospital. Even later in life, after being diagnosed with Epilepsy, I never felt the danger or fear so often associated with illness. These were simply the patches holding me together, fragments of my life that defined me from others.

These memories surge into my head as I receive a wake-up call from my mom: 6:30am. "Daylan's in the hospital; he's had a heart attack." My mind is mixing reality with sleep as Mom pauses, waiting for me to fully grasp what she has said. I can tell from her voice that she is shaking, like a little girl in high heels, not sure how to move, how to act. I can't imagine how she feels, waiting like so many years before, waiting to know if her child will be OK. I spend several hours feeling hot and nervous; I call back to check on his status. No heart attack.

I'm relieved, then spun once again into a panic as Mom informs me that Daylan, my big brother, has apparently been living with the same condition I was born with. He had it first, I will learn, and suddenly I'm forced to realize what it's like on the outside, to feel that pit of concern, stress, and worry over something which I cannot control. My brother, this enormous bear of a human being, suddenly shakes the immortal, superhero glow I remember growing up with. I'm forced to see him not as this gladiator but as a human being—as fragile as we all are. I'm forced for once to be the observer, to know that the pain of loving someone who is ill might be every bit as challenging as being ill oneself.

I want to joke with him, ask him, "So are you contagious or am I?" but my words are uncomfortable, like sandpaper on the skin, as they exit my mouth. I manage an equally awkward prayer because in times like this you forget what you want to believe and head for the nearest immediate comfort. And I'm not sure if I should feel relieved or concerned . . . they've made huge advances in the treatment of this condition; no more experimental medications, no bidding between open heart surgery or a brand-new laser ablation, but there is still nothing for those waiting. Nothing to take away the fear and anger. I'm learning now what my family has been living with since the day I was born, and only now am I discovering how easy I've had it. How much I've taken for granted.

How to Write a First-Person Narrative

Andrew Shepperson

FIRST, YOU'RE GOING TO HAVE TO BRAINSTORM ABOUT YOUR NARRATOR. IF YOUR narrator is fully formed as a character before you begin writing, if you have a clear vision of your narrator from every possible angle, then you will save yourself from writing all those ugly drafts that more often than not end up in the fire or the recycling bin. Do this and have fun with it; let your mind wander to unexplored corners, and perhaps your story will be something worth reading.

So, pick a character, any character. And by pick, I mean create one, even if it's based on a real person. And by creating one, I mean that you're going to have to ask a whole lot of questions about this character, even if some voice is already speaking to you from the great beyond, as it should be, as it must be if you're thinking about using it to write a whole story. Ask yourself—out loud if you're alone, in silence if in a cubicle—whether or not this voice in your head belongs to a man or a woman, boy or girl. It may be that the voice is a voice of a sexless angel or that of a sexy she-male. If it be the former, ditch it. Have you ever read a good story narrated by an angel? But if it be the latter, run with it, tap on that keyboard as fast as your little fingers can. Trust me on this: everyone loves a wily hermaphrodite.

However, if the muse has refused to bless you with such an inherently conflicted creature, then you will in all likelihood be stuck with a man or a woman, or a boy or a girl. Ninety-nine percent of the time this is true, so don't sulk and shy away just because Danny got the she-male and you got the pregnant IT clerk with smelly armpits and a nasty Gobstopper habit. If this is your woman, if this woman's voice haunts you in your dreams and follows you to the bathroom and makes you mutter to yourself about oversized Victorian nightgowns and the man who mocked her idea to turn their small rowboat into a crib, then she is worthy. She is your narrator.

Oftentimes the characters that would be considered ordinary and insignificant in real life make for great narrators. Before you start to argue, ask yourself: does anyone seem all that normal or unimportant once you get to know them? I didn't think so. Take Huckleberry Finn, for example. We all know about Huck Finn, right? The boy who escapes from his drunken father downriver with a runaway slave? Mark Twain? Masterpiece? Yes, you have that book, right, the one that's been collecting dust on the shelf ever since sixth grade? Get it down, open it, and follow along with me.

Huck is a nobody, a scoundrel, a piece of poor white trash, a boy you'd pass on the street and look down on for being wrapped in filthy rags. Huck is a boy who "didn't care no more" about Moses because he "don't take no stock in dead people" (14-15). This is a boy with a reoccurring fascination with death, a drunken, homicidal maniac for a father, and a best friend whom he lets boss him around, even as he knows that this friend is full of lies. This is a boy that nobody knows even exists outside his little town in Missouri, yet Twain saw greatness in him and so chose him to narrate his novel, a novel that's come to be considered one of the most important ever written.

Now, most likely your work won't turn out to be a masterpiece, but you have to trust that your ordinary woman narrator has enough substance and life for a whole series of great American novels. So use her, mold her. Right now she is a clichéd lump of clay. Recognize this, and think of her as something else, something alive, a possible person, not a piece of pottery that will eventually shatter beneath the weight of the story. Keep asking questions. How old is she? What does she think about being pregnant? How pregnant is she, anyway? Is she one of those tiny pregnant women you see in tiny pregnant business suits nibbling granola bars on the subway, or is she more like a beached whale in spandex? Considering her Gobstopper addiction, she'd probably land closer to the beached-whale end of the spectrum, though this doesn't mean she has to be some humungous Blue Whale. She can be beautiful and whiney, like an Orca, which is really part of the porpoise family anyway. That's it—she's something beautiful who's been misplaced. She works in a cube but belongs in an ocean. How will she get there?

Before you go on with this idea, make sure you have all the basics in line and ready to be displayed on the page when the story calls for them. Besides the fact that she's pregnant, what does she look like? Eyes, hair, ears, mouth, height, stare, weight, race—these are all important. You should know them, even if they don't make it into the story. It's important for your character to have a sense of her own body, but don't feel as if you have to force any visuals where they don't belong. She will be the one telling the story, remember, so let her see herself naturally. Being pregnant, she will probably overreact to certain comments on her appearance, whether they are positive or not. Use this, but don't abuse it. Your story can't be only about her insecurities.

Analyze how Twain gets Huck's body onto the page. Huck is a presence, not merely a voice. Study his clothes, his hair, his movements and posture. Sometimes a sight of a narrator may come from another character, as I suggested above. This following excerpt comes after Huck has griped about his caretaker, Miss Watson, forcing him to wear "new clothes," which made him "sweat and sweat, and feel all cramped up" (14). Here it is:

> Then for an hour it was deadly dull, and I was fidgety. Miss Watson would say, "Don't put your feet up there, Huckleberry;" and "don't scrunch up like that, Huckleberry—set up straight;" and pretty soon she would say, "Don't gap and stretch like that, Huckleberry—why don't you try to behave?" (15)

Here Twain has given us a clear view of Huck's mannerisms through Miss Watson scolding him for "misbehaving." This is a clever way of letting the reader see Huck from another person's perspective. Coming at the beginning of the novel, this enables the reader to get a sense of Huck's preferred manner of behaving and provides some building blocks from which the reader can start to form a mental image. Huck is continually aware of his own body and appearance throughout the rest of the novel. Whether he is killing a spider on his chest, spinning around to prevent bad luck from cursing him, or dressing up in women's clothes, Twain always gives us some visual of Huck to play around with in our own imaginations. So be aware of your narrator's body as you're writing. Make a conscious effort, and the reader will be more engaged with the story.

Now that you're comfortable with your narrator's body, it's time to give her a name. At first, you might be enticed by some unattractive, old-fashioned name like Martha or Mary Jane. Resist these names. You know she's not old-fashioned, and neither were her flower-power parents. Yes, they were stoned, stoned and tired of names like Autumn and Chloe and Breeze. They wanted their child's name to be an original, yet malleable enough to be shortened into something traditional, just in case she turned out to be a politician instead of a poet or, let's say, something like an IT clerk in a law office. So they named her Cadence and called her Cadie. Only when someone asks does Cadie reveal her true, full name. Cadie could care less that "Scarborough Fair" was playing at her moment of conception. She likes industrial music and mystery novels. Anything too poetic has always made her angry, like she's missing something that never needed to be there in the first place.

Now, in the midst of all these initial attributes, we've only barely touched on her personality, her sensibilities and worldview and voice. To make a story more alluring for a reader, Cadence must have an active mind and at least try to play an active role in the world that surrounds her. Preferably, she will be hyperactive in both, having the ability to keenly perceive and interpret her world and the compulsion to act on her perceptions. Most first-person narrators are active in mind as well as body.

Again, let's take a look at Huck. He is one of the most active narrators you will ever encounter, and one of the best. Here he is in action, faking his own death in order to escape from his father and the rest of the people in town that will only try to civilize him:

Well, last I pulled out some of my hair, and bloodied the axe good, and stuck it on the back side, and slung the axe in the corner. Then I took up the pig and held him to my breast with the jacket (so he couldn't drip) till I got a good piece below the house and then dumped him into the river. Now I thought of something else. So I went and got the bag of meal and my old saw out of the canoe and fetched them to the house. I took the bag to where it used to stand, and ripped a hole in the bottom of it with a saw, for there warn't no knives and forks on the place—Pap done everything with his clasp-knife, about the cooking. (45-46)

This is a telling example of Huck's ability to analyze a situation and then act in accordance with his analysis. Now, the actions that he takes may not always be the most prudent, but they are almost always lively, dramatic, hilarious, and true to Huck's agile imagination and skewed sort of pragmatism. He does this because he sees it as the only way he can get what he wants: true and absolute freedom. What better way to ward off those who bother and abuse you than by making them think you no longer exist at all? And this is no plan that's been thought up for months or years or even weeks. Huck's just thinking as he goes, which makes his plan seem all the more daring and ingenious to a reader.

It's easy to get bogged down in a narrator's thoughts, so try to keep your narrator in motion as much as possible. Even in those static moments, find something that Cadence notices. Maybe she has a cat, an orange tabby she adopted from the neighbor girl Ramona when her family moved away and couldn't take her. Ramona, not knowing any better, had named the cat Garfield even though she was female, so Cadence calls her Garfy. Garfy's wild, used to being an outside cat, but Cadence is trying to tame her. She dangles a tin tea strainer full of catnip by Garfy's bowl to lure her into drinking this water instead of running water from the sink. She used to squat and do this, but now she sits on the cool, white tile of the kitchen, leaning back against the garage door beside the bowl, listening for her husband's return from another late night at work. He's had a lot of those lately, and Garfy's jabs at the catnip offer her a strange sort of comfort, as if she were training her to be a prizefighter instead of a normal housecat. After a good workout, the sink is always waiting as a reward. She knows this only validates Garfy's misbehavior, so she makes sure to shake her finger at her before she turns the water on.

This is great. This is action, even when sitting, even when alone. But all this action will prove to be worthless if the spatial relations of the setting are not properly put in place. If a character has no space in which to act, then your readers will have a damn hard time trying to visualize the scene in their minds.

Huck is another great example of this. Whether he is the one committing the actions or he is merely observing other characters around him, there is always a space in which these characters breathe and walk and run and even die at times. Take a close look at this scene in which Huck is observing young Buck Grangerford and another boy fight off an attack from their rivals, the Shepherdsons:

I took up the river road as hard as I could put. By and by I begin to hear guns
a good ways off. When I come in sight of the log store and the woodpile

where the steamboat lands, I worked along under the trees and brush till I got to a good place, and then I clumb up into the forks of a cottonwood that was out of reach, and watched. There was a wood-rank four foot high, a little ways in front of the tree, and first I was going to hide behind it; but maybe it was luckier that I didn't. (132)

Here we see Twain place Huck in a perfect vantage point from which to watch the ensuing gun battle. This might seem like almost too perfect of a place, but considering Huck's character—his daring, adventurous spirit and insatiable curiosity—his climbing of the tree and viewing of the battle are more plausible than him cowering away from the scene. Now, Twain isn't content with Huck just watching the scene unfold before him, as he is in some other scenes, but here he has Huck become an active participant. Huck says that he "sung out to Buck and told him" when the Shepherdsons had retreated and even asked him "what was become of young Harney and Miss Sophia" (133).

Huck's participation would seem ridiculous if Twain had not set up the spacial relations so well as Huck was climbing the tree. We know that Buck and the boy are shielded by the wood pile right in front of the tree from which Huck is watching and calling out. This imbues Buck's subsequent death with even more heartbreak and emotion, as Huck has spoken to him and has done his best to help him in his final moments. These emotions don't just arise from the ether like smoke in the opening credits of a James Bond movie. They happen in a fully realized, very specific place. Huck sees Buck's dead body "laying in the edge of the water," and so we see it and feel for Huck and immediately recognize his devastation.

Now, think of your narrator: think of where Cadence lives and works; think of where we will find her when the story opens. Maybe she is lying on the couch with a bag full of Cheetos and a jar full of Gobstoppers. The room is large but not enormous, covered by a spotless gray carpet and several pieces of modern-looking furniture. The TV, framed by two black-and-white Ansel Adams photos, gives off a pale blue glow, which is the only light in the room. Cadence isn't even watching anymore, doesn't even really listen. Her husband has just called. He has to stay late again. He's always staying late recently. Even though he calls from his work phone, she suspects that something is awry—another woman, another man, she can't be sure—but she never calls back to try and catch him. Instead she grows restless and sweaty, aches to be somewhere else, somewhere different.

Cadence stares at the ceiling fan whirring above her and then lifts her head off the couch. It's a black leather couch, which makes her back sweat profusely. She would get up, but no longer can Cadence simply sit up. Seven months pregnant, this takes effort, this takes time.

She digs her outer elbow into the cushion and rolls onto it. Her curly black hair drops over her round, pimply face. She flicks her neck so that the hair springs back over her shoulder, pushes up with the elbow and pivots her legs around in a grunt. Her toes dig into the gray living-room carpet, and the ceiling fan whirs and clicks above her. She leaves Animal Planet on to pretend she's not alone and holds her belly as she squats up from the couch. Her feet swell with the weight of her unborn son. The back of her violet nightgown, damp with sweat, clings to her skin. She pulls it away and fans her body with the fabric. It hangs loosely around her stocky legs until they begin to waddle toward the backyard door a few feet behind the couch.

She pulls at the fabric again and opens the door. The hot, humid air rushes through the screen door and envelops her. She tries to separate the sweet scent of the magnolias from the general rot of the soil that nourishes them, but fails and gags and feels her son squirm inside her.

"Garfy," she yells. "Garfield, I know you're out there. I don't much plan on leavin' this door open for two nights in a row, I hope you know!"

Cadence scans the figure-eight design of the lawn and the patches of flowers that border it. She listens for the bell jingling around Garfield's neck but only hears the squeaks and squawks of the Wilson boy practicing clarinet next door and the rustling leaves of the poplar tree in the corner of the yard. That's where she first saw Garfield, a beautiful orange tabby perched on a branch, swaying her white-sock paw. She senses that Garfield is elsewhere, but gives the yard one final look. It gets dark so early now. She realizes the summer is almost over and she hasn't enjoyed an hour of it. Rubbing her stomach, she turns back inside.

So now you have your place—a sketch of a place, but still a place, one you can realize more fully as the story unfolds before you and the drafts keep forming and re-forming until the place is a place you know as well as your home, Cadence's home. And a place is all well and good, a necessary ingredient, to be sure, but how does she see it, what does she think about it? How does she see the world outside her home? Does her husband remind her of that snake Richard the Third, or Bateman in *American Psycho*, or Jafaar from *Aladdin*? Obviously, you like to think of him as a rather villainous character, but that's beside the point, really. These opinions and perceptions must be conveyed, but how does she convey them? What language does she use to narrate her story? All of these questions have to do with voice, and what better character to illustrate all the wonders and joys and idiosyncrasies of a strong narrative voice than, once again, the great Huck Finn.

So what's so great about Huck's voice? What can you learn from Twain's creation to help construct a proper story-telling voice for Cadence? The most salient and arguably most effective aspect of Huck's voice is the lazy, conversational dialect that he uses to tell his story. Here is a great example, excerpted from a scene in which Huck has just arrived in a "one-horse town" with Jim, the Duke, and the King:

> All the streets and lanes was just mud, they warn't nothing else *but* mud—mud as black as tar, and nigh about a foot deep in some places; and two or three inches deep in *all* the places. The hogs loafed and grunted around, everywheres. You'd see a muddy sow come lazying along the street and whollop herself right down in the way, where folks had to walk around her, and she'd stretch out, and shut her eyes, and wave her ears, whilst the pigs was milking her, and look as happy as if she was on salary. (156)

This excerpt represents the way Huck narrates the entire novel. It has a rather charming, mellifluous rhythm to it, and the dialect is sprinkled into the lines as a spice, not slathered on thick as gravy. Everything we see, we see through Huck, in his language—his rich, often impromptu phraseologies combined with his lazy, conversational tone. Huck doesn't just say that a pig was walking down the road; he says that she was "lazying," a word that he uses time and time again throughout the novel. It's a word that can mean multiple things, depending on Huck's mood or the situation in which he finds himself. "Lazying" can mean swimming, sleeping, rolling along down the river, sitting, swaying, lying in the grass, or basically anything else that Huck wants it to mean.

It's a telling word, packed with a deeper significance than the various contextual meanings that Huck has chosen for it. From this word we can see and hear that Huck has a way with language. However, he doesn't know enough words to always assign a different, proper word to the thing or situation he is trying to describe. The ability and desire to capture a scene are there within Huck, but the proper education and vocabulary are not. You can see Huck making up other words as well, my favorite being in the following excerpt:

On the river front some of the houses was sticking out over the bank, and they was bowed and bent, and about ready to tumble in. The people had moved out of them. The bank was caved away under one corner of some others, and that corner was hanging over. People lived in them yet, but it was dangersome, because sometimes a strip of land as wide as a house caves in at a time. Sometimes a belt of land a quarter of a mile deep will start in and cave along and cave along till it all caves into the river in one summer. Such a town as that has to be always moving back, and back, and back, because the river's always gnawing at it. (156)

So, what do you think my favorite word of Huck's is in this passage? You got it: "dangersome." What a word, and true to his character as well. He obviously knows the word *danger*, and so thinks of a way to use it to describe the river eroding away at the land beneath the houses of the town. Huck loves the suffix "some"—he's always talking about how the river is so "lonesome," instead of saying that he feels lonely—so it seems logical for him to tack on the suffix in order to form the adjective that he needs. Now, the one controlling this use of language is not Huck, quite obviously. Huck is a fictional character, created and written by Twain. But the language that Twain has attributed to Huck tells us so much about Huck's character, and so should Cadence's narration as well.

As a tip of the hat to Twain, maybe you give Cadence some southern roots. But she's beached, remember? A porpoise out of water. So you have her migrate to the north for college, to Chicago, but she drops out after two years. Luckily, she's good with computers, so she finds a job at Roper, Roberts & Michaelson, a small firm on the north side of the city. This is where she meets Rob, her husband, who eventually moves on to some swankier firm in the financial district. This is where he says he is all those nights he doesn't come home for hours and hours and hours. This is where he says he is on the night your story occurs, when Cadence comes out to the garage to look for her cat. Perhaps, this is how it begins:

No, she wasn't out back, so I figured the garage would be worth a try. That damn cat had been out as much as Robbie lately, so I didn't have much hope of wrangling her in. But I needed some company, at least, and all the baby was good for was kicking my insides. He feels a lot stronger than seven months, to be sure, but it ain't like I can talk to him.

So I open the door, the brass handle cool on my sweaty palm, and waddle out into the gray, empty space of the garage. Even though it reeks of rubber and cat piss, the damn place is spotless from Rob's anal-retentive weekly cleanings and from general underuse, I guess. Myself, I like nice yellow light, but Robbie had to save him some energy, you know, so now I'm left with these ghostly white rows of fluorescents. They hurt my eyes, but his toolbox sure does look nice and shiny, perched up on that steel, black table, over there on Rob's side, the right side. Above the table hang three saws that I've never seen him use, a hatchet I've never seen him use, and a yellow flyswatter with one brown smudge in the upper right-hand corner, left by me, of course, after some housefly got what was coming to him.

And then there's my side, empty save for Garfy's litter box and the tiny green rowboat I inherited after my father passed a few weeks ago. Oh, Robbie yelled and yelled when I told him I was taking the goddamn thing back with me no matter how much the rental truck cost. I work. I drive. So I just went ahead and did it. Two days from Georgia, and I got myself back one of the dearest things I ever had. Last time I saw Ashley was in that boat, when she touched me and pressed on me like I never been pressed before.

It was a dreary fall day on the lake. Drizzle on and on. A Sunday, and we were bored beyond believing, so we got my father's poles and went down to the docks. Ashley was always underdressed, so it was no surprise that all she had on was a tank top and skin-tight pair of warm-ups. Me, I was in my old red Bulldogs sweatshirt. Damn thing was so saggy and I wore it nearly all that fall, so I'd be surprised if anyone had even noticed yet that I'd blossomed a fine pair of tits over the summer. I mean, it wasn't like they were watermelon tits or anything, but they were definitely there and new and frightening—nice rounded cones like two little anthills.

And so it begins, which brings to mind another thing about writing: don't be afraid to rewrite. I say this now because I can't help thinking that this story might be better in third person. Sounds like an intriguing idea, right? So maybe you should just start over. Maybe you should try it that way instead.

Work Cited

Twain, Mark. *Adventures of Huckleberry Finn*. New York: W.W. Norton & Co, Inc. 1985.

Underwear

Siera Cerny

I AM TRYING ON UNDERWEAR AT GAP KIDS. THEY ARE BABY BLUE WITH WHITE clouds on them and a white elastic band that is tight against my narrow, pudgy hips. I look into the mirror. The dressing room is larger than a normal one; I think it is so kids and parents can try on clothes together. The fluorescent lights illuminate the creases on my eleven-year-old stomach. Pale pink and lumpy, like clay. I lean one way and then I lean the other and watch the skin fold like hands pressed together to pray.

I put my hands up to my eyes and cover them. Surely darkness will overtake the ugliness I see. But it's still there. I'm still here. I can feel the folds: I envision them. The tears come after a heavy sting in my nose and eyes and ears.

And here is my mother. She's come into the dressing room. I don't know how she knew or when she came in, but that doesn't matter. She sits on the chair where I've piled my clothes, pulls me to sit on her lap. I cry into her white linen blouse. The wetness of my tears, the soft, expensive, faded smell of her perfume, her voice reverberating from her chest to mine: I've felt this before.

When I was eight-years-old, I got lost at Disney World in the Epcot Center, the park with the big, golf ball thingy that towers over everything. At some point, I noticed that the sidewalk sparkled as if it were magical or something. My eyes were glued to the ground just long enough that when I finally looked up, the lines of people crossed like plaid in front of me, and my family was nowhere to be seen.

Not knowing what to do and unable to find reason to panic—I *was* in Disney World, after all—I began walking. The park is set up like a donut with the big golf ball in the center and sectioned off into the different countries of the world. I remembered my father telling the rest of the family that he wanted a beer and that the Mexico portion of the park was the only place that served alcohol. I used that as a lead and was off.

Small crowds gathered to watch acrobats hop on each other's shoulders while juggling with orange and red and blue bean bags. Families posed for pictures in front of women with white-painted faces and pink and gold silken robes covering their whole bodies. A man wearing a black beret painted an exaggerated portrait of an older couple in front of a miniature version of the Eiffel Tower. It was warm during the day, but as the sun began to set, a chilly breeze made the hair on my arms stand up. I checked my new Tigger and Pooh watch, realized it was after seven and the fireworks show would start soon. Panic was about to set in when I found my mom.

She was walking towards me, so quickly she passed right by, her white linen blouse billowing behind her. I almost didn't want to call out because she looked angry. In reality, she was scared, nervous, *terrified*. Her little girl had disappeared into a park filled with pedophiles, lonely strangers, big, deadly machines where ghosts of the children who were never found lingered like steam after a shower.

But I had to say something; she was getting away. I called, "Neesee..." I used her nickname because I figured there were a million other ladies named "Mom" and didn't want to confuse anybody, and it was the first thing that came out of my mouth. She turned on the spot, wild-eyed, her brown hair falling around her face. She looked above me at first; her eyes were bigger and bluer and more frantic than I had ever seen them.

And then she was hugging me. Bent down to my level, or maybe she picked me up, it doesn't really matter. I didn't know I was going to start crying. But suddenly her warmth took over and I could feel her choppy breaths, heard her say my name, her voice reverberating from her chest to mine: it was a familiarity I didn't know I'd missed until it enveloped my entire physical being.

And here we are, back in the over-sized, Gap Kids dressing room. She's holding me, comforting me, just like before, but something about this is different.

I don't feel relief. I feel fat. I stand and look in the mirror again. My stomach is like half-baked dough and my skin is pale and I hate everything about my dumb body and there isn't anything anybody can do.

My flesh is slightly red from my attempts to stretch it, pull it, make it flat. My mother watches as I stare myself down, telling me she understands. She's sorry because "I have her body."

"No curves," she says. "I know. We are like boxes. Totally square."

My 16-year-old sister Quinn enters after hearing me sobbing and complaining. Her hair is brown with blonde highlights, pulled back with a heather-gray scrunchy. I can see the bumpy pimples she has attempted to conceal with a layer of gritty peach-colored powder that makes the complexion on her face a different color than that of her neck. She says, "Yeah, you and Mom *do* have the same body type... straight down. No hips."

Standing next to Quinn in the mirror, I look like the little kid I am and feel silly in the sky-blue underwear, my own pink ones sticking out from the leg holes. The dressing room is meant for two people, not three and I can smell her Bath and Body Works body spray and look at how her braces make her glossy lips puff out.

"See?" Quinn says and slides her hands down her sides. She over-exaggerates the wide-skinny-wide shape. "See how it gets wider at the bottom? That's because I have *hips.*"

I nod as I watch her in the mirror, my lips pulled down into an exaggerated frown. I look like a sad clown.

"You don't have hips, see?" From behind me Quinn's hands outline my lack of curvature as they move straight down: two parallel lines. "It's more boxy than curvy. Why is your skin so red?"

I exhale loudly, sending a piece of my hair away from my eyes. I say, "It was itchy."

"Oh . . ." She moves her hands away from me, probably thinking I have some sort of rash. "Well, you're still young, CC. You haven't even gotten your period yet. And at least you don't have a huge ass like me . . ."

"Yeah, CC!" my mother says excitedly, as if she's just thought of some brilliant idea. "You've got that great little butt. I remember when you were born, six weeks early. They were worried you wouldn't have developed all the way because you were so premature, so they brought in this specialist doctor in case you were missing any body parts—fingers, toes. But, you arrived with everything you needed! Ten fingers, ten toes. You were perfect, barely even cried! And this doctor, this *specialist,* she was, like, *disappointed* that you were perfect. She *stormed* out of the delivery room saying how *they shouldn't have called me if they didn't actually* need *me!* What a nut job *she* was!"

"I've got some stuff I'm going to try on still," Quinn says. "I'll see you guys out there . . ."

"OK, Quinny," my mom says, then continues, "and then I get you home from the hospital—you were *so little*. And then I suddenly realized"— a quick, smiling gasp— "*Oh my God! She doesn't have a butt!* We needed that doctor after all!"

She shakes her head and groans, and it is like she is reliving it. "I mean, changing your diaper! I didn't know what to do!" Her hands spread out in front of her in exasperation; then she presses them to her forehead. "It was just flat! I was—I—I—it was *so* bizarre! You would not believe . . . I was worried, really. Until one day—out of the blue—*you had a butt.* Just like that! There it was. But this wasn't just any butt, CC. This was the most perfect bubble butt I had ever seen. I was *so relieved*."

My face flushes; I am smiling. My mother stands and hands me my clothes; they are warm from being sat on, and I wipe my face with my jeans, though the tears have already dried. She pinches my butt; I squeal and giggle reflexively and she says, "*And you still got it!*"

I sniff some snot back up my nose as she leaves. My insides still sting, but there's a sense of calm coming over me, like the cool, wet air after a summer storm, the sudden lack of humidity making everything lighter and clearer, a little more illuminated. I've heard the story before; I've always liked to hear my mother tell it, but hearing it again won't make my body suddenly appear pretty. I turn from the mirror and pull the shirt over my head. Covering my body, covering my feelings, hiding it all because there is nothing else I can think to do.

Eight years later, I'm staring into the toilet bowl which I grip with shaky hands and sticky fingers. A thick, discolored string of saliva dips into the water where brown chunks of partially digested steak and baked potato float like debris from a sunken ship.

I breathe out of my mouth, refusing to smell or taste it. It stings my throat, burns my eyes, weakens my knees, and rots my teeth, my body, from the inside out: all of this is happening, has *been* happening, to my spirit, self-esteem, and outlook on life. I know all of this. I hate all of this.

And then, at the other end of the narrow bathroom someone pounds on the locked door: "*Siera!*" The dizziness I've already been feeling makes the earth sway harder and slower and faster and the sound of my mother's voice is worse than the sharp tang of vomit that coats my mouth. This noise zaps my eyes into focus. *"OPEN THIS DOOR* RIGHT NOW!"

I rush to the sink and put my hands under the faucet that's already running because I needed to muffle the sounds of my gags and the splatter of my recently eaten dinner landing heavily into the toilet. I flush, wipe my eyes, grab a toothbrush, shove it in my mouth, and open the door.

Her eyes are glazed, frantic, and narrow. She's not worried like at Disney World; she's not oddly sympathetic and kind of evasive like at Gap Kids. No, she's mad. Surely she feels those other feelings, but the wine stains on her shirt and the way she forcefully exhales through her nose—so loud I can hear it—she's overcome with . . . something. And when she says, "So is this how you do it? Is this how you've gotten so skinny . . .?" I know there's satisfaction hidden inside of her. She's solved the mystery! She's seen it with her own eyes! *Gotcha*!

This twisted pride I sense from her (and perhaps the stench I know will escape from my mouth) keeps the toothbrush pressed firmly between my lips: I do not speak. We stare at each other.

She doesn't enter the bathroom, just leans in at the door. The hallway stretches out on either side of her. I hear a door to my bedroom on her left shut and think about my sister Mollie hearing this, and everyone else I know she will tell. Only one year my senior, we are best friends and worst enemies; we are each other's rock, as well as the cement blocks that have the potential to drag us to the bottom of the ocean. Quinn, who moved away to college eight years ago, does not have the same effect. Mollie and I, on the other hand, have gone through our whole lives together; when my parents are at their worst, we have an unspoken pact to stick together. Recently, however, my behavior has ignited heated whispers from everyone around me.

Lost in thought, stifled by embarrassment, I don't answer my mother's question. Truth is, I don't think I'm skinny. I see myself in the mirror as a blur of pale skin and dark hair; my eyes are still watering from all the self-inflicted puking. It's like that most of the time. And really, what am I supposed to say? Yeah Mom, I admit it. I've been puking up my food for six months and that's how I've lost all this weight . . . seven whole pounds, down the toilet. Here, let me rub your face in it a little bit because I think that's what you want.

She breathes, I stare. And finally, like a bull raging toward the red cloth, she bursts into her manic, hand-wringing, spit-flinging rages that she seems to save for those she claims to love most in her life. "Oh! Oh! OK. Fine!" Reflexively, I take a step back as she takes one unsteady step forward, crossing the threshold, shouting, "If you do it, then I will too! I'll go *gag* myself right now. That way I can be skinny, just like you!"

Her exit is as swift as it is brutal, humiliating. Hands shaking, I've barely brushed the toothpaste against my thinning teeth. My heart is pounding and I want to die, but I'm kind of calm, because what am I supposed to do? Panic? If I freak out, I'll feel even more exposed. I'll be as bad as she.

It's been going on for years now, my mother's instability. Being the middle child of nine children—seven girls—couldn't have been easy for her. Body image for me is nothing compared to what my mother must feel. I mean no offense to my aunts, but her beauty was unmatched by theirs. This opinion was shared by the many men (and some women) who courted her. Age hasn't been unfair to my mother. She has the kind of beauty that will last forever. What happened was, time went by and she married too early, and she had her children, and the suitors dwindled, leaving the forced, twenty-five-year-old compliments from my father as wilted as her self-esteem. The desperation that has fermented under her surface has mani-fested itself in the man she is having an affair with.

He was one of the men who helped renovate our house five years ago. I nicknamed him Moth. A roughly built man in his thirties, he was a hard worker, wired, fidgety, always looking for something more to fix. He and his whole crew seemed to buzz with frenetic energy. We didn't know it yet, but that buzz was the result of chronic drug abuse. They were all meth heads. One day, as Moth sipped my mother's homemade lemonade under the umbrella on our newly remodeled deck, he said to her, "Me and the guys were wondering . . ." She looked up from watering the flowers. He was almost bashful; she nodded him on. "Are your, uh, are those . . . real? Your breasts?" And a button was pushed, and a light was reignited in her, and her immediate reality—submitting to the demands of a family, thankless and greedy; a life of driving a minivan, cooking and cleaning and watering the fucking plants—became dismal, unfulfilling. For years she had been doing this. Too many years to count, she was almost *fifty!* And the button sent a shock through her, as the realization set in: her youth had been stolen. *Of course*, her breasts were real! And she couldn't remember the last time somebody paid them any positive attention. And here was this man, this younger guy, complimenting her. As crass as it was, she was somehow invig-orated by the honesty, the unprovoked bluntness the man was expressing, not to her fourteen-year-old daughter (me, at the time), but to *her*.

The chemical reaction that occurred at that moment triggered a chain of lies, neglect, adultery, and numerous toxic relationships that overshadowed most of my high school life and forced my father to move out of the house six months into my senior year. A few months later, I graduated and left home and started a life in Chicago.

A year later, back for the holidays, I stand in the bathroom, silent, my toothbrush raised to my mouth. Where my mother just was, my sister Mollie now stands.

"Wow," she drones, disgusted. I want to cry. But I don't. Instead, I look her up and down out of the corner of my eye and spit in the sink.

Compared to me, her hair is five shades lighter, her skin is three shades darker, she is one inch taller, and two sizes larger. She too is angry, but also, of course, somehow proud, exhilarated. Her perfect nose flares; I see her ever-present cleavage rise and fall with each breath. She's voluptuous with curves like Beyonce. I've told her that before, but she took it as an insult; up until her recent two years in college, she was the skinny one. She's staring me down with her sky-blue eyes, outlined in navy-blue liner, surrounded by thick black mascara. People always ask if those are her "real" eyes, as in, they are so blue, they look fake. Well, they are real, like everything else on her. She doesn't know how fake I feel about my condition. She thinks I enjoy it. I know this because we're sisters and I can tell by the way she speaks to me. In her passive-aggressive, intensely belittling way, Mollie states: "Good job, CC. Now Mom's going to be bulimic . . . because of you." Her eyes narrow for effect, and she says it in a whisper, like it's one word: "Wayda-go."

I shrug and nod. It's a totally bitchy thing to do. But I'm caught off guard and don't know what to say. I can see it in her eyes, the way she's picking apart my brain and body and thinks I'm smug and skinny, the type who does whatever she wants because she lives away from home and she thinks I'm happy because I'm skinny because I barf up all my food in order to keep my stomach flat (there's still a pouch under my belly button), and my legs from brushing together (they still touch), and my arms thin and weak (never thin enough, not really weak). And it's disgusting and I'm mortified and I wish I could flush myself down the toilet. But no matter what I say or do, it's not going to make the situation any better. So fuck it. Let them think that, Yup, I'm really fucking smug, I'm better than everyone.

With a scoff of incredulity, Mollie is gone. I close the door and watch myself move the toothbrush around, mixing the mint with the vomit and all the acidic words I've just consumed. Words I tell myself a lot because it's easier to hurt yourself, insult yourself, when you kind of hate yourself.

I wouldn't be doing this if I thought I deserved something better. I'm depressed and nobody notices. And maybe I puke for attention—so people will look at me and think: Hey . . . something isn't right. She must be hurting. I wonder how I can help. But at the same time, I know what people think. I'm not surprised at the reaction of my family. I'm not happy at being found out. It's not something I'm proud of. I'm ashamed. Fucking *ashamed* that I do this to myself. I realized a long time ago that I was going to be stuck with the body I have. I heard it all the time from my mother. She told me over and over again: I have her body and that's just the way things are. And when she looks in the mirror, she sees ugliness. She says it out loud, "Oh God. I'm so fat. I look like a great big *toad*. And *my butt is so flat* I can't even keep my pants up!" A toad. What a terrible thing to compare yourself to.

I don't want to see my mother like that. I don't want my mother to think of herself like that. Because . . . what am I supposed to see when I look in the mirror? I see *her* body. But this is *me*. Why should I settle for something so imperfect? If I can do something to change myself, to offset the trajectory of what they tell me is my fate, why not? This is *my* life. I control what I do . . .

And yet, when I look in the mirror, do I see a flat stomach and a nice, long torso with round, perky little breasts? No. No matter how long I stare at myself (which is a lot, because when you have an eating disorder you tend to spend way too much time in the bathroom, on the scale, pinching, poking, sucking, sighing, crying about how ridiculous your life has become . . . so alienated and alone and really, seriously *stupid*), I don't see anything but a reflection of impermanence. Because really, how long can I keep up this charade? I can't barf up my food forever, can I? No. Especially not after today. And yet, I don't want to quit.

And it's awful. It's awful to pretend like I believe that I'm OK with this. It's awful to lie to myself and pretend that what I'm eating right now won't be coming back up in a half hour. It's degrading. The condition itself is making my condition worse. One part of me thinks, I've gone this far, why stop now? The other part is like, This isn't right. Think about Beth's anorexia in high school. Remember how you'd offer her food at the lunch table, knowing she wouldn't eat it? Remember watching her watch you eat a breadstick or a bag of chips? Her eyes blinked heavily and she chewed her yogurt in calculated slow motion, to make it look like she was consuming more than 500 calories a day. You saw a certain satisfied jealousy in her sallow face as you ate your food while you endured the same sick satisfaction of her not eating food: these aren't secrets to anybody but you. The disorder is the blinders, binding you to it. Did she know that you wished you were that skinny, that you had that much control? Remember how you would make lists of things you could and couldn't eat . . . only living up to the "diet" for two days at most? She was mentally capable of naked salads and zero carbs, but what about how physically weak she became? How frail and unstable from the malnourishment? Remember the resentment you felt because she acted like she didn't know why she would pass out randomly, why she nearly drowned while swimming in the lake, why she never got her period? Ever wonder why your teeth are so sensitive? Your nails are thin as paper. Your hair is, too. And the headaches? The sleeplessness? Ever wonder about these things, CC?

No. Yes. Maybe.

Mollie shows up again right as I open the door to leave the bathroom, a cordless phone in her hand. "Yeah, she's right here." She looks at me with her blue eyes as she holds the phone out, "Dad wants to talk to you." I want to sigh, but for some reason, my chest seizes and I realize I'm holding my breath. I take the phone, slip into the guest bedroom because it's closest to the bathroom, and close the door.

"Hi," I say into the phone. Letting my legs bend beneath me, I roll onto my back, stare at the white, bumpy ceiling. I'm exasperated and can't believe he wants to talk to me about this.

"What's going on, Siera?" he says. He's calling from his own small apartment, seven miles east of the house.

"I don't know," I say.

"Well, what you're doing is really stupid," he says. Like everyone else, he seems angry. Annoyed, even.

"Dad," I say, covering my eyes with the hand that's not holding the phone, "I *really* don't want to talk about this. Really. I don't."

I'm still short of breath and a silent sob rises in my chest as I imagine him staring out of the windshield of his BMW, his white hair whiter in the moonlight as he's parked outside the apartment complex where he lives alone. Although he comes over for dinner most nights, like tonight, his unspoken loneliness isn't something I like to think about. I mean, he's still married to my mother and she invites him over and he accepts, so it's not that bad, I guess. But then again . . . what else will he eat? Ramen Noodles? And who else would she cook for? . . . Oh wait. She cooks for two men, actually: her husband and Moth, the drug-infected insect she loves more than herself. I might not have mentioned before that Moth is known in many counties as a repeated drug abuser, thief, and gun possessor. It's not something I like to talk about, or think about, or admit to anyone. But I suppose it is an important aspect to how and why things have come to . . . *this*. How my mother has let herself fall into this totally fucked-up world. More than anything, time has become her enemy, but since time does not have a face, I feel like she looks at me as the one who stole her youth. After all, she lost her perfect body and creaseless skin after she had her first baby. I complain about what I look like, but what do I know? I'm still young and firm. Yeah right, I scoff, and my teeth are going to start falling out any day now.

"What did you say?" my dad says, harshly. I snap out of it.

"I said I'm sorry for being . . . the way that I am. I just . . . I'm sorry, Dad." Goddammit, my voice is shaking; I take a deep breath and realize how terrible he must feel. In my efforts to redesign my fate, I've found myself causing the same amount of trouble as my mother. All of these insecurities, they aren't just mine. They're part of those around me. They're seeping slowly into my father and it's too late to make it stop. This isn't his fault. And it's not my mother's either . . .

"You're not going out tonight," he says, and I exhale.

"Uhm . . . OK," I say, and I know he doesn't buy it.

"I mean it, Siera. You can't . . . go out and get drunk on an empty stomach like this; it's unhealthy."

Duh. "Yeah, well. I promised Nick I would go to Kyle's for Cara's birthday celebration . . . so, it's kind of too late. Sorry again, Dad." As bad as I feel, I know I'd feel worse if I had to stay at home tonight. There's no way I'm sticking around here.

"Siera . . ."

"Love you, bye," I say, and hang up.

I storm out of the house and drink a whole bottle of whiskey with my friends, with girls who no doubt have had less to eat than me today. Less to eat, less to gag up. Their legs are like twigs, their faces gaunt. Even the boys have their own svelteness about them; everybody around me, in the magazines, on the Internet, everyone has the look. And I delve into it, allow myself to grab hold of something other than what is going on at home, all the while cursing the piece of steak that seems to be lodged in my throat, an irritation that leads my thoughts to giving up food altogether so I won't have to force myself physically to give it up. Because no matter how many times I swallow, it feels like there is something stuck inside me, refusing to go down.

Trying to Get Home

Courtney Howard

START HERE: A GIRL SITTING AT O'HARE INTERNATIONAL AIRPORT, NEBRASKA bound, wearing a Cubs T-shirt (I don't even care about the Cubs), sipping on iced tea, and watching all the people go by in a hurry. Whenever I am in Chicago, I yearn for home. I call Nebraska home because it smells sweeter and the water tastes better and my family lives there and they are most important to me. When I'm in Nebraska, under my parents' roof, residing in the bedroom that I grew up in, drinking gin and tonics with my father (you want a double?), I speak of home as if it's a place far, far away. Home is wherever I am not, and home is a place that I am always trying to get to.

My very first job, like most twelve-year-olds in Nebraska who want to buy televisions and DVDs, was detasseling. They employ twelve-year-olds because no stable-minded adult would do what we did for $6.75 an hour. Every morning at six we had to be at the buses with our sunscreen and our working gloves and our packed lunches of cheese and crackers and Kool-Aid. We'd ride the bus out to the country, every day a new field, even more vast than the day before, and we would climb on top of a detasseling machine, going up and down every row, plucking the tassels off each stalk of corn. This was to control reproduction. The machines just looked like big tractors with wings, and on each wing were three bucket-like platforms that held two people each.

Every morning it was nearly freezing, and everyone wore long jeans and sweatshirts and swept their hair behind a bandana. By noon, it was blistering hot, and most had stripped down to bikini tops, or in the boys' cases bare chests, despite the horrible, unavoidable corn rash. Out in the cornfields, we'd find some of the biggest garden spiders I'd ever seen. They had big yellow abdomens and long, thick black legs. There were grasshoppers and praying mantises and little gnats that we called salt-and-pepper bugs. By the end of the summer, I was plucking tassels gloveless, not caring about the dirt under my fingernails or the insects or the prickly little hairs all over the corn leaves that left tiny cuts everywhere.

But the worst days were when we'd show up and they'd inform us that we were to be roguing. To rogue, everybody carried around shovels and walked up and down the rows of corn or beans hacking out all the weeds from the soil. It was backbreaking after a while and my shoulders ached afterwards. But the worst part about roguing corn was not seeing where you were for a very long time. For all you knew, all of your friends were roguing so much faster than you, and they could be miles ahead of you, and you'd be lost in a corn maze until sunset with those stalks towering over you, and all you would think about were crop circles and scarecrows and the *Children of the Corn*. By the end of the summer I had put $250 in my savings account and bought that new digital camera I wanted.

I would tell my family the following things: sometimes, I see people on the street who remind me of you and I choke back tears; you are lovely. I think mostly of you, Mom, when I see a woman with eyes like yours, gray and green with invisible eyelashes, wearing unflattering jeans and a floral blouse. These women have little wrinkles around their eyes and I think that they must have seen a lot and loved a lot, and I feel your compassion. You funny people, I worry about you, please take care of yourselves. Dad, you must get your sleep, and please watch your midnight binges on the sweets left in the cookie jar. For some reason, it makes me so happy to think about you around 8:00 p.m. and know that you're filling up that gigantic cup with milk and adding ice cubes.

Ashley, you are my sister and I'm sorry I always talk about myself, and I'm sorry it took the better part of twenty years for us to get along. Austin, I love the way your beard is always different and always a darker red than your curly hair. I picture you wearing aviator sunglasses and I hear your laugh and I see your nose scrunching up and your eyes watering and you look just as you did as a child, so graceful and silly. Tell the woman you're marrying that I love her too, and that I've never seen a couple have so much fun together. I wish I was near you more often. Sheldon, sometimes you text when I'm worrying about my homework or trying to get laid, and I'm sorry I ignore you. I can't imagine being the last of four left in that house. You are seriously the funniest seventeen-year-old I know, and I miss the way we bicker and the way you call me compadre when we play Super Mario Brothers together. When I'm sad, the only thing in the entire world that I want is to watch *Futurama* with you.

This room isn't bright enough; the sun only warms the walls in window-shaped squares in the late afternoon, and the light is fickle and fleeting. It's warm, in purples and blues and pinks. There are maps and pages of the yellow calendar taped randomly about; there is a postcard from the Art Institute and a mattress on the floor. There is a laptop and a cup of coffee and important documents, and a painted ceramic fish named Zach who holds old hemp bracelets, bobby pins, an origami rose made by my ex, Nivan, and one Cadbury Egg. There is a pink painting with black lines forming edges and pathways; it looks like a maze, and it's been hanging in my bedroom my entire life, although my bedroom has been in many places now.

It was my grandfather's first painting; I never met the guy, but I heard he used to finish a cigarette in two drags. My dad tells me the story of how he died. He says he collapsed in their office, and my dad did CPR, and he cried when he said, "I've saved many people, but I could not save my own father." My dad says that my grandfather was rushed to the hospital and flatlined for a minute. He awoke suddenly, with enough time to say, "I saw Jesus," before passing. That's how the story goes anyway. I used to spend hours trying to interpret the abstract lines in this painting but never made any sense of it; now just looking at it puts me in a creative mood.

It was some humid night in the middle of July and I was fifteen. My family, like everyone else in central Nebraska, had their eyes glued to the radar on the local evening news. The green blobs on the map were creeping closer, and soon they'd settle in right overhead. I couldn't wait.

I stepped out onto the front porch. The sun had barely started setting behind our house, and the white clouds like mountains hung in the distance.

Every couple of seconds the clouds would flash, but we heard little thunder. A wave of lightning bugs unfolded over the lawn and flashed like the clouds.

"What are you doing?" Sheldon asked. He'd followed me to the front porch. Predictable, he was still in the phase of following me everywhere.

"I'm watching the storm come in."

"We should go up the hill," he suggested.

"You're absolutely right." I opened the door to the house and yelled into the living room, "We're going up the hill to see the storm!" Neither one of my parents answered.

There's a diagonal street jutting out from the corner of our yard. It goes straight uphill for half a block and then meets a cornfield. We literally live right on the edge of town, and that cornfield opens up the horizon to us in three directions. Sheldon and I used to go up the hill at night and scream, "Bloody Mary! Bloody Mary! Bloody Mary!" before getting scared and running all the way back to the house. But this night in July we watched the sky turn violent. First it got kind of purple, and it might have been the setting sun, but then it got brown, and there wasn't even the slightest breeze and not a single blade of grass whispered but some of the crickets still croaked.

"Kind of spooky, eh?" I said.

"Yeah, let's go back."

"Please, don't be a baby. Come on, the house isn't that far. Let's stay longer."

That's when the brown sky started to move, as if it had fallen asleep standing in line and someone behind pushed it along. The big white clouds were now black and the lightning more than harmless flashes, but giant, striking blades.

"Court, let's go."

"Sheld, shut up. It hasn't even started raining yet."

"By then it could be too late. Come on."

"We don't have a problem unless it starts to hail."

"You're the problem. I'm leaving."

Sheldon meandered down the hill, and the wind picked up, and in my stomach I knew I should not have been there, but my feet were like stubborn bricks, unable to move until they were satisfied. I heard the sirens go off, those dreadful sirens that I remember hearing during breakfast as a kid, those sirens that always mean nothing to me, those sirens that have yet to scare me more than annoy me. Nothing bad has ever happened. My dad stood on the porch using all the air in his round belly to whistle to me, the sign to come home. I could always hear that whistle from anywhere in the neighborhood. I stayed where I was. Dad put his fingers in his mouth and pierced the evening one more time.

"Come up here!" I shouted. It really was unbelievable to watch the sky twist itself like that. Dad jogged up the hill, well, halfway up the hill before he ran out of breath. He walked the rest of the way.

"Court, come inside. The sirens are going off."

"They're not for us. They never are."

My dad saw it first; it must have been about eight miles away. At the opposite end of the cornfield, or perhaps in the neighboring cornfield, a massive twister swayed. It was so wide that it appeared as sturdy as a house, barely seeming to move at all except for those rotations in the black clouds. We saw it spin and curl, but it never came closer. Dad ran down to the house to get the video camera and I stayed put. I watched it for minutes by myself, and tears built up in my eyes for its magnificence and its power. Never before had I seen nature so uncontrollable, and never again after that.

Everyone falls in love with Dana. Everyone I know, anyway. Let's see, I've had one ex-boyfriend, two roommates, one best friend, one boss, and a handful of acquaintances fall to her charm. I haven't fallen in love with Dana, but that's because I've seen so many people torn to shreds because of her beauty—men and women, it doesn't matter. Even when she's talking about diseases or vegetables, she just oozes sex; it spills out like she didn't know she had so much, and I have to interrupt the conversation to say, "Dana, why is everything you say so sexy? Be careful." Then she giggles and I roll my eyes. Oh, to be gorgeous, she must think.

Every Thursday night Dana and I buy two bottles of eight-dollar merlot and sip until our lips are stained purple, and we cry talking about our mothers and our periods and our past lovers. I cry because she tells me that I'm a goddess, and she cries because she misses home. Home for her is Jordan, although her family now lives in Dubai, and it makes me feel like I need an appendectomy just imagining a family on the other side of the world. Nebraska already feels so far. She ties her wild black curls up in a lump on top of her head, and her eyes like big brown moons reflect any shimmer to be found in her dimly lit studio apartment. We drink and we drink and we drink until I finally yell it; I scream it to the world, and I write it down on a napkin so that I will never forget how I truly feel, if truth can be found in cheap merlot: "I love Chicago, I do. I love Chicago!"

"I'll miss it," Dana says.

Dana is moving on to bigger and better things: a theater company in Dubai seeks her talent. I feel cold, realizing she'll be moving soon, and so I must have fallen in love with her a little bit because I can't imagine loving Chicago if she isn't in it.

I listen to Yonder Mountain String Band's "Criminal" when I smoke cigarettes in my bedroom. The song lasts exactly as long as my smoke, and the bluegrass really brings me back home. I picture driving down Alda Road with my windows down and the sticky summer heat pouring in, smoking a cigarette and scanning the fields for signs of bald eagles and redtail hawks and deer. I usually wear my great-grandfather's flannel jacket when I smoke, although I don't think he wore it a single day in his life; it's probably better that way.

My great-grandfather was a wretched man, a man with no boundaries. He lived in Plainview, Nebraska, a town of one thousand, as plain as it is named, and it must have spoiled him. I only knew him as a painfully old man, a man in his late eighties wearing denim overalls that hung from his broad, farmer's shoulders. A man who spit when he cursed and cursed with every sentence. This man told my older sister not to date niggers at college. This man told me, when I was twelve years old, when I was wearing a frumpy black dress that my mom picked out, when I was with a family in mourning at his own wife's funeral, that I would always be the fat one. Ashley stood next to me, five foot ten and lanky, practically pointing her ballerina toes like she was ready to dance, and she had no idea what to say. Her bottom lip fell a bit and her eyes looked so desperately pained. She wanted to help, but she was the problem, the perfectionist, the beautiful statue that could never be lived up to. After that, my great-grandfather crowded my great grandmother's casket, hovering over his wife's body, then fell into it, clinging and weeping until my uncle finally pulled him off of her. I was weeping too, but not for his loss.

When he finally died, at the age of ninety-five, it had been eight years since I'd spoken to him or seen his wrinkly, gray face and crusty, square jaw. I learned of his death through a text message from my mother as I was preparing to go to class. She wrote, "I understand if you won't come to the funeral." She understood because he used to touch her the way he touched me after Grandma died, after he spat the words, "You're looking mature."

I later had a dream about him. In my dream he was long gone, just a ghost in a giant, terrifyingly dark castle. My cousin told me, "Bill left you something, a gift. It's upstairs." I climbed the cobwebbed, spiral staircase to find a pink dress with a big bow set out on the queen-sized bed in the corner. I picked up the dress and knew it was an apology.

I wear the jacket when I smoke now because I have forgiven him, and because it's so big it practically drowns me, and I don't mind making my memory of him smell like cigarettes.

I say good-bye to my parents and my little brother at the Omaha airport before security. My dad squeezes me and cries and holds me for about two minutes, and I try to be a rock for them, to not let my weakness without them show, but after just one minute of being captured in my father's arms, it is more complicated than that. I hug my mother and her face gets puffy around her eyes, just as mine does before I cry. I say, "It's only two months before we see each other again. Piece of cake." I hug Sheldon and he shows little emotion, but as I'd packed my bags the night before, he had begged me to stay. The problem is, our visits are getting fewer, and it is usually more than two months these days, and I have nothing to console them with. I love them and need them and appreciate them more than I appreciate the first full day of sunlight in April, but I could never tell them that it's not enough for me anymore. That I need Chicago.

I get on the plane and sink into my seat. I stare out the window. The flight attendant asks me what I want to drink and I say, "Nothing," despite how parched I really am. I smile at her and lose myself as the plane takes off, and I see the flatness of Nebraska before me for miles and miles, sometimes coated in white snow, sometimes green in squares and rows of agriculture, and sometimes dead and brown. I sob, uncontrollably; I should know by now not to wear mascara on travel days. I think, here I am, going back to the world I've missed of fast-paced people and art and drugs and lovers and friends and wine and trains and buses. I think, wow, it'll be a long time before I am back here, a long time before I taste such sweet water. I think that my family is my heart, but the people I've come to associate with in Chicago are my bread. Although one cannot live on bread alone, one can live without heart longer.

I cry for almost the entire duration of the flight, a little over an hour, but by the time that we land I am dry-faced and prepared to blend in with the city.

And I asked someone, "Has the park turned pink yet? I don't want to miss it." Adam said, "I think you already missed it." In my mind there was no way; the park was pink last May, a week before school ended, the week of important discussions on the woodchips and on the benches. Discussions about giving up on love and confessing to cheating with the hot magician roommate who looked a lot like Leonardo DiCaprio only with tricky hands.

The first time I saw the pink park in all its glory I shouted, "Wow! I think we've just walked into a children's book!" Every tree was a pastel pink that smelled as enticing as perfume, and all the petals floated and swirled through the air, and each petal was like a thought and each thought was significant.

For my twentieth birthday, my roommate Tyler, Dana, and I ate mushrooms and walked to the end of the world at four thirty in the morning to watch the sunrise. The end of the world, or so we call it, is out past the museum campus; if you follow the winding concrete path all the way around to where you can't see any buildings anymore, and the sky blends with Lake Michigan, you might believe, especially if you're tripping, that you've lost all connections with civilization.

The sun peeked its golden forehead over the horizon and we stood near the water and urged it on. We felt like children, giddy and curious and innately happy for no real reason at all, like we hadn't yet been corrupted. When the sun finally made its full debut, we gave it a standing ovation, and big, sloppy mushroom tears pushed their way out of the creases of our eyes. Then we plopped down in the grass, absorbing the sunlight until we were disrupted by a stranger.

A thirty-something man wearing ripped jeans and a sweatshirt asked if he could sit next to us. Being that we were impaired, we invited him into our circle.

"Do you guys need any shrooms?" he asked.

"Um, hello!" I said. I laughed until I fell to my side.

"Why else would we be out here so early?" Dana asked.

"Cool, cool," the man said, and watched the sky with us for a few more minutes before moving on to someone else who might have been lacking in psychedelics.

After he left the sky revealed a giant question mark in the clouds. This was definitely a real question mark and not a hallucination. We took pictures of it on our phones for proof. A man on a bicycle rode down the path, and Dana yelled, "The question mark in the sky! Do you see it? Do you?"

But the man must not have heard us, or cared.

"It's from God. He's saying, 'What the hell are you guys doing?'" Tyler said.

"It's from the universe. It's saying, "Really? The only time that you appreciate me is when you're tripping?" Dana said.

I said nothing at all because the question mark made me sad. The question mark was from my mother and my father and my teachers and all my old friends from high school. The question mark was sarcastic and menacing and I didn't care to look at it much longer, so I suggested that we leave. We walked slowly back to civilization but our bodies still churned on the inside with revelations that would soon be forgotten.

The Sound of the Man Hitting the Piano

David J. Bauer

JOHN WAS SITTING ON THE PIANO BENCH, LIGHTLY PLAYING A CHRISTMAS TUNE as the symphony that was Marshall Field's at Christmastime swelled about his small person. He hunched and played.

One day, say, oh, around one thirty—maybe it was even a Saturday, business in full swing, and then *whap!* It felt like Little League all over again, a right-handed kid cursed with the awful ability to be left-handed— why, cruel fates? It meant at least one—if not two—forty-mile-an-hour beanballs per game on the bony shoulder blade.

Then there it was again, like, *whap*.

Suddenly there was a nearness, a heat that meant a body was close. Looming over John was an elderly man, an ancient mountain swaddled in a fog of overcoats. He arrived like a weather front and loomed in John's airspace.

The man had a salt-and-pepper mustache and one eye that didn't seem to work. His hair was sparse and fluttered from the sides of his oval head. He looked somewhere above John's head and, casting a long-knuckled index finger at him, said, "Son, you are wasting your art."

John said, "Did you punch me?" He was rubbing his shoulder. A few people with large paper bags for hands stopped and wondered, Where has the music gone? It was an oddly lucid observation for such shallow individuals.

The man stood near John for a few seconds, wavering a bit, like his three heavy wool overcoats were a burden weighing him down. He shook and shivered a bit. Then he turned and made for the jewelry counters, and he was gone.

John sat there for a moment considering the man, wondering, was my playing really that bad? And then he looked down and saw, on the plush red carpet where the man had been standing, one dead cockroach and one dead millipede. John shuffled a few pieces of sheet music around, cracked his knuckles, and played.

What was it? Where did this come from, all this piano nonsense? Surely not Mom or Dad. They listened to big band on the radio and tapped their toes. Love and all, there was little artistry blooming inside their working-class bodies. Alas.

What was it that he saw, this boy John? Eighty-eight keys before him. Thirty-six black, fifty-two white. As he closed his eyes and plucked with his fingers notes that were buried somewhere in this vast whale of a piano, he saw this. See it:

88

It was beautiful to him. A pair of infinities side by side, modest in their love. Two infinities.

He got the gig at Marshall Field's on State Street when he was fifteen years old. To get there, he took the train up from Blue Island at 123rd St. It was a flag stop, and he stood on the empty platform and nearly leapt out of his sneakers trying to sufficiently hail the train. These were bright, cold, bleak-branched, snot-nosed winter days, often spent gazing out the train window as the opulent homes of Beverly Hills gave way to hatred, violence, and struggle. That was somewhere around Hyde Park.

His first time at Marshall Field's, on instinct, he slipped into the piano vendor's area in the basement, kind of near the cookware and the candy. He slunk behind a big beautiful Baldwin and began to silently fiddle, his ears held close to the keys, feeling for the delicate action, the kiss of wood and felt, so soft and resistant.

He was caught by a salesman who demanded he explain himself.

Sitting there on the piano bench, his fingers still meekly poised over the keys, John said, "Sir, I have a deep love for pianos in my young heart. I only seek to play pianos all day. I despise words, Sir. I have no use for them. They do not live, not to me. I wish to speak in sounds. I wish to spend all day speaking in sounds here in your fine store."

The man said, "Do you know 'Sleigh Ride'?"

John said, "Yes."

"Ah, but do you know 'Silver Bells'?" And he added a haughty smile.

John said, "Yes," and played a pleasant little blues quietly on the low keys. The piano purred, and John scratched its belly.

"Do you know 'Holly-Jolly Christmas', 'Most Wonderful Time of the Year'?" His arms were shooting out wildly.

"Yes!"

"'Rudolph', 'Frosty', perhaps you even fancy yourself 'A Little Drummer Boy'?"

John said, "I am acquainted with such music. Please give me a job. Everyone will love it." It was the bravest he'd ever been in his life. John was a bit of a pushover. A waffler. Wishy-washy. Flip-flopper. Chucklehead. Nudnik.

But the people who knew said he played a mean piano. Juilliard, the University of Chicago, Stanford. They'd all been hounding him about studying with them, but he hadn't much gotten around to opening the letters that arrived about once a week. He preferred to go to Field's. Before he had gone through the revolving doors, he had prayed for strength in his convictions. He really wanted to play piano for them. He was something of an obsessive kid.

The piano dealer referred him to a man on the fourth floor who referred him to a woman on the sixth floor who referred him to a nice man back on the fourth floor named Charles.

Charles was a man with blue eyes that happened to tear up at the merest provocation. The joy that a new toy brings to a child. Loving couples leaning over brightly lit display cases, rows of them. Swooping spans of red ribbon. And the tree. The tree that is an institution, holding court over the grandest of atriums.

John was a little ways off with the tree to his back, and he could see into the large room that held jewelry, swirling circles of ties (color coded), and high-end men's shaving appliances, among other things. An ivory or oak handle for your disposable razor, perhaps. Alas.

He wanted to pluck at the piano keys and speak to Field's. He hadn't been blowing smoke when he talked to the man in the piano department. Words meant very little to John. He often spoke in nonsense and was not surprised to find it didn't make much difference. He only spoke when he played piano. He would hunch low over the keys, his rib cage folding in on itself to accommodate his long gangly legs. His ten fingers were garden trowels and he was a gardener digging at black-and-white soil, seeking whatever knowledge was underneath, buried somewhere in the piano's cavernous body.

Sound was all.

One day, early in December, John was deep into a long spell of playing. The Christmas songs were beyond boring him. The fifteen or so holly-jolly songs he played were more or less a shower routine by this point.

But he'd gotten soft. At the outset he had told himself: Discipline. This is a gift, this gig. Don't blow the whole damn thing. Don't expand. Challenge yourself to stay inside the lines. Very Zen, perhaps. Or not. Alas.

He'd catch himself drifting, throwing in a left-hand stride here or there, aping Art Tatum and his cutting contest style, right hand flying quiet and wild, striving to destroy and improve Christmas songs the way Art Tatum did to "Over the Rainbow."

And one day his kind boss, Charles, the man with the leaky blue eyes, who always seemed to be wearing the same broad suede suit and purple-shaded glasses, spied him from a nearby pillar.

Charles, who was a nice person, had made his way to a rather respectable position as a floor manager. It was unprecedented. No one expected him to get anywhere near that. He was a nice man, and subsequently life made a point of shitting on him whenever it could. He was often emasculated by his boozy, three-drink-lunch superiors, never allowed to be part of the boys' club. He thought of this as he listened to John play. He watched John's face. John's parted brown hair fell in his eyes as he bore down into the piano, as was his nature. He wore a tuxedo, black and sharp at the shoes. Charles listened to John take "Sleigh Ride" and repeatedly roll it up and unroll it, like a sleeping bag. The song became the beautiful, troubled sister of "Sleigh Ride." The one you secretly wanted to fall in love with.

And Charles, caressing the suede lapel of his jacket, felt that there was something exalted in the way John played. He cut a striking figure, seen from the shoulders up behind a black grand piano, gleaming in Marshall Field's exaltation. The sound shot up in a column, filling the atrium's space, tall and gorged with winter light. He saw at every level, people leaning over the railing, their necks stretching into the airspace, like they were savoring the smells John's piano made. They fairly sniffed in delight as he danced around the compositions, taking a few seconds here and there to leap around high and low, dragging chords behind him like a runaway horsecart. Everyone listened.

A beautiful woman who exuded brightness and warmth came up next to Charles and said, "My name is Ruth. I'm from the *New Yorker*."

Charles, always such a nice fellow, said, "Hello."

She said, "Are you the manager here?" She had an accent acquired in classrooms with many levels of chairs, where the professors walk around with phonographs around their necks that beseech the girls to be *charming*, be *delightful*.

And indeed she was. Alas.

Charles said, "I'm the floor manager."

She was looking at John at the piano. His left hand was churning on the low keys, getting a little worked up.

"He's really something."

"Boy-howdy," Charles said, whatever that means.

She decided to write a piece on John for the magazine. It was very long. Nearly ten pages of small print in a January issue. She was very thoughtful and sensitive. She presented John like a misunderstood savant. A beautiful genius who may be on the brink of a major breakthrough or on his way to losing his mind. It was readable and thoroughly interviewed.

John told Ruth about the elderly man. The way he had punched him, sternly spoken to him. He told her that the man's words haunted him at night and that often he'd wake in lonely, cold sweats. Charles's family, besides being comprised of ugly people who spent their free time making Charles miserable, happened to be rich, and he became the closest thing John had to a friend. After all, John was hard to talk to sometimes. He only answered in notes. The family was filthy, stinking rich, and they got John a modest flat for himself and his insanity like it was a new dinette set.

Ruth, the writer, and John, the piano player, sat side by side on the piano bench and talked while he played. She marveled at the way he bent towards the keys and managed to hold a frighteningly insightful conversation. He was like a mechanic the way he approached the instrument, always peering in, searching for answers in the machinery. For half a second she wished he was ten years older. Even eight.

The article was a big hit. John became something Worth Seeing, which is good as gold today. We all want to feel that we're worth seeing, don't we? The store began to take on record numbers. The escalators gargled shoppers up and down their throats. Elevators dinged, and a deluge of bags and heels and mittens clipped to cuffs all tumbled towards the big open atrium like flies that bump into windows because they yearn to be outside.

At this point the tree was gone, and John occupied Marshall Field's most awe-inducing atrium, which it mostly owed to its vast size. Other atriums in the building possessed more artistry, more sensitivity. This one was tall and broad and scoured with bright winter light. Sheer volume in space. A piano kid's dream. And the customers ate it up. By this point he didn't even bother with Christmas songs. The compositions were his, and they were made up at the moment his fingers touched the keys. Instant composing. His playing would often begin lightly enough, playfully lilting around the high keys, maybe slamming once in a while for fun, loosening up, playing around. Then he would decrescendo and linger somewhere in the low depths, wondering. John did his thinking down here. Then, without warning, he would hop, leap, and skip up and over black keys, striving for high notes. And that's about all it took. From there his body simply spoke to the piano, which in turn spoke to the building. And thus the three—boy, piano, building, were one in sound. And everyone heard it. Alas.

John had just chugged his way through a major building portion of music, and he was relaxing somewhere in the middle of the keyboard. Nothing too rigorous. Then, for some reason, he was possessed to linger in silence. This never happened. Something in his personality demanded constant, precise, piano movement. He was merciless in the way he pushed himself to achieve.

The elderly man's words would chastise his sleep and cause his heart to ache. To question one's own motives can often be dangerous territory.

It was strange, and everyone seemed to feel it, this strangeness. It filled up space like a balloon, rose right up to the boarded storage room windows near the misty tops of the atrium.

Then the piano was crushed to bits. It didn't stand a chance. First there was silence. Even the dynamo cash registers, even the traffic outside the building—everyone remained still with John, still with him.

The piano crunched like an elephant and leaned forward like a broken camel. The keyboard nearly flew up and broke John's nose from underneath. Something had landed on the far end and sent his end hurtling upward. Right in the middle of that silence. Or at the exact end of it. John had even caught his hands—the devils—poised up in the air with dramatic gusto. But instead, a small plane crashed into a symphony, or at least that's what the piano seemed to want you to think.

The sound the piano made echoed through the silent store. A few concerned voices could be heard from the balconies up above. But no one moved. John crawled around the piano on his hands and knees as the whole store watched, breathing dust the whole time, and he found—lying there amongst shards of wood and lacquer and steel wire—the elderly man. Alas.

It was him. He had plunged. John looked up and considered that tall space, so full of whatever exalted pieces of space are full of. Again the man's words, "Son, you are wasting your art." John looked at all the people, who seemed to be waiting. He said, "I quit." And that was that. Alas.

He began making recordings with avant-garde college kids from Evanston. He found them boring. Mostly they smoked weed and drank dark beer and agreed that they all, each and every one of them, liked the same obscure, soul-touching artists. He played piano at gigs and made some money, but he was miserable. Alas.

He spent all his time in his bleak studio apartment. Cigarette butts abounded. A few shoes here and there, a minimalist mat to sleep on. A small kitchen the size of a walk-in closet.

And a piano. The whole point of it all.

He spent all his waking time at this piano. Sometimes he napped on it and woke up with red lines on his face. His hands drifted, searched, left no rock—no key—unturned. He was obsessive.

The elderly man had certainly made his point. John devoted himself to turning the elderly man into sound. To make him live in a composition of piano that somehow spoke to who he was, whoever he happened to be. It would be beautiful.

It was driving John insane.

He played Debussy's first etude over and over again, the lonely little scale periodically razzed by atonal notes. It was bleak and made his empty apartment feel bleak. It was also kind of funny. Alas.

How to do it? How to capture the elderly man in sounds? This was John's conundrum. One thing felt OK. An idea: The notes (on the piano) should be staccato. Dot dash. Dot dot dot. Like when you ride the subway and those long fluorescent lights streak by, one after another, and your face strobes sadly. It should sound like that, at least at first.

To describe the weight with which he moved. His jitters. Something on the low keys, minor key, sad. Plodding, leaden with heft. But then there was his lightness in approaching those heavenly jewelry counters. Warm and loving major chords trilled and resounded and seemed to swaddle his sad notes in blankets. The man approached the escalators; the notes began quietly and gently trilling upwards, up, up.

Perhaps John was on to something. Perhaps not. Alas.

But as the man successfully mounted each escalator, the piano's risings became more pronounced. They swelled with crescendo and foreboding, still making us aware of the overcoats and the weight.

Perhaps, perhaps not.

They grew and grew. The piano began humming, the room began thrumming; John felt all of his body, numbing, except the hands. They flew like pigeons as the elderly man, in John's roiling mind, approached a lofty banister and looked down on a space taken over by a young man and a piano as shoppers and art aficionados looked on.

It was here that John reacquainted himself with that silence. In fact, silence terrified him. Sleep was murder. The man's words chastised and lashed him, and every day that he didn't have a breakthrough was more anguish. Alas.

But after all, wasn't it silent then, right before? A second—no a half-second, no a hundredth of a second before the man hit the piano, there was nothing but silence. Silence in that big, big building. Funny how fast things could go from quiet to loud.

And here was the wall. How to get that sound? The sound of the man hitting the piano. Oh sure, he'd mashed his arm, fist to elbow, against the keys. But that's kid's stuff. Sophomoric.

How to do it? Alas.

Well, it didn't come. And neither did sleep. John found himself rarely leaving his apartment, rarely eating, rarely talking. All he had was sound.

He worked and worked, and his work, instead of making more sense, made less sense, and it continued to do so at an alarming rate. His work and his sanity were ground into powder like corn in a gristmill. Alas.

Then one day he was walking down the hallway outside his apartment. His building was five floors of relatively peaceful, dank living. The stairwell weaved round and round. He could see the teal-and-white tiles of the ground floor, and there was a big beautiful space of quiet air. He got a great idea. He called his only friend Charles, who he only talked to once or twice a year, and who was quite a pushover, and got him to get a few guys to move his piano down to the bottom of the stairwell. It was no grand, just an upright. They came one Saturday and John sat with his feet up on the windowsill, reading Wordsworth. Words still meant nothing to him. Perhaps that's why he loved the poems so much. Or perhaps not. Alas.

After the men finished, John offered them a drink from his small kitchen and they politely obliged. John had read that this was what you did. They drank water and stood in the silence.

One moving man, big and brawny, said, "What's the book?"

John looked down at his hand which, strangely, had a book in it instead of a piano.

"The book," John said, "is Wordsworth. I suppose that answers your question."

"Do you like it?" The man was quite thoughtful for a mover. Whatever that means.

"Words mean nothing," John declared. He had said it often before but not in many years. Not since he was playing at Marshall Field's and everyone was reading about him in glossy magazines. Not since the days when he got invited to parties as the fiercely interesting young prodigy. John didn't feel interesting at all. At least, not when he was away from the piano. He held a watered-down drink in his hand and declared to a group of successful, middle-aged individuals, "Words mean nothing."

But now it felt sort of false. Automatic. It felt nice to talk. He stood still. His hands stood still. They men were silent in the apartment, and they drank their water, and that's all it was. Then the movers left.

John held the book of poems for a second longer, then he went out the door and approached the balcony over the stairway and plunged. As he fell, he asked many questions. For example: the elderly man. As John plunged in his own, personal way, he asked the elderly man: When you jumped, did your overcoats flail like pigeon wings? Did you feel the cool breeze in your celestial wisps of hair? Did you speak to me in your descent? Did you even remember me?

Son, you are wasting your art.

John plunged down five flights and slammed into the piano. It sounded like the Macy's Thanksgiving Day Parade having the pavement pulled out from beneath it like a rug. Everything slammed and rang. Alas.

With the shards and protruding edges all around his face and organs, John heard the echo, the resonating ghost of a man plunging into a piano. He saw his Wordsworth book nearby, and, strangely enough, considering the moment, opted for words:

He said: "I hear, I hear, with joy I hear!"

Alas.

Basketball Is Gay,
from "Fly, Grounded"

Chris L. Terry

BEFORE PE, KEVIN OPENED HIS GYM LOCKER. THE SMELL OF PAINT AND SWEAT washed over him. Locker doors banged and Demetric's voice floated by from a row over, echoing off the concrete floor.

"Stinky finger, man."

Demetric's friend Maurice said, "Word?"

A bookbag zipper *voop*ed open.

"Yeah boy."

"With who?"

Maurice's voice rose and the "ooh" noise in "who" hit a high note on the ceiling. The inside of the lockers made a metallic rumble as one of the guys maneuvered his bookbag into the narrow metal cubby.

"You know Deja?" Demetric asked.

"Naw, man."

"Deja Eliot."

Maurice grew serious, "Stop playin', nigga."

Kevin stood frozen, staring into the shadows of his locker. There was a tap as Demetric's rubber-soled gym shoe dropped to the floor. Deja Eliot was a quiet girl with huge, inviting eyes that popped off her dark skin. She was new in town, from Alabama or somewhere country.

"Naw, for real. You know Deja. From math class."

Demetric was one of those guys who was in the smart classes, but people didn't clown him, because he was cool. Let Kevin try that sometime.

Maurice was Demetric's old friend who hadn't become as popular as Demetric had in middle school. He said, "Oh, wait. Deja. Churchy girl with that yellow coat?"

"Yeah, her."

Holy shit.

"Nigga, you did not."

Kevin stood there in his boxer shorts, not wanting to rustle his clothes and drown out their conversation.

"Yeah, boy!"

Demetric sounded casual about it. Like he went around fingering girls every week. Kevin hadn't even kissed anyone yet and here went Demetric, getting to third. When would Kevin's time come?

"Ha-ha! . . . Nigga, I ain't slappin' your hand. Who knows if you washed it since!"

"I used my other hand anyway."

There was the clap of them giving each other five. Kevin stepped into his gym shorts. The damp sweat in his socks was cool on the floor.

"Is that where you was at yesterday?"

"Yeah. Both her parents work 'til five. We got at it on the couch," Demetric snickered.

Maurice hooted. More guys came into the locker room and Kevin sped up, not wanting to hang out half-dressed. He rooted around in his bag, lifting up textbooks and looking for his PE shirt. Then it hit him—it was still in a ball on his bedroom floor, where he'd ditched it Tuesday after Mama caught him with the red shirt on, lip-synching to the Eddie Murphy tape.

If you don't dress out once, you get a warning. Twice, you get a detention. Same with the third time. Then you get in-school on the fourth, and on your fifth time, you fail. This was Kevin's first miss. He laced up his sneakers and hoped that he'd only get half a warning since he had his shorts. Mr. Bisceglia might not even notice. He was known to miss all sorts of cheating because he stayed busy looking at the bottom of Chiffawn Marion's booty poking out of her rolled-up shorts.

As Kevin sauntered out to the gym, there was a hip-hop tape playing in Mr. Bisceglia's boombox. It was so loud that the music was reduced to static and drums slapping off the cinderblock walls. Mr. B hated rap. Once he'd called it "crap with a silent C," and it took the class a minute to get the joke; then they still didn't laugh. He usually played some rock 'n' roll station that had songs he liked back when he had all his hair. Every now and then, he'd play a tape of some country bullshit and make the class hit a volleyball around while some cracker sang about being in the Ku Klux Klan or whatever.

The gym was alive when Mr. B wasn't there, and it excited and worried Kevin. He loved the energy and the music, but he sucked at sports and would never participate in these pick-up games before the bell. Tyrell the bully, his henchman Leo, and two other guys were playing half-court. They were balling rough and close between the free throw line and the basket, hardly passing, just shooting, shoving each other for the rebound, then shooting again. The way they jostled made each shot look like the ball had been squeezed out between their bodies and popped into the air. It rarely went through the hoop.

Demetric came out and joined the game, and Kevin watched his fingers spread as he dribbled the ball. Had he washed them since yesterday? Did they still smell like pussy? Was he getting pussy smell on the ball?

Mr. Bisceglia followed his paunch into the gym, wearing black sweat-pants and a Dallas Cowboys T-shirt and carrying a maroon can of Tab soda. Kevin fingered the hem of his T-shirt and hoped Mr. B wouldn't notice that it wasn't his gym uniform. The neon lights in the cages high up on the ceiling reflected off Mr. B's bald spot as he bent to click off the tape, then blew his whistle for everyone's attention. Leo took a last shot, which went off the backboard and through the hoop, and Mr. B blew the whistle again, harder. The players all turned and the ball left the net swinging, then bounced into a far corner.

Mr. B punctuated his announcement with two claps at the beginning and end. "All right, everybody, basketball today. Let's get four teams going."

Reading from his attendance sheet, Mr. B pointed people to different cor-ners of the gym to separate the teams. The two teams on the right side hit the bleachers and the two on the left took opposite ends of the basketball court while Mr. B fiddled with the boombox until some rock 'n' roll that sounded like a beer commercial came on. Tyrell took center for the other team. Kevin stood near Demetric on the court, looking away, but sniffing in his direction to smell his hand. Floor varnish and leftover sweat stung his nose.

Mr. B blew the whistle for the tipoff. Demetric trotted toward the center, tapping Kevin's shoulder in passing and saying, "You're on defense."

Kevin twisted his neck to smell the side of his shirt. Which hand did he use to tap me? Nothing. He walked to the side of the free throw line and stood with knees bent, hands on thighs, and hoped the ball wouldn't come his way.

Don't take this wrong, but in gym class, sometimes Kevin wished he was a girl. That way, no one would expect him to do anything but get flustered when the ball came at him. He could scrunch his face and throw it badly and things would work out fine. That's about what Kevin usually did anyway, but if he was a girl, no one would care; no one would hit his arm and go, "You fucked up," and hey, he could also go into the girls' locker room after class and watch them change.

The guys who were really into basketball took all the forward positions and wound up doing a lot of the defense, too. It was like there was a ball game between six guys, with Kevin and three others, usually girls, standing on the outside of it, following at a safe distance as the pack of hardcore players charged up and down the court, all elbows. Some people played, but people like Kevin just passed their time before it was their turn to hit the bench. There'd be three games, the third being where the winning teams from the other two matches played each other.

Mr. Bisceglia called this "elimination, bracket-style," and would shout things from the sideline like, "C'mon final four!" That man was corny.

But things were going OK today. Kevin was hanging back on defense, and Mr. B hadn't said nothing about his blue shirt. Kevin was trudging across center court while his team was shooting on the basket when Tyrell broke out of the knot of players under the hoop, jumped out, arms up to catch a wide rebound, then came dribbling upcourt, slamming the ball to the floor, moving away from the sideline and right towards Kevin.

The rock music and the squeak of gym shoes on polished wood and Chiffawn's honey-coated legs dropped away, leaving Kevin, Tyrell-the-charging-bull, and that dark orange ball that boomed off the floor every few feet as it drew closer to Kevin. Sweat dripped off the tip of Tyrell's nose and sprayed to the sides with each exhalation. Kevin remembered his own surprise at the high arc of the lit cigarillo that he'd thrown back onto Tyrell's balcony the day before. Tyrell could be got. And Kevin could get him, starting with this basketball. Kevin crouched and glowered at the approaching bully.

Tyrell was set to pass five feet to Kevin's right. His eyes were locked on the hoop as if Kevin wasn't there. That was how little the other guys thought of Kevin in gym class. They thought they could just fly by without any worry of losing the ball. Kevin spread his arms into defense position. That wasn't true.

Kevin scissored his legs and cut back diagonally, going for the ball as Tyrell was reaching the three-point line. When Kevin leaned in, Tyrell popped his arms up for a jumper and elbowed Kevin in the side of the head. When Tyrell heaved his grizzly bear body into the air, Kevin's face mashed on the front of Tyrell's sweaty gym shirt.

Most guys bring their PE clothes home every week or two to put them in the laundry, but not Tyrell. And that shirt stank like cabbagey old sweat, tobacco smoke, and the oily smells that linger near the body. Upon impact, Tyrell made a deep woofing noise and his left leg splayed out to the side. He had to grab his knees for balance, but stayed on his feet. Kevin spun away, blind from Tyrell's stinging sweat, and ran three steps to keep from falling. Kevin stopped in his team's paint, head housing a dull ring from Tyrell's elbow. Someone on the bleachers yelled, "Dag!"

Kevin stood there, arm jutted out, hand clapped to his warming ear. The shot went crazy and the ball hit the ground short of the hoop and ricocheted out of bounds, bouncing off the gym wall and rolling right back to Tyrell's mammoth feet.

Tyrell picked the ball up and overhanded it off Kevin's exposed side. The air inside the rubber ball made a ringing noise after it hit. Kevin's hand fell from his ear. Now, Kevin had been elbowed in the head, hit in the ribs with a ball, had some wind knocked out of him, had never fingered anyone like Demetric, and had Tyrell next to him, hopping on his toes, yelling at the sidelines, "Mr. B! He fouled me, Mr. B! I need a free throw!"

People on the bleachers were murmuring and pointing. The ball lay dead on the ground between the two boys. Kevin looked over it at Tyrell and hated him more than he'd hated anyone since his pop moved out. If Tyrell wasn't there, there'd be no problems. Ever. Kevin yelled back, "You fouled *me*, asshole!"

During the shout, Kevin's voice moved from a croak to a squeak. He clapped his lips shut, not believing that he'd just cursed in class. Tyrell got blurry. Kevin's eyes were wet and he automatically reached both hands up to wipe them off. Mid-wipe, he realized that he looked like a baby in the cartoons when they ball up their fists and wring them over their eyes with tears shooting out, yelling, "Waaah!" Everyone was looking at him. Necks cocked, eyes wide, mouths hanging. It was silent in the room like when you expect noise any second, and the strong wind of anticipation fills your ears.

Before today, Kevin had never missed dressing out, he'd never cussed in class, and he'd never even raised his voice. Mr. Bisceglia must have been shocked because he didn't say anything about any of it. He looked from Kevin to Tyrell, who had his arms spread, palms up in the classic "what the fuck?" gesture, and said, "You guys both fouled each other. Let's do a tip off with . . . Demetric and Leo." He gave his head a fast, tiny shake then clapped twice and boomed, "Come on, everybody, heads in the game!"

As Tyrell turned to take his position midcourt, he called Kevin a bitch. Kevin crossed the floor to his position, looking at the red paint in the free throw area, when Mr. Bisceglia went, "Wait, Kevin. That's not your gym shirt."

Kevin's eyes were still wet. He didn't look up, just down at his sweaty blue T-shirt. The class was back to staring at Kevin, seeing if he'd shout again. Kevin took a big breath that shook when he exhaled.

"I know," he told the floor.

Mr. B tucked the basketball against his hip and said, "Why didn't you dress out?"

"I did." Kevin pinched the right leg of his red shorts and pulled it out, stretching the Richmond Public Schools logo.

"But where's your shirt? You've gotta dress out all the way to play." Mr. B stood there in that circle in the middle of the court like he ran the whole world. A guitar solo started on the boombox. Mr. B's hand moved to the whistle around his neck. Kevin said, "Well, I'm already playing."

Mr. B couldn't write Kevin up halfway through class for being halfway dressed. It wasn't like he'd not dressed out so he wouldn't have to play. He'd really tried. Demetric looked at the clock behind the cage on the wall and made a hissing noise with his teeth, like he was deflating. Tyrell rocked his head side to side, stretching his neck with a look of bliss on his sweat-glossy face.

"Not anymore. Sit down!"

Mr. B stomped his right foot and pointed to the bleachers. The whistle swung back and forth. Kevin hated him so bad right then. Mr. Bisceglia hadn't been good enough at sports to go pro, and he'd never even be good enough at watching them to be a ref, so this was all he got. He just got to boss around middle school kids who he thought were too young to tell how much of a loser he was.

"Fine by me. I didn't wanna play gay-ass basketball anyway."

Kevin heard his own voice echo and made a beeline for the bleachers, which got blurry before his eyes.

"What did you say?" Mr. Bisceglia thundered. Kevin kept walking. Mr. B blasted his whistle. Chiffawn laughed.

"He said basketball gay, Mr. B."

Thanks, bitch.

"Basketball ain't gay!"

Crap. Tyrell was back in the mix. If Kevin had said that basketball was gay, that meant that the people who played it were gay too. And what did Tyrell, and all of the other really big dudes like to do? Play basketball. So, when Kevin got mad at Mr. B and called basketball gay, he'd also called Tyrell, Leo, and every other big dude at school gay.

"Aww!"

A rustle and a holler went up through the class. Kids were yelling and stomping on the bleachers. Maurice put a fist over his mouth and staggered behind Demetric, laughing. Mr. B dropped the ball and came trotting after Kevin, who changed his path and headed for the locker room door.

Leo picked up the ball and arced a shot from halfcourt. It nose-bombed ten feet short of the basket, slapping noises echoing with each bounce.

"Basketball ain't gay. *You* gay!" Tyrell yelled.

Mr. B stopped and turned, then pointed at Tyrell, "You. Office. Now."

Kevin kept going for the locker room door until he felt Mr. B's hand on his shoulder. He stopped. Tyrell was ranting and raving like Taz on the cartoons as he walked across the gym and shoved open the door to the hall. Mr. B said, "Kevin. What the hell?"

His cracker accent made *hell* into two syllables, "hay-ull." He walked around to Kevin's front and leaned in, speaking quietly in a buddy-buddy tone. It sounded like Kevin had let him down somehow. Chiffawn's hair, forehead, then eyes peeked over the side of the bleachers. Kevin looked from her to the locker room door three feet beyond Mr. B. and wanted to push past him.

"You're never like this. What's goin' on?"

Mr. B's breath was hot and sour. The skin on his forehead was rougher than the smooth part where his hair used to be.

"Nothing. I just . . . left my shirt at home."

"You can't talk like that in class (*clay-uss*). Or anywhere."

He leaned back a little and swept out his right arm, pointing out the entire world that would be pissed off if Kevin called basketball gay again.

"OK. I dressed out as much as I could."

Kevin couldn't say sorry. He couldn't say it to that man, because he didn't mean it. This man with his diet soda and his eyes that looked at the girls who were twenty years younger than him. This guy who ran the class that Kevin hated the most.

"I see. But I've still gotta write you up, Kevin. You can't act like that in class."

He looked sorry to be writing him up. But if he was really sorry, he wouldn't do it. Kevin hated his bushy eyebrows that were almost as big as his stupid black mustache and how he looked like he felt sorry. And getting written up! Man, that meant he'd call home and talk to Mama, and Kevin would get grounded for even longer and wouldn't be able to go to the movies and see *The Mask* on Saturday. His eyes blurred all over again and he hung his head, away from Mr. B's face and breath. He moved his hand from Kevin's shoulder and clapped his back.

"Hit the locker room and get changed, Kevin. Stay on the bleachers for the rest of the class."

Kevin walked into the musty quiet of the locker room and passed Demetric's locker. Had his stinky finger touched one of those locker handles? He sorta wanted to smell them, to see if he could tell which one it had been, and to see if pussy really smelled like fish like people said.

Getting written up was for bad kids. Kevin wasn't a bad kid. He didn't go around getting into trouble, but lately, it seemed like trouble had just been getting into him.

Everything that Kevin did echoed alone in that locker room, and he took his time changing, easing the shorts down his legs and sitting in his boxers on the wood bench, trying to figure out what to do about that phone call that was coming after school. Never mind Tyrell.

Central Standard

Matt Martin

The heart has its reasons
which reason knows nothing of.
–Pascal

I STOOD ON THE EL PLATFORM AND LOOKED DOWN TO THE STREET. TOPS OF heads below moved around like pieces on a sidewalk board game. I walked to the opposite edge of the platform and looked north towards the approaching train. People all around me stood at the ready to rush to work, start their days, and enter their cubes. They were covered in mittens and scarves, down parkas and boots.

I pulled out my phone and looked at the time. It was inside of 9:00 a.m. in the Central Standard Time zone, Chicago, Illinois. The Green Line train at Clark and Lake pulled up and opened its doors as the working poor prepared to board. I didn't have the heart to sit inside my cube today. I didn't have the heart to deal with the public.

My compatriots in the morning workforce boarded, hound-dog looks in their eyes, computer bags exploding. I let the doors close and proceeded to walk in the opposite direction of my brethren. Instead of boarding the train to work, I left the train station for a bar.

I lit a cigarette as soon as I hit the stairs and slowly walked down, taking each step one at a time, landing with both feet at a step before starting the next, like a confused ring boy in a wedding procession. My left hand braced me on the stairwell, while my bag hung on my right shoulder. People were running up the stairs as an approaching train sounded off in the distance.

By the time I got down each stair, the train was in the station above me. An announcement that was supposed to alert riders that doors were closing sounded like "life imploding," and I grinned as I neared Monks, a shithole Chicago dive bar, like every other bar that stood trapped in the time warp of a long forgotten era.

The front of Monk's looked like the side of an oak wine barrel with a door in the middle. A bright "MONKS" sign in yellow lettering was stenciled over the door. It looked like it could have been a hidden door in the middle of a Medieval drawbridge.

My cigarette was about done, and it started to snow. Three city workers in green and yellow neon safety vests stood in a triangle, smoking, their heads tilting back as they exhaled. Specks of snow and other old train track dust that fell from the platform met their smoke as it traveled sky-bound, the smoke illuminating the dust and landing on top of their heads. I flicked my cigarette and walked into the bar unnoticed.

Inside, I found darkness, a long bar to the left, the TV, hanging above the far end of the bar, blaring cable news that was barely audible, and beyond that, a clamoring of pots and pans and a couple of muffled conversations in Spanish. To the right, nothing but a wall with yellowing photographs showcasing Michael Jordan, Mayor Daley, and Al Capone in various modes of undress.

I removed my sunglasses and took a deep breath, hoping the recycled oxygen would instill some warmth in my blood and lessen the redness of my face.

I threw my bag underneath the bar without any care for its contents, and it banged hard against the wood paneling. Two men with gray moustaches and sweaters that buttoned at the bottom looked in my direction. I looked at them, tension thick between us, until they went back to their quiet conversation revolving around deliveries and check stubs.

The bartender, a girl in her late twenties, brown hair in a ponytail, no jewelry to be seen, shuffled towards me, her brown eyes fixated on a container of cocktail straws. "Good day, huh?"

I feigned a tilt-necked smile with a sarcastic nod that didn't warm the situation and said, "You can pour me three fingers of Jameson and a pint of Old Style."

She rolled her eyes, never taking them away from the brown box of cocktail straws, shuffled away towards a sink underneath the beer taps, and pulled out a spotted pint glass.

I took off my coat and placed it on the stool next to me, pulled my white sleeves down from underneath my suit coat arms, and twitched my neck to the left, as the reason for my malaise came back to me.

She was young and dizzy, five foot four, with a deplorable attitude and a strong vocabulary. I saw her name on a piece of mail that morning as I walked out the door of my three-flat. The letter was sitting on a rusty-colored desk near the front door. The normalcy of her letters had become less normal, so this one took me by surprise. I usually carried the letters she left me out of the door to throw in the garbage can on the way to the train, but this one stayed in my pocket, and now its white top was peering at me from my coat, which hung on the stool next to me.

The bartender came over and dropped a couple of glasses in front of me. I looked up at her and saw that she was missing half a tooth in her own version of a patronizing smile.

"Don't worry, I have cash," I said, as I dug in my back pocket for my wallet. I threw out twenty dollars on the bar and reached for my glass.

"She's not worth it."

I coughed up a little of the Old Style back into the glass. I wiped my nose with my hand and swiped the beer off my face. "What?"

She just walked away and went back to her brown box, this time filled with white beverage napkins. She stopped to briefly listen in on the two moustaches talking at the other end of the bar.

As long as I stared at her, she never peeked back at me. She just looked up to put napkins in the straw caddy and then back at the two guys, who looked like they could have been my gym teacher in grade school or a fire chief or a retired professional wrestler.

My eyes drifted down and away from the scene going on quietly in front of me to the letter that ached to be opened.

I gripped my Jameson and took a small pull. It slowly slipped down, coating my smoke-scarred throat. I swallowed again after it was down, and looked up at the bartender.

She was standing in front of me again, a different kind of smile on her face, her hands on her hips. "You're a player. So, I know it hurts a little more when you get hurt. But like everything, this too will pass."

I smiled, took a much bigger sip of my whiskey and said, "It's funny, ya know?"

"What's that?" She smiled back.

"Ya can throw anyone behind the bar, and all of a sudden they think they have a little movie magic in 'em." I sipped my beer. "But it's fun to listen to the musings of an arm chair psychiatrist, so, go ahead, Dr. Drew, I'm on *Loveline*."

"I won't begin to understand the mind of someone who drinks at," she looked back at the cable news station, "9:15, but I will say this: she's not worth it. Take that for what you want. Shit, go ahead and ruminate on my armchair psychiatry and know she's not worth it."

It was my turn to roll my eyes, and I smiled and nodded. Took my whiskey and finished it, slammed the empty with only a few ice cubes remaining, and said, "It appears my glass is empty. Would you be so kind?"

She took the glass off the bar and turned, shuffling away, taking all the time in the world, because after all, I was her only customer. At some point during our rousing conversation the two moustaches had slipped out the back, and it was now me, her, and another talking head on TV mixing with the awkward air in the room.

She came over and put the glass of whiskey down in front of me. She pursed her lips as I smiled at her.

Then, in a rare moment of honesty, I said, "Listen, she left a letter in my apartment and I'm afraid to read what it says. The only reason I'm in here is because of what it might or might not say. It's," and I looked up at the cable news station, "exactly 9:22 Central Standard Time and I'm freakin' the fuck out. I don't drink this early in the morning, usually, so you got me pegged, to an extent, and well, fuck it, I need your help."

She looked for a brown box of straws or napkins, anything to pick up as an excuse. "What?"

"Will you read it?"

"What?"

I leaned down and slid the letter out of my jacket pocket. A whiff of perfume hit my nostrils.

I handed her the letter.

I sat at the bar, my eyes on the bartender, my elbows on the bar, like a little kid waiting for the teacher's notes. After a moment, she folded the letter, put it back into the envelope, smelled it, and placed it in front of me.

"You have to read this letter for yourself."

I slid it down the bar and tilted my head back as my whole body fell into the black-backed stool. "Women have never helped me with anything. One more Jameson please."

She shook her head gently, and her eyes blinked with purpose. She took a deep breath in and leaned forward into me. "Drinking is not going to make this any better."

"I didn't ask you for advice on my drinking. If my money's no good here, then I can take it somewhere else."

She shook her head again, though this time not as gently. She walked to the bottle of Jameson and pulled it from the rail. She walked two feet to me and slammed it on the bar, just hard enough not to break it all over the place.

"Fine, you fuckin' pussy. Fine." She pulled a glass from her left and sat it next to mine. She filled both glasses, gripping hers with one hand and pouring with the other. She tilted her head back, and threw the whiskey down her throat, and slammed the glass down next to mine.

"You want to know what the letter said?"

I raised my glass and tipped it towards her like Dean Martin in black and white, and said, "That's why I had you read it." I sipped the whiskey slowly, before finishing the whole glass.

She poured two more shots into the small rocks glasses and left them there. Her body was rigid; she ran her hands through her short brown hair.

"Fine. She said sorry. It was her choice, not yours. She couldn't trust you or herself to do the right thing when it came to the kid. She misses you like crazy and wants to see you." She raised her glass and did not wait for a "cheers." The glass was back down barely a moment before she was filling it.

"But, if I was her, I wouldn't want to see you because you're acting like a selfish baby brat. You have no idea how hard it is to do what she did, your help or not. So, this fuckin' melancholy, poor-me act is weak, Sean." I looked at her, not breaking her gaze, and took my shot of whiskey. It slipped down my throat enough to burn away the knot that was starting to form.

"I feel for her, and I feel for you. But if you want the truth, which is not in this bottle, than you need to face up to it and go meet her. Call her. Call her right now."

II

Roughly a month ago, I was sitting where I am sitting now, in the kitchen nook in my apartment, on a Wednesday. I had just gotten home from work.

I was picking at a French-bread pizza and spinning my phone on the table while I read some novel by Richard Price. I had an old Zeppelin record on, and I think I was burning some of her candles.

She came in, drunk, slammed the door, walked right past me, without a look, took an abrupt left and walked into the bathroom. The door knocked a painting of a yellow dog off the wall.

I smiled, flipped a page, and said loud enough for her to hear through the bathroom door, "*Somebody's* taking advantage of her day."

I heard the toilet flush and the sink turn on, and the door spun open; in the frame of the door stood the potential mother of my children, jeans around her ankles, a toothbrush between her teeth and cheek, an unzipped fleece, and what appeared to be faint red coloring on her underwear. She stopped brushing. "You don't want to know what my day was."

"I think you must've spilled some wine on your pantaloons there, boozy."

She looked down at her jeans, at her underwear, at her body below the waist. Her eyes came up to greet mine. Shallow pools filled her eyes, and for a second she looked like an actress who had just been told she had won an Academy Award.

Then, she dropped. Her body crumpled to the ground like pants thrown against a wall. Her legs slid out from under her, and her head just missed the toilet.

I ran toward her and accidentally tipped over the vase; water rushed off the table onto the ground. She was lying on the cold bathroom tile in the fetal position. I tried to fit into the space between her and the wall, but there was no room, so I stood above her looking down, casting a shadow over her body. She had covered her eyes with her arm, but the toothbrush was still in her mouth as she sobbed. It was bouncing up and down like a gangster chews a toothpick. I let out a small laugh. I reached down and grabbed it out of her mouth; a mouthful of spit and toothpaste stuck elastically as I pulled it out. It reminded me of taking a plastic mouthpiece from a football player.

In my best, non-patronizing, shoulder-patting, hair-holding, friendly voice, I asked her, "Baaaaabe, what happened?" I am not sure if I succeeded.

She sobbed at me with unfocused eyes. I tried to pull her up by her hand so I could give her a hug and somehow console her, but her body was dead. Everything was limp but her chest, which heaved with each wail.

"Baby, get up. What's wrong with you? What happened?"

"You happened."

That was a response I didn't expect. I shook my head. "What?"

She took her arm from her eyes and glared up at me. The white in her eyes was gone. It was replaced with a Mr. and Mrs. T's Bloody Mary Mix red. It made the blue of her eyes that much more sharp.

She shouted, "You happened." She rolled on her back. "I *swore* I would never do this. *Swore.* You fuckin' asshole."

I don't respond well to name calling, especially when I don't know why I am being called names. "What the fuck are you talking about?"

She kicked at the door with her feet; her body wiggled, but her jeans, acting like shackles, prevented her from doing much.

"I didn't want to tell you."

"Tell me what?" The initial sensitivity lacing my voice was gone. Instead, everything came out in a bark.

She kicked at the door again. Her foot slammed the handle and broke it off.

"Jess, please. What the fuck? Quit this shit."

She looked up when I said her name and looked at me. Her eyes darted left and right, trying to focus through the alcohol. Her yellow hair was spun like pasta, matted to her forehead by tears, "I hate you."

"OK. I'm done. This is Re. Tarded."

She screamed out, "FUUUUUCCCKKK YOUUUUUUUUUU!" Her vocal chords couldn't accommodate the strength with which she screamed. She sounded like a two-year-old who didn't want to go to bed yet.

"What the fuck, Jess?"

She screamed again, sobbing through the sleeves of her worn beige fleece. I walked out of the bathroom, grabbed a paper towel, wiped down the table, sat where I was when she had barreled through the door no more than fifteen minutes before, picked up my book, and pretended to read.

After a minute, the sobs slowed down, and within a minute of that, the bathroom was silent and the room started to feel a little dizzy as "Tangerine" played on the record player.

Measuring a summer's day
I only find it slips away to gray,
The hours they bring me pain.

She pulled her pants up and wiggled her way into them. She looked into the mirror and wiped up the wetness from her face. She looked out to me, sucked in the remaining snot in her nose, and said with a blink,

"You were almost a father today." The record was the only thing I heard.

Thinking how it used to be
does she still remember times like these?
To think of us again?
And I do.

The look on my face must have scared her, because she instinctively backed up.

I still didn't register much of what she said; my head fell into my arms on the table. My sleeves felt wet. I looked up at her, and my eyes must have mirrored the color of hers.

She walked over to the fridge and opened the freezer door, reached for the flask we kept in there.

I felt her gaze on me, but didn't want to look at her as she crossed back to the front of the bathroom.

I stared at the black-and-white tile on the bathroom floor. The bare, hanging lightbulb glared into my eyes. Everything went silent. My eyes closed. My eyes opened. "What did you say?"

If her cry sobered her up, the tip off the flask put her back to drunk. "Before I got *an abortion* this morning, you were a *father*."

Somehow, thought passed through contemplation and directly to reaction and I didn't know what else to say. I tried to summon positive memories from the last year and a half that I had spent with her, the last three months living in the same house. I tried to recall the reasons why I thought she was the one. I tried to remember the excitement I'd felt just a week before as I was pricing engagement rings.

Unfortunately, none of those things came back, so I looked at her for one more beat; my chest felt tight, and I was out of breath, but I got through it and said, "Get out of my house."

She smiled a boozy, ugly smile I had never seen on her face and said, "Fuck you."

"I'm serious. Get the fuck out of my house."

"This is as much my place as yours."

"Well, you don't fuckin' pay rent; your name's not on a lease; please, before I LOSE my MIND: Get. The. FUCK. Out."

She stood there for a while and swallowed.

I never thought about hitting a girl before then, so instead, while she stared at me, swaying, tears dripping off her chin, her pants unbuttoned, one sock off, hair in her face, I walked past her and slammed the door behind me.

III

I fell into the bottle pretty hard after that. I took days off work, sat in corners of bars, silent. Shot dirty looks under sunglasses to women who resembled her.

At some point, we started texting. I should say, she started texting. She sent. I read. I deleted. That's how it went for a while. Then, I started responding, mostly things that I shouldn't have said. Mostly things I regretted immediately after sending.

"Cunt face whore" was a favorite. "Lying shit-neck bitch hole" was one I read when I woke up one morning and laughed to myself about. I deleted her number from my phone after that, and for the most part, didn't have it on very much.

Now, I was sitting in the kitchen nook, looking at my phone, her name on the screen, the vase filled with dead flowers, day drunk, again.

I put my arm up on the back of the couch like I had so many times with her sitting there. I felt her stupid body. I felt her lying cunt face whore self and well, the whiskey got to me a bit. I started to cry: nose-pouring, Adam's apple hurting, unattractive tears, the kind that only came out when someone died or maybe when someone was born.

Through my squinting eyes, I looked at the phone. I picked it up and let my thumbs do the talking in 170 characters or less.

"Babe, I'm sitting here pouring my eyes out and everything in my head is telling me to hate your fuckin' guts. But I can't."

I put the phone on the table and looked while the screen went from a clock, to a check mark, to a sent. The flask hit my lips and the whiskey my throat. It felt like I was swallowing a grapefruit.

My phone vibrated; "one new message." Fuck. The phone looked at me, blinking its red light, and I pushed the button.

"Don't leave. I'll be right there."

I started coughing the moment she walked in the door.

She put her bag down and took off her coat. She placed it on top of mine with a wince, as she caught wind of the rotting chicken in the garbage can.

She put down her cup of coffee and went under the sink, grabbed the bag, and walked back out the door, turning the deadbolt so the door didn't lock behind her.

When she walked back in, she looked at me contemptuously. The last two years of our lives gave her the right to be indignant. I just looked at her blankly. She flipped open a garbage bag like a white sheet out of the dryer, and put it in the can. She grabbed a can of Febreeze and sprayed it in the air.

"You look like shit," she said, as she put the air freshener back in the cabinet.

"Feel like shit, hon." I pulled a smoke out of the pack and lit it. I exhaled up into the fading sunlight, which was still peeking through the window above my head.

She walked to the table, pulled out an old kitchen chair with a plaid padded seat, and sat down. Her chin fell into her hands as her elbows hit the table. She shook her head at me; I gave her a crooked-lipped smile.

"Ya know, you're a regular prick." She reached over and grabbed a smoke out of my pack. She lit it and leaned back into her chair.

"Ya know? You're a regular little baby killer." I tried to smile, to let her know that I was just trying to be cute, but she didn't like it, and started to cry.

"I don't want to be here if you are going to be like this." She looked at me out of watering crooked eyes, swallowed, blinked a few times as the tears hit her cheeks, and went to the fridge. She reached above it for the old cigar box with pictures of Havana on it where she kept her tea. "Do you want a cup?"

I nodded.

I opened the cap of the flask, and she turned to look at me. I shrugged my shoulders and smiled, took a sip and put it down.

She loosened her soft, gray scarf and filled the kettle. She put it on the stove and pushed her hair back behind her ears with both hands.

She talked as she grabbed cups out of a cabinet and put them on the counter. "I've been playing that day back in my mind ever since it happened."

Things were starting to get unruly in my head, the alcohol, the smokes, and the lack of eating. "Can we eat something?" I asked.

"Yeah, do you have anything?"

I shook my head.

"Fine, I'll order some Thai, but really, Sean, let me get this off my chest."

I nodded. "OK, you're right." My words were starting to get heavy as the weight of the situation and the whiskey took its toll.

She moved around the kitchen, wiping things off counter tops. She filled one side of the sink with hot water and tipped in some dish soap to get it sudsy. Making her way back to the freezer door, she stopped, her eyes focusing on the letter that was taped to it.

"So, you read it?"

"Kind of."

"And that's why I'm here?"

I looked at her. "You know what gets me? The what if. What if she was beautiful? What if she loved me? What if she looked like you?" I started to cry a little. "What if she made us better?"

Tears started down her face. "Look at you right now. You're day drunk on a fuckin' Tuesday, and what is it, one o'clock?" I wasn't quick enough to answer. "You're a mess. Was I supposed to believe that you would have been able to hold it together if our kid got sick? What if, Sean? What if? Well, what if she came out sick? What if she came out deformed? What if I had to do it by myself?"

"Oh, fuck this. Fuck you."

"No, you can't say that shit to me. I had my reasons. It was my choice, Sean. It was my choice."

I looked at her a little clearer now, tears stopping. "I know. I believe that too, but—"

"No buts, Sean. It's my body, my choice."

"Yeah, I know, but—"

"But what?"

"What if she was beautiful?"

I couldn't hold it together. I tried. But booze, no food besides a Popsicle, and the image of my sleeping baby smiling through a dream took over my mind. My head dropped to the table and hit the wood; I didn't even attempt to pad it with my arms.

I felt her come over to me and put her arm around my back. "I've always wanted a little someone to look at me like that, like I was the only one in the world that could make her all right," I said. "And you didn't even have the common decency to fuckin' ask me how I felt."

Her hand stopped comforting, stopped running in concentric circles. She stood up and went to the stove.

"I understand it's your 'choice,' but fuck, dude. You should have fuckin' told me." I stood up and walked past her, my shoulder brushing against her shoulder, and opened the fridge. I opened a beer. "Tell me how you think that's right."

"Choice is a really weird word, Sean."

"You know what name I liked? I liked Samantha. I liked Brooke. I liked Sarah. But my favorite," I slugged the can of beer, "my favorite was Nora."

"Look! This isn't fuckin' easy for me, Sean."

"I know, let's all sing a fuckin' song about it."

The kettle went off, screeching. It snapped me out of a bit of my drunkenness. She put away her cup, turned off the stove and poured the water down the dish-filled sink. She put the kettle back on the stove, empty. I was standing behind her; my back was strong, but my knees were weak. She turned to walk past me to grab her coat, but I wouldn't let her by.

"Let me go." I grabbed her and pulled her into me and the tears came out. She cried like that for what turned out to be just long enough. Nothing was said. Just her crying into my chest as I rubbed her back. When she stopped crying she looked up at me, and I didn't know what to say. She just looked up at me, her chest pushed against my stomach. The look in my eyes must have said it all. She grabbed her coat, and I didn't say a word as she walked out the door.

The Lonely Man

Justin Bostian

THERE WAS ONCE A MAN WHO WAS LONELY ALL HIS LIFE. HE WAS BORN TO A MOTHER that fed him with the milk of her breast, to a father that taught him to hunt and to grow and to be a man. They clothed him, sheltered him, raised him, and stayed with him, even loved him, in their own quiet way, but still he was lonely. When he was a babe crawling on the earthen floor of his house, he was lonely. When he was a boy running through the hot desert, conquering new territory and fighting imaginary demons, he was lonely. When he was a man and his parents caught sickness, and all he could do was to stay with them and offer what little comfort his silent figure provided, he was lonely. When his father's spirit returned to the earth, and his mother's spirit quickly followed, the man was lonely.

With the bodies wrapped in coarse cloth, the man went into the desert to lay them to rest. He walked in the midday sun, too hot for sweating. The bodies were light with the loss of their spirits, and the harsh years kept them as dry and weathered as the sands from which they had scraped their lives. The man carried them until he felt the need to stop, the feeling that *this* was the place and he need not go farther. With his hands he began to dig into the hot earth, descending into the layered ground. Bit by bit he displaced the sand, then the dirt that lay below the sand, then the stones that lay below the dirt. Finally his hands, raw and quaking, felt the smooth, moist clay that lay beneath everything. The rich, red flesh—the heart of the desert—slid between his cracked flesh and torn fingernails, soothing his pain and filling the empty places stolen by his efforts, by the sharp stones and cruel sands.

He wept, then, his wet tears falling to the ground and disappearing into the thirsty soil. He wept not because he was lonely, for he had *always* been lonely. He wept because he was lonely *and* alone. There was nothing but the desert, a bitter and difficult companion, and the man. He cursed his fate, to be forever set apart from anyone, from anything. He cursed his mother and his father for leaving him behind, for leaving him with the burden of life that weighed so heavily on his heart it drove him down into the ground and stole the breath from his lungs. All the while he wept, his pacing steps and endless tears softening the deep red clay. He cried for a full day, and when he had nothing left in him, he lay in the warm, wet pool that filled the grave. Tired and empty, he looked to the black sky and its numberless stars.

Why, he asked, must I be alone? Why must I be lonely? His hands dug in to the clay, squeezing it through fingers and allowing his mind to wander through the pliable earth. Soon his shapes took form, a small figure of a woman that he pieced together from memories of his mother when she was young and he but a child. Images of her tilling the soil, her dark hair trailing to the ground in a thick braid, beads of sweat rolling down her warm brown skin. He stroked the figure longingly, then turned his attention back to the sky. Did not the gods create man from the dust of the earth? Why then, should *he* be alone? And then he worked, slowly, thoughtfully, with the precious clay, shaping and molding the form of a woman. He made her legs strong and thick so that she might work with him in the fields. He made her hips wide, that she might bear him many children. He made her hands carefully, delicately, that she might cook and sew and touch. She was beautiful, even then, all dirt and mud, a featureless golem with soft, round edges and a pleasant shape. Two stones, sleek, shimmering, black as the night sky, served as eyes. He kissed her face, then sculpted full, soft lips over the prints his left behind, and wrapped her head in cloth he tore from his own garment, so that he might run his hands over her hair.

When he was done, and she was a complete, beautiful thing, he spoke to her. He called her forth from his heart, and from the earth, from all of the places that grow and blossom and flourish. He called her into the body he had fashioned, into the vessel that he had poured all of his hurt, all of his longing and despair, and his small, pitiful measure of hope. Her dark eyes saw, and saw only him, and she fell upon him with gratitude. He had given her form, a shape to fill and move, to love. Together, they climbed from the great grave, and walked past the mounds of displaced soil that his hands had made, past the two bodies wrapped in rough fabric and lying side by side on the desert floor.

There was love, then, and the man was not alone. She was good to him, and he was good to her. They planted crops together, and her harvest was vast, even in times of drought. It seemed that everywhere she stepped, green things shot from the ground and curled around her feet, and the man grew accustomed to the fresh flowers and green grass and bountiful fruits, and the way that she cooked for him. Every meal was greater than the last, as if every ingredient had no purpose other than to be on his plate, to fulfill *his* hunger. They touched and she was smooth and soft and cold. She smelled of the earth, of the great hole that he had dug with his hands, of the hidden secret places of moisture and growth in the deep desert. He was satisfied with her, and she was made to love him, so she loved him. She loved him purely, unselfishly, a love that no man could ever feel, having been made for other reasons. She loved him with her whole being, with her every motion and thought.

The man was not satisfied forever, though, as the woman would not give him any children. While she was soft and pleasant and welcoming, her womb was barren and she would not, she *could* not, bear him sons or daughters. In the beginning, this was nothing to him. He had love, and he was happy. As their lives grew long, he began to dwell on it more and more, and became resentful of his clay wife. He knew that any fault with her was a fault of his, being her creator, and began to treat her with a coldness that she had never known before. She began to show signs of wear and age, no longer soft and smooth as she once was. Cracks branched away from her shining black eyes, like the desert floor after the rains have gone and the earth has claimed every drop of moisture. Her hands grew stiff and clumsy, drying out slowly as her husband drew further from her. With his waning love went her deep red color; now she was a pale and chalky thing. Her harvests were no longer abundant, nor was her food marvelous or her touch soft. From the fields she brought pitiful things, dead for want of water and care, and served them uncooked, unwashed and unprepared. The green things that grew around their home became yellow and brittle, flaking to nothing at the slightest touch. She scratched him with her fingers, rough and cracked, though she meant only to love him and to show him her love. The harder she tried to please him, the colder he grew, and the colder he grew, the dryer she became.

One day, the man could not take it anymore. He cried out at his wife, blaming her for his bad fortune and cursing her infertility. She opened her mouth to speak, but her throat was as coarse and empty as a dead riverbed. Jet black eyes glittered at him from her pale, dry face, and he could see that she still loved him, through all of his distance and cruelty. This so enraged the man, this selfless display of unconditional love, that he stepped close to his wife and struck her hard across the face. Her body crumpled, shattered, and fell to a pile of sand and dried clay. A cloud of dust, red and thick and woman-shaped, hung mournfully in the air, filling it with an awful weight and choking at his lungs until he swung his fists again and again, sending it away with the wind. He saw what he had done, and knew that he was a fool. He had love, perfect love, and now he was alone. He was alone and he was lonely.

Overcome with grief and sorrow, the man ran into the desert. He would find the place where he had fashioned her, the woman that he had loved, and beg the earth for another chance. He would not be alone again, he *could* not be lonely anymore. He ran and cried, sucking in the hot, dry air and drying out his body. When he found the place, the great pit ringed with mounds of long-dried dirt and sand and clay, he fell to his knees and covered his face. There, lying side by side and staring at the night sky with bleached-white grins and hollow sockets, were the bodies of his father and mother. The wind and elements had stripped them clean, to smooth, pale skeletons, leaving scraps of tattered fabric clinging to their bones, decaying strings blowing about in the wind. The man cried and threw his face into the sand, for he knew he had done such wrong that he could not be forgiven. The desert breeze, a cloud of red dust that smelled of the deep wet places in the earth, swept among the empty bones and twisted around the lonely man,

The small stones all around began to shake together, rattling with the skeletons that moved and rose from the desert floor. Ancient joints scraped and scratched as they danced in the moonlight, circling the lonely man and taking his arms in their sharp, dead hands. He yelled and fought, but their grip was strong: "You will not be alone again."

Their voices were like death itself, empty and cold and hissed between wicked grins, forever bared: "You will not be alone again."

They led him into the dark hole, the great grave in the deep desert: "You will not be alone again."

Their thin white fingers raked the soil, pulling it down into the places between their ribs and the hollows of their skulls. The lonely man was buried with them, filled completely with the red dirt and clay and dust that fell all around him. In the ground, deep below the surface, he felt his loneliness slip away, replaced in his eyes and his nose and his lungs with the rich, ancient earth. He felt the hands on his arms, tight and unmoving, and he was not alone.

My Bad Genes

Josh Alletto

I GOT BAD GENES. MY MOTHER ALWAYS TOLD ME THAT. "YOUR DADDY HAS terrible genes, and I don't have good genes either, so now you got two pairs of the worst genes you can get." So I got bad genes, which is why I'm fat— really fat—350 and counting. It's why my face is spotted with blackheads and puffy around my tiny blue eyes. "Like a catcher's mitt holding two robin's eggs," is what my mother used to say. She's dead now. Bad heart.

So, since I grew up always knowing I had bad genes and always knowing I was fat and always knowing that no one in my family ever lived past forty-seven years old (my sister died at twenty, stomach cancer), I guess the big surprise wasn't that I got diagnosed with diabetes, but that it didn't happen until I turned forty-one.

"It's not all that surprising," Doctor Schlitz says to me in his office. He does little to hide his amusement. He's one of these really chiseled guys with a jawbone that's thick and curved around hard like a ram's horn. He's got pictures of himself all over his office: pictures of himself shirtless, sailing on a boat called *The Annihilator*, his abs oily and glowing. He's got pictures of himself on the high school football team, of himself French-kissing some blond woman with plasticky-looking skin on a beach somewhere where the sky and the ocean are the same bright blue.

"Diabetes, Mr. Gustavo, is a serious disease. Especially for someone in your . . . physical condition," he smiles. Then he leans back in his leather swivel chair and folds his hands over his tight abs. He seems content with his office, his chin. He grins so I can see a row of shining teeth.

And I don't really know what to say, because all my life I've known I got these bad genes and there was nothing I could do about it, so I just smile back and ask: "What should I do about it?"

Dr. Schlitz frowns. And it's the look on his face that makes everything feel suddenly like it's happening in fast motion, but all twisted, too, like life's shooting through a blender. He scribbles a prescription, mumbles something about injections, and hurries me out the door.

"Ask the pharmacist," he says.

It's really hot, and it's not helping that I have to carry this lute around all day. It's really squeezing against my chest because the strap is way too small. I'm doing this book on medieval instruments, and the publishing house keeps sending me these replicas so I can get the "feel" of things in order to write about them more accurately. I have to send them back when I'm done.

When I did my book on amphibians they kept sending me cages full of newts and frogs, which were nice to have around until they all died for reasons I still can't figure because I thought I was doing a pretty good job taking care of them, but I guess not.

The lute came this morning, before I left to see Dr. Schlitz, so I figured I should put the thing on and wear it around for a day, it being the instrument of the traveling minstrel and whatnot. It kind of looks like a guitar with a tear-shaped body, but when I pluck the strings, the noise is higher, like a harp. My editor, Ron, says we have to give people an experience. "We're not just listing facts," he says. "We're painting a picture of people's lives."

As I'm walking to the pharmacy, I think that maybe I'll swing by the library and tell Barbara about my diabetes. Barbara's the head librarian over there, and I think that maybe having diabetes is a good enough excuse to start talking to her. I've had this thing for her ever since I started going there. I almost talked to her last week, but the timing was all wrong. I mean, don't misunderstand me, I've talked to her before. I have to do a lot of my work in that library, and I ask a lot of questions.

You may have seen some of my books in the bargain bins at your local bookstore: *1001 Questions and Answers: Holocaust Edition; Everything*

You Ever Wanted to Know About Bugs . . . And Some Things You Didn't; Mysteries of the Universe Revealed: A Top Ten List. It's an easy enough gig. I look up a bunch of facts and then list them in a logical order and provide an extensive index. The publisher adds a bunch of colorful pictures, usually stock stuff so they don't have to pay a photographer, and there you go.

All of the world is categorized in the library. I just take pieces from a bunch of different categories and put them together into new ones. Find ways to connect things. I can do a whole book in about a month if I work hard at it, which I almost always do because I almost always don't have much else going on, which is fine with me.

I have to go by the library anyway to check up on some facts for the new book I'm working on: *Medieval Musicians: Soundtrack to the Black Death*. Ron says he wants me to capture the romance of a simpler time. "I can't give this project to anyone else," he says. "They don't have the sentimentality." Also, I remember that one time I overheard how Barbara's grandson has diabetes, and when Dr. Schlitz told me in his office, the first thing I thought about, after I thought about how my mother said I got bad genes, was Barbara at the library.

I know she's got one grandson living with her because I overheard her talking about him one time when I was researching holistic medicine for a book called *Voodoo: Just the Facts*. So she's a grandmother, which you'd never know because she doesn't look seventy-seven at all. Really, she doesn't. The only reason I know she's seventy-seven is because I was in the library two years ago on April third, and some of the staff had hung a banner for her that said, "Happy Seventy-Fifth Birthday! We Love You!" And there were red balloons around it because I think that is her favorite color. She has this red cardigan that she wears every Thursday that I think is really pretty.

On my way to the library, I figure I'll stop by the pharmacy. While I'm waiting in line I feel the woman behind me brush up against my arm a bit, and I look over and she's leaning all the way to one side. "Sorry, I was just trying to see around you," she says, in this shy kind of way. When you got bad genes you always know it but sometimes aren't always thinking about it. But now I'm really thinking about it, and when I turn back to the pharmacist to get my prescription, I think about Dr. Shlitz's boat and his abs and his chin, and when the pharmacist asks, "Have you used syringes before?" the world's going through the blender again, and I just say, "Yeah" so I can get the hell out of there, even though needles scare the hell out of me, and there is no way I'll be able to stick myself with one.

I have to go pick up these overdue books from my apartment before I
go to the library, and while I'm in the hallway of my building messing with
my keys, Ricky from across the hall shows up.

"Hey, big guy," he says and mock punches me in the stomach a few
times. He wears his clothes too big, and it makes him look runty; I never
know why I feel so intimidated around him, but I do. He leans away from
me a bit and turns his head to the side, "Heeeyyyy. You know I'm just
messing with you. Right Chief?" He slugs me one on the shoulder, and I nod.

Last week Ricky invited me to watch wrestling over at his place with
some of his friends. At first I was a little thrown because Ricky hardly ever
made eye contact with me when we passed each other in the hall. I felt really
odd at the party, and I didn't know where to stand. His apartment is really
small, and it was packed with people dressed in black wrestling T-shirts who
had lots of tattoos and leather accessories. Everyone there was younger than
me by at least fifteen years. After about an hour I thought about leaving, but
Ricky called me into his bedroom. He had something to show me. The
something he had was a one-piece spandex suit, and he wanted me to put it
on. "It's an exact replica of the Death Blob's uniform," he said, smiling like
he had discovered plutonium and couldn't wait to unleash it on an unsuspecting world.

Death Blob was, as far as I could tell, an overweight wrestler that most
of the wrestling audience despised for being an unfair fighter, but whom, for
some reason, Ricky and his friends idolized. He always walked into the ring
with a hunk of ham or a whole turkey leg in his fist, and his "special move,"
Ricky told me, was holding his opponent's head between his thighs and
shooting "grizzly farts" over him until he passed out or gave up.

So here's the part that I regret, but I have to tell because it's what happened. I took the costume from Ricky, went into the bathroom, and changed
into it. I'd never been to a party before, and even though I knew then that
the only reason I had been invited was to play wrestler for Ricky's friends,
at least I was part of the party in some way. Standing out there earlier, in my
pressed slacks, feeling like an obstacle for everyone to maneuver around,
was horrible. At least now there was a place for me at the party. A category
for me to fall into, even if it was "Entertainment."

And it worked, too. I came out and everyone cheered and roared and
slapped me high fives, and when the fight was over and everyone was pretty
drunk, and because the costume was this bright red thing with a thick black

belt, one of the girls came over and sat on my lap and told me that she wanted a dollhouse for Christmas, and everyone burst out laughing. I laughed too. Then other girls started lining up to sit on my lap, and some of them whispered things into my ear, and some of them laughed, and soon I started to get really into it. I was saying, "Ho ho ho," and, "Have you been a good girl or a naughty girl?" which got a huge laugh, and everyone was really having fun, except for Ricky. He was in the corner biting on his lip a little and staring straight at me, right into me. And I knew right away when our eyes met that he had noticed how hard all the lap sitting had gotten me. I had been trying to hide it with some subtle adjustments in the chair, but it was getting more difficult as girls kept getting up and then plopping back down on my lap.

Eventually, Ricky started to roll a giant grin over his face, and he yelled out to the whole party, "Look out ladies, Santa's north pole is rising!" And everyone looked down at my crotch and they could see. The worst part was that this really pretty girl named Lisa, who had big, green-meadow eyes, made a face like she'd just eaten a dog turd she thought was a Tootsie Roll and leaped off of me like I was on fire.

The guys at the party all fell over laughing. I was used to that, but the women didn't laugh. They gagged and sniffed and moaned, and that's when I stood up, and that's when I started to feel really dizzy and lightheaded, and that's when I fell to the floor and blacked out.

Next day I wake up in the hospital. Mild heart attack.

Day after I'm plugged with needles, lots of tests.

No one visits.

Two days later I'm in Dr. Schlitz's office, staring at pictures of his tight abs, learning about my diabetes, and thinking about my bad genes.

The rest of the walk to the library I think about Ricky's chuckling friends, and by the time I arrive, I'm so achingly in love with Barbara I don't think I'll be able to talk when I see her.

"Hello, Mr. Gustavo," she says when she sees me coming; I forget sometimes that she knows my name.

She's behind the counter checking in some books, and I walk right up to her and I say, "Can you tell me where the books about diabetes are?"

She smiles her thin-lipped smile and pushes her round glasses up her nose.

"That looks interesting," she says.

"Excuse me?"

"That little guitar you have there."

"Oh, it's a lute," I say. I try to hold it up a little, but the strap is pulling it too tightly to my chest. I think I may need to cut it off with scissors when I get home.

"How adorable. Do you play?"

"Yes, I do," I say.

"Oh, how lovely. My grandson plays the guitar. I'm sure you're much better than he is, though. I think it's a great skill, playing an instrument. I wish I had learned."

"Yes," I say. "It is a fine skill."

"Are you on your way to a performance?"

"What?"

"Do you always just walk around with your guitar?"

"Lute."

"I bet you could teach my Joseph a thing or two. I swear, the racket he makes on that electric guitar."

After that she points me over to the medical books, and I spend the rest of the day looking up about diabetes, which turns out to be a much more awful disease than I could have imagined. I can't sleep that night. All I think about is my feet getting gangrene and falling off.

Next day I start learning how to play the lute. Ron calls to see how the book is coming along. I say fine. I don't spend any time on it the rest of the week. Instead, I spend every day hammering out "Twinkle Twinkle Little Star" on the lute, and in the process, I completely neglect my diabetes medication.

I have dreams like black-and-white movies. I'm saving Barbara from tall castle towers. I'm saving her from the angry talons of a dragon. I'm playing her to sleep on the lute.

A week or so later I find Barbara's address in the phone book and walk over to her house. I go on Sunday, so I know she's not working.

I stand on the doorstep feeling dizzy. I think maybe I should just drink what's in the little vials because by now the thought of trying to use the needle is making me want to puke. I ring the bell twice. The door opens.

"I came to give your grandson some lessons."

She looks puzzled at first. She looks like maybe she wants to close the door.

"You said he made a lot of racket," I say, and just when I'm feeling like this is a mistake, she smiles, lets her shoulders drop a little. Her grandson is not home, she says, but she invites me in to wait.

"I'm sorry I didn't call first," I tell her. "Traveling minstrels usually announce their arrival with a song."

"How lovely," she says. And she is beautiful today; her hair is long and gray but pulled back into a ponytail like a little girl's.

In the living room, she offers me tea. I accept. There's a dish of peppermints on the coffee table. I eat one. We sit. I want to say something else, but my head is full of cotton balls, and I feel like I might fall over if I open my mouth.

After a long silence she says, "I think this will be really good for Joseph. I was glad when he started playing the guitar, but that music he's into . . . so angry."

"I have diabetes."

Barbara clears her throat. "Well, that is awful."

"Yes, it is. They gave me these injections," I say, and I reach into my bag and pull out the little vials and a few syringes. "I have no idea how to use them."

Just then, the front door opens and in walks a grumpy-looking kid with black hair that hangs in his face and a long chain swinging from his belt loop. Almost under his breath, as though the word weighs a hundred pounds, he manages, while looking down at his feet, to say only, "Hey," before dropping his book bag on the floor and running for the stairs.

"Joseph!" Barbara's call to him is desperate. "Come here, young man. I have someone I want you to meet."

Joseph comes in, his eyes still on his feet. "Hey," he says.

We are in Joseph's room. The boy looks puzzled, angry, shy. He's holding a black electric guitar, the body of which is made up of so many sharp edges I find myself telling him to be careful with the thing at least four times.

"So, how long have you been playing guitar?"

"I don't know."

"What kind of music do you like?"

He shrugs.

"You ever see one of these before?" I hold up the lute.

"Is my grandmother paying you?"

"Umm."

"Are you another shrink? Because I hate shrinks so much it makes me want to . . ." He stands up from his bed, holds the guitar up over his head for a moment and grinds his teeth. He closes his eyes, starts to mouth something under his breath. He calms down, sits again.

"Sorry. I got anger issues. I have to do this counting thing."

"Does that help?"

"I just don't like shrinks, OK? I've seen about a hundred since my mom ran off."

I'm starting to feel really sick again. I pull out the bag of medication. "You know how to use these things?" I ask, pulling out the vial and a syringe. The kid looks confused.

"I have diabetes," I say.

"So do I," he mumbles.

"I know. I don't want my feet to fall off. Can you please help me with these things?"

"I don't know."

"Please?" At this point I'm feeling worse than I did at Ricky's party. Joseph pushes the hair out of his eyes. He reaches over and grabs the bag. He fills the syringe.

"You gotta lift up your shirt," he says.

"Are you sure?"

"Maybe I should go get my grandma. This is too weird."

"No no no. Fine."

I roll up my shirt. Joseph leans in and bites his lip, like he's trying to solve a puzzle. He reaches over and grabs a hunk of me, squeezes it between his fingers. His hands feel small, cold, but gentle. I can't remember the last time any part of me was held like that.

"This is going to hurt like hell," he says, and shoves the needle in. It hurts. I feel a pressure as he pushes down on the plunger.

Barbara opens the door with her backside and walks in with a plate of cookies and two glasses of milk. "And how's it going with you two?" she asks. Then, noticing us for the first time, she drops the tray on the floor and screams.

It takes us a while to calm her down. After we convince her we're not doing drugs, she seems to get the picture. She tells me to leave. She says if she sees me again, at work or at her home, she will call the police.

A week later, I'm getting used to doing the injections myself, but it still hurts like hell. Also, I had left the lute at Barbara's and was pretty sure I was going to have to pay for it. Also, Ron was not happy when I finally turned in my draft of the book because I had to do most of my research on the Internet since there was no way I could go back to the library and I wasn't really too picky with my sources.

There's this knock at the door while I'm on the phone with Ron. He's saying how disappointed he is in me, and do I have any idea how much of his money I'm wasting?

I answer the door and it's Joseph. He's staring at his feet. He's got the lute in his hand.

"You left it."

I wave him in while Ron is yelling about quality, organization, about how our readers want something that is informative and easy to understand. I'm not sure anything is like that. "What you've given me here is disgraceful!" He's really shouting.

Joseph sets the lute down on the couch. He turns to leave, then stops. "I tried to play it," he says. "It sounds weird."

I nod my head.

"Fix it," Ron says and hangs up. I toss the phone down and let myself fall onto the couch. Joseph is still standing by the door like he's waiting for me to say something.

"I can't play it at all," I say.

"I figured," he says. He comes back over and picks up the lute again. "It really is a lot like the guitar."

"I can't play that either."

Joseph strums a few chords. "My grandma is so mad at you." For the first time I think maybe he smiles a little.

"I know."

"She hates you."

"I know."

"Do you have some sort of thing for her?" he laughs.

"Sort of. Maybe. I don't know."

"That's gross," he says. He plays a little more on the lute. He points over at my syringes on the kitchen counter.

"How's that going?" he asks.

"Good. Better."

He slaps the side of the lute hard a few times like a drum. "Well, I should get going." He stands, puts the lute down. "This thing isn't really that hard to play," he says. "I could come by and show you another time if you want."

I shrug. "OK."

Joseph walks to the door; he stops again and turns.

"Don't worry so much about my grandma. She probably doesn't hate you." He leaves.

Caged

Sarah E. Doyle

MARY-ELIZABETH ABERNATHY KEPT ONE OF HER RIB BONES IN A JAR FILLED with pink liquid on a shelf in her room. She didn't want it there; her mother forced her to. She would lie in bed, her purple covers pulled up to her chin, and stare at the jar. Sometimes, if the curtains were open, the moonlight would cascade over the jar, illuminating the bone in a soft, pinkish hue. Mary-Elizabeth Abernathy was only seven, so the bone wasn't that big and neither was the jar. The liquid wasn't even so much of a liquid. It was more of a slime: a little thick with a few air bubbles. And it sat there, in the middle of her bookshelf, between a picture Bible and a collection of *Winnie The Pooh* books; and like a bright lightbulb shining in her eye, or a jackhammer outside her window, or a cold breeze coming in through the air shaft, it kept Mary-Elizabeth Abernathy from falling asleep.

Mary-Elizabeth lived with her mother, Louise, in a very small town—only a couple thousand people—outside Memphis, Tennessee. Mary-Elizabeth's daddy had died suddenly one night when a flash flood washed his truck off the road into the Mississippi when she was three years old. Louise didn't have what some people might call a "normal" childhood and had some health problems after Mary-Elizabeth was born, but it was after her husband's death that she really lost it for good. She lost the color from her once soft pink cheeks that Mary-Elizabeth always thought looked like peaches. Her blue eyes turned gray and lost all their sparkle. Her hair lost all its body and fell limp at her shoulders. Louise slowly began to turn on Mary-Elizabeth, blaming her for her daddy's death. The Abernathys had never been too much of a religious family, but suddenly Louise started dragging Mary-Elizabeth to church all the time. Louise said she needed to be cleansed.

One sticky, hot Sunday morning, the preacher at Holy Trinity Baptist Church was reading excerpts from the book of Genesis and told the story of Adam and Eve. He talked about the beauty of the Garden of Eden, and how God created Man from nothingness, but created Woman from taking a rib by Adam. And they were pure and free of sin and evil. That may have been where Louise got the idea.

On the car ride home Louise said nothing. She stared intently and unflinchingly while gripping the steering wheel, turning her knuckles white and stretching the skin tight and thin over the bone. Mary-Elizabeth dared not look or speak to her. She let her head hang low at her neck and played with the lace on the bottom of her yellow church dress.

Louise pulled their old, clunky, white Volvo into the garage and sat in silence as the garage door closed behind them, shutting them out from the light outside. Louise sat there, motionless, with her hands still on the steering wheel.

"Mary-Elizabeth," Louise said.

"Yes, Mama?" Mary-Elizabeth returned, her voice cracking with dryness.

"I want you to go inside and go down into the basement and wait for me."

Mary-Elizabeth's bottom lip dropped a bit and began to tremble.

"What for, Mama?" she said, her voice beginning to wobble.

"Just go, Mary-Elizabeth."

Louise was raised in the South. But not just any South—the deep South. And not just any deep South: the deep, southern part of Louisiana. She was orphaned as a baby and found in a Dumpster by a small Haitian family. They took her back to their tiny, one-bedroom house that had a tin roof and was home to five people: three women and two boys. And now one baby. They named her after the state she was found in, Louisiana, but everyone just called her Louise.

The head of the house was a large woman named Aloquacious Jones. But she was Gramammy to the family. She wasn't fat, just large: over six foot two, broad shoulders like she permanently had football pads under her clothes, long thick arms like tree trunks, and a huge bustle of hair that she tied down with a red bandana.

Josephine was Gramammy's sister and was the ying to her yang: short and spritely, thin and wiry. She had long, perfectly straight hair that she always wore a flower in. Monarch was Josephine's eleven-year-old daughter. She had a face as bright and round as the moon, with blue eyes that were deep and wide. She had tiny legs so it always took her longer to get places. Pete and Raymond were the twins, also Josephines, so identical that Josephine had bows tied around their wrists with their names on them.

They raised Louise as their own. Aloquacious always loved a baby and was eager to do something good by saving the life of the poor child. Louise grew up on their meals, which were caught fresh from the Mississippi; she grew into Monarch's hand-me-down clothes, although almost all the pants were too short on Louise. She grew to drown out the chickens clucking outside in the backyard, and she grew to understand and live the family religious tradition: voodoo.

Sometimes a typical family night was sitting down to a dinner of pulled BBQ pork, cornbread, catfish, and sweet tea; sometimes, however, it was a night of ritual cleansing for folks from around the small town they lived outside of. They would come over to the Jones's house to cure anything from depression to cancer. On a night like that, the small front room was dusted with candlelight, and if it was raining, the tin roof rattled with noise from the loud raindrops falling onto it. Josephine and Gramammy were dressed in beautiful, multicolored skirts that looked like melted crayons. They had on long, flowing white blouses. Gramammy wore a heavy necklace laced with full chicken bones that beat against her body as she moved around. Their faces were lightly painted white and they had their hair all wrapped up in cloth. While Pete and Raymond beat their palms vigorously on small, round drums, Aloquacious methodically danced around the room with a live chicken in her hand, doing a classic waltz step. The chicken squawked and cawed, flapping its wings out, making a sound like the sail of a boat being caught by the wind. But Aloquacious kept him still with her hand around his neck. As she danced around she plucked feathers from his body, dropping them on the floor. Louise watched all of this happen from the corner of the room. Eventually, Pete and Raymond taught her how to play the drums, and eventually Gramammy taught her how to slice a live chicken down his stomach and boil his blood to cleanse the souls of those living in despair. And she taught her how to pluck a hair from unsuspecting victims and cast a spell on them with a specially made voodoo doll.

Neither Mary-Elizabeth nor Louise went down into the basement often. It had been where Mary-Elizabeth's daddy spent most of his time. He kept his tools and things down there. Mary-Elizabeth opened up the door and pushed it all the way open, letting the light from the hallway drizzle into the dark space ahead of her. She reached her hand around the side of the door frame, searching for the light switch. The lights came on in stages and revealed a light brown wooden staircase. She took each step slowly, turning around every few steps to see if her mother was behind her. When she finally got to the bottom, Mary-Elizabeth just sat down quietly in a dusty brown leather chair and waited.

Louise came slowly down the stairs, each one making an "*errr-reeeu-uuhh*" noise as she stepped on it. She stood in front of Mary-Elizabeth, staring down at her with most of her wavy blond hair covering her face. She picked Mary-Elizabeth up under her armpits and sat her down on the cold, porcelain-enamel washing machine. She pushed the dryer right up next to it, making a flat surface just big enough for Mary-Elizabeth's tiny body. Louise bent down a little, putting her hands on her knees so that she was looking Mary-Elizabeth in the eyes.

"This is for your own good, child," she said.

Mary-Elizabeth's mouth turned down at the corners and her face turned as stark white as the machine she was sitting on.

"Now, be a good girl and lie down on your back," Louise said.

"Mama?" Mary-Elizabeth said, but it was barely audible. Louise started to push her down and grabbed a roll of duct tape from the shelf above. She ripped a small piece off and held it with both her hands above Mary-Elizabeth's face.

"Daddy . . . ," she whimpered.

"Your daddy's dead, little girl. And you killed him."

Louise slammed Mary-Elizabeth's head down against the washer as she covered her mouth with the tape. Mary-Elizabeth could feel a vein pumping so hard in her neck that she was sure it was trying to escape. Should she try to escape, too? Should she run? She could see the basement door open and the light trickling down the stairs. She could make it out if she jumped up fast enough. Or was Mama right? Was she evil? Was there something evil and terrible inside her that made her daddy drive into the Mississippi?

Louise grabbed both of Mary-Elizabeth's arms, which were at her side, and yanked them up and above her head. She crossed her wrists over each other behind a metal pipe that came up from the ground, and with her free hand, picked up a worn, brown leather belt from off the ground. She slipped it between Mary-Elizabeth's skin and the cold, dark metal and pulled it tightly through the buckle. Mary-Elizabeth curled her fingers in and out. Louise disappeared behind the dryer and emerged with a long, hemp rope that was heavily frayed. She wrapped it three times around Mary-Elizabeth's ankles; it tightened, pinched, and burned her skin. Louise tied her ankles to the metal pole. She took a pack of Marlboro Reds out of her front jean pocket and lit up a victory cigarette. She inhaled slowly, making a sound like a radiator letting heat escape, and blew the smoke over Mary-Elizabeth's body. She took two more drags and gently tapped the end of the cigarette over Mary-Elizabeth's head, letting the still burning ash fall onto her hair. It burned her hair a little. Mary-Elizabeth took a deep breath and the smell of burnt hair and laundry linens tickled her nose.

I stopped mid-spin as I noticed something out of the corner of one of my eyes. I typically don't notice much; when I'm working on a new web I become very focused. And, to be honest, not much has really happened in the basement since the tall, dark-haired father stopped inhabiting the area. But now, the two women of the family were both down here at the same time, which was very strange. The mother had the daughter, Mary-Elizabeth, tangled up into a web of her own, it seemed. But the mother, Louise, had disappeared now. Mary-Elizabeth was stuck all alone. As a mother of thousands myself, I wasn't sure what it was she was doing. Why did she leave her child tied up and alone? I decided to abandon the web-weaving for a moment to investigate. I swung over to a pipe that ran the length of the basement. As I crawled very slowly along, I remembered when Mary-Elizabeth was smaller and she would wander into the basement when her father was down here. She noticed me crouched up in a corner and wasn't at all afraid to get up close. It was strange for a girl her age to not be afraid of a black widow spider. But she wasn't; in fact, she seemed quite intrigued. She even gave me a name, Clarisse, and asked if I could be her pet. She came down and tried to find me all the time. Her father saw her talking to me one day and explained to her that she had to be careful around black widows like myself, because we have a very powerful poison that could harm little girls like her. I resented that statement. I would have never harmed little Mary-Elizabeth. We were friends.

As I made my way closer to her, I saw Mary-Elizabeth struggling in her captured state. I knew this movement so well, as all the moths and bugs I caught over the years made the same movements. She definitely didn't want to be there and it wasn't a game. She was trying to escape. I lowered myself down, not really sure of what I was planning on doing. I crawled up the side of the machine she was laid out upon. She didn't notice me as I scurried up behind her head and over to the side of her face. As I was trying to decipher how to help, a wave of light washed down from the basement door. Louise was coming back down. As she made her way down the steps, and I cowered behind the knob on the washing machine, I noticed she was holding something silver, pointy, and shiny in her hand. It was a knife! In her other hand she was holding a clear bottle of some pinkish liquid that I couldn't make out. She came closer, hovering over Mary-Elizabeth, examining her like a surgeon.

"That rib has got to go, baby," her voice boomed.

Mary-Elizabeth began to sob, very softly though. I panicked. Why was Louise talking about taking her rib? She rolled up Mary-Elizabeth's purple shirt and poured the pinkish liquid on her torso area. It splashed towards the back of the machine.

"This will only hurt a bit," Louise said.

I watched as Louise pointed the tip of the knife into Mary-Elizabeth's pale skin. Louise stopped, picking up the blade momentarily, as if she was second-guessing herself. I jumped, without hesitation, onto Mary-Elizabeth and crawled towards her gash. Louise stared down at me, quickly pulling her hand away, and without thinking, I sank my fangs into Mary-Elizabeth's spongy skin.

Mary-Elizabeth began to convulse, her eyes rolling back into her head, looking like two cue balls. Louise jumped back, dropping the knife onto the concrete floor.

"I knew it!" she screamed. "I knew she had the devil inside her!"

Louise cowered back against the stairs, hiding as Mary-Elizabeth's body slowly stopped moving. Soon her body lay nearly lifeless. Louise crept up back around the stairs and cautiously stepped towards Mary-Elizabeth, like her daughter was a snake that might dart out and bite her.

"You alive?" Louise asked, but Mary-Elizabeth didn't move. She could see that the girl was still faintly breathing though.

That devil. It knows, Louise thought to herself. But she can't die. No. If she dies, then he'll come after me.

Louise rapidly untied Mary-Elizabeth, took her in her arms and rushed up the stairs.

I could feel the slow, trickling, hot poison wrapping itself around my tendons and muscles. I felt it seeping in my pores and washing over my bones. I felt it seize on my heart a bit and unfocus my eyes. They rolled backwards and around in my sockets and stopped facing the back of my head. Everything turned gray and it all stopped hurting.

It started like the rabbit hole: I fell and fell and fell towards nothingness, feeling nothing, not even the absence of gravity. I began to hear my father whisper, "Mary-Elizabeth," which I knew was my name, but it didn't feel like he was talking to me. Eventually I stopped falling. I was back in the basement, but I was no longer tied up. No, now I was trapped in a giant spider's web. I tried to move, but was paralyzed. I tried to shout, but no noise would escape. I heard my father say, "Mary-Elizabeth," again and I thought hard "I'm here!" hoping he could hear me. I saw something rustle and move around in the shadows of the basement, but it didn't feel like it was my father. A long, prickly-haired leg stepped from behind the dark curtain and revealed a giant black widow spider who had been lurking around. I shut my eyes tightly. She spoke to me in a kind voice, the voice that had sounded like my father's.

"Mary-Elizabeth, I saved you," the voice said.

"No you didn't! You bit me!" I shouted back, my eyes still closed.

My stomach began to heave. I felt my insides burning with liquid trying to escape. My body jerked and spasmed in the web. What was happening?

Mary-Elizabeth's eyes were caked shut with eye gook and leftover tears. Her eyelashes flicked off the goop as she blinked more and more rapidly. She rubbed at her eyes with her fingertips, smooshing them around in the sockets. She was just remembering the lingering details of her dream when she realized she wasn't at home in her bed. She sat up quickly and a thin, plastic tube tugged at her skin from behind her elbow. She winced. She saw the white curtain at her side and the small, staticky TV hoisted up on the wall. She could hear the beep-beep-beep of the heart monitor and turned to look at it; the little green line on the screen began making bigger mountains, faster and faster as her heart thump-thumped. She could smell the over-whelming stench of the blue and yellow chemicals resting in their jars. They had all kinds of scary, silver tools in them and the word *sterile* written in black. The smell wafted into her nostrils, tickling her tiny nose hairs, and up back into her throat, burning as it went down her esophagus and into her stomach, punching and kicking its way down to her intestine. She wrapped her arms around her waist and let out a tiny whimper. Mary-Elizabeth was in a hospital.

"Oh, you're alive," a voice said.

Mary-Elizabeth looked up and leaned over to the left a bit to see her mama sitting in a chair, menacingly eating the vegetables from Mary-Elizabeth's dinner plate. Louise sat very still, quietly sticking steamed car-rots and green beans in her mouth, never taking her eyes off Mary-Elizabeth.

Mary-Elizabeth was startled and sat back a little quickly on her bed. A sharp pain leaped up from her side. She clenched her stomach and moaned with soreness. She hurt all over, but mostly at her side, on the left, near her ribcage. She slowly lifted up her light purple hospital gown to reveal a yel-lowish bruise surrounding two small, puffy red holes. She ran her fingertips over the top and even the light touch was painful. What had happened? Why was she in a hospital in such pain? She didn't remember anything after her mama had tied her up and came back downstairs with the knife. Mary-Elizabeth froze. She looked back down at her side and felt the pain flame up again. Had her mama really done it? Had she really taken her rib? A sudden banging noise brought Mary-Elizabeth back to reality.

In front of her, on the table connected to the bed, was a small jar filled with pink liquid and a little white bone floating very still inside of it. Her mama's hand was resting on the lid. Louise and Mary-Elizabeth stared at each other, like two mannequins.

"A spider bit you. That little black widow yer always talkin' to," Louise said, breaking the silence.

"But don't you worry. I got yer rib all the same. I saved you, Mary-Elizabeth. I can't have that devil inside you coming after me. I'm a decent person, Mary-Elizabeth. I'm a God-fearing woman. And I saved you for your own good."

Mary-Elizabeth held her breath in her lungs. The heart monitor started beeping even faster. Beep...Beep....Beeepbeeepbeeepbeeepbeep. Louise came around the side of the bed and leaned over into Mary-Elizabeth's face. She breathed heavily and her breath smelled like cigarettes and carrots. Louise went back to her chair and shoved the jar into her purse, just as a nurse rushed in the door.

"You all right, Mary-Elizabeth?" the short, brunette nurse asked as she jolted towards the heart monitor. Mary-Elizabeth's lip quivered a bit as she looked up at the friendly nurse's face. She traced her eyes down her white coat to a name tag that said "Darlene." The nurse fiddled with a few buttons on the heart monitor and the beep-beep-beep began to slow down.

"There you go," Darlene said with a softness in her voice. "Did you just wake up? Probably wonderin' why you're all tied up in tubes, huh?"

Mary-Elizabeth nodded her head.

"Well, you got bit by a little old spider, a black widow in fact," Darlene said, bending down so she and Mary-Elizabeth were eye-to-eye.

"Clarisse?" Mary-Elizabeth finally squeaked out.

"Oh, is she your friend?" Darlene asked, her eyes widening a bit.

Mary-Elizabeth nodded.

"It seems Clarisse might not be the best friend for you. Turns out you're allergic to the little bit of poison she keeps inside her. So when she bit you, your body didn't like it so much," Darlene said, her voice raised up an octave or so.

"Clarisse bit me?" Mary-Elizabeth asked, nearly in a whisper. "Why would she do that?"

Darlene paused for a moment before responding.

"She might have felt threatened by something or someone."

Mary-Elizabeth's eyes slowly fell onto the chair her mother was sitting in. She squeezed the scratchy hospital blanket into her palms and met eyes with Darlene again.

"I don't know about that," Mary-Elizabeth said.

Darlene and Mary-Elizabeth shared a long stare for a few silent minutes. The nurse stood up and looked at Louise, who was staring out the window, fiddling with a ring on her finger.

"The good news, Mary-Elizabeth, is that you get to go home today," Darlene said with a smile and little clap.

Louise's neck shot towards the bed, so quickly you would've thought she had broken it. "Nurse, are you sure? I mean, maybe she should stay here a few more days," Louise said, feigning concern, but mostly just sounding afraid.

"I assure you, Mrs. Abernathy, she is ready to go home."

Louise came over to the hospital bed, putting her hands on the bar on the side. She gripped it tightly.

"I dunno, nurse. She still looks a little pale."

"It's fine, Mrs. Abernathy. I promise, she's all better and if anything else happens you can call the hospital right away. Just keep her outta the basement."

Louise's eyes widened to the size of silver dollars and she looked at Mary-Elizabeth as if to say, you better not have said something.

Nurse Darlene helped Mary-Elizabeth out of the tall hospital bed and into the bathroom where her clothes were. The door clicked shut and Mary-Elizabeth was alone. She didn't want to leave the hospital because she felt safe there. She listened at the door, hoping Darlene would still be there after she dressed. She didn't hear anybody leave, so she put on her blue jeans and purple top, laced up her white sneakers, and opened the door. She peered her head around the door and saw Darlene cleaning up her bed area. She looked over at her mama quietly putting on her jacket. For a second she thought about running, but she couldn't get her legs to move.

Mary-Elizabeth crawled into the back of Louise's rusty, white Volvo. It was dusty, but not completely covered in dirt; it reminded Mary-Elizabeth of an undershirt that desperately needed to be washed. She missed her daddy's red Chevy pickup. It was always dirty, too, but her daddy said it added character. It always took her a few tries to hop into the front seat, which felt like it was as high up as the Appalachian mountains. But she always refused her daddy's help; she just had to do it herself. Once she made it in she could barely see out the windows, but she would wiggle her legs underneath her butt and sit on her knees. They would go for drives through the plains for no reason at all.

Louise and Mary-Elizabeth sat in silence on the car ride home. Mary-Elizabeth rested her head on the door, watching through the window as the tree tops passed by so quickly. She became hypnotized by the repetition and it lulled her to sleep. She was jolted back awake when her mother yanked open the back door. Louise reached over, unbuckled her from the seat, and grabbed her coat from the floor.

"Don't forget your rib, little girl," Louise said with her back turned.

Mary-Elizabeth grabbed the jar from the seat next to her, shut the Volvo door and slowly followed her mama back into the house.

Belmont to Bridgeport

Alexis Thomas

IT TOOK ME A FEW YEARS TO REALIZE I WAS SCARED OF MY BROTHER BECAUSE HE killed that old Korean man at Belmont Harbor. At the time, I don't think I felt much other than wanting to punch somebody. And what made it all even worse was that I just couldn't sleep. That's the way it is whenever shit pisses me off. Instead of dealing with it, I store it and let it build up, and then when I try to fall asleep, I have a panic attack.

It's been like that my whole life, and no matter what, there is nothing I can do about it. The only person that knew how to deal with it was Frankie. Every night, when he was still living at home, he'd poke his head in my room to make sure I was sleeping. Even if he was drunk and it was five in the morning, he'd still check up on me. And if I were awake and trying to fake like I was sleeping, he'd know it and would sit on my bed running his mouth off with his stories to distract me, until I'd have no choice except to fall asleep.

But it wasn't like that after Frankie was convicted and got ten years in prison. He spent his nights sleeping in East Moline with thousands of other prisoners, and I spent my nights in my apartment with my boyfriend Marco, since I ran outta the house before even finishing my senior year of high school.

I'd be in bed kicking my toes like a tadpole. Our room would echo my twists and turns because it wasn't more than a pile of clothes and a mattress and some blankets Marco stole from his mom's. He'd roll into me, wrap his arms around my stomach, and say, "Megan–shhhhh. Just re-lax." Humboldt Park buzzed outside our bedroom window. Even at two a.m. in April, Chicago was a bust down. And Marco would say, "Please—just go to sleep so both of us can." Because ever since Frankie's trial, all I'd do was yell at Marco and throw things at him and tell him to fuck off, pushing him to the point of smacking me. Just like his dad did to his mom.

The problem was, when I slowed down and wasn't at work making shitty smoothies or drunk at somebody's house, everything that had happened would keep replaying in my head. It'd always start with my brother. Frankie's face was round but bumpy like an orange. He had Dad's Irish skin and Mom's farm–built cheekbones. His eyebrows hugged his forehead. He was tall and thick and mean like Logan Square, but his head was shaved and his Doc Martens were concrete.

All my brother wanted to be was Belmont and Clark. Just like Dad. And that'd always make me think about Dad's store Chaos and all the screen-printed band shirts and the *fuck the police* fabric patches and the suspenders and Doc Martens and creepers.

Frankie screwed everything up at Belmont Harbor. It was Frankie, Chris, and me, sitting at the rocks drinking, and Chris was trying to grab my boob, and Frankie wasn't doing nothing about it. He let his own best friend grope his sister. I might have been his family, but Chris was his boy. And Frankie, like the idiot he was, dropped the pint of whiskey. I remember hearing Chris lose his shit because it was too late to find a liquor store that was still open. I knew we shouldn't have ever been at Belmont Harbor. Whenever I think about it, I always regret seeing the old Korean man sit down ten feet from us, on the rocks with his backpack and fishing pole and tackle box. Even at that moment, all drunk, I knew something was gonna happen. That's when Chris stood up. I heard the leather in his Docs crinkle. And he hollered, "Go catch some fuckin' sushi, Jap-ass-bitch!" while he ran over to him and started kicking him in the ribs until the man was on the ground. I looked up at Frankie, and I'll always remember how he was shaking in his bomber jacket, his shadow tick-tick-ticking in Lake Michigan. And the waves swallowed the rocks, and Chris kicked and yelled, "Give me your fuckin' wallet!" Frankie ran toward them. I stood up and cupped my hands around my mouth so he could hear me over the waves on the left and Lake Shore Drive on the right.

"Frankie! Stop him!" I screamed. But all he did was push the old man into the lake. He thumped, and it thumped through me and I bet it thumped all the way to the West Side where nobody notices thumps because all they know is death.

Frankie looked back at me as Chris started to run, "Come on man!" And Frankie yelled, "Megan!" But I wasn't gonna move. So he left me. My big brother left me. I looked over the rocks and I felt like I was gonna barf because the old man was stuck on them like a plastic bag. And he wasn't whining or crying or nothing. Lake Michigan covered him and then pulled back. I started to unlace my boots because they were so heavy I'd drown. I crawled down into the rocks and tried to pull the old man up, but he wasn't moving. He outweighed me. But I couldn't just leave him.

I stayed with that old man for almost an hour before someone on their morning jog came by. I looked up as the man yelled, "Holy shit!" and I barfed up French fries and cheeseburger all over the dead man.

Sometimes I can't sleep because all I can think about is Belmont and Clark. I see my dad standing in front of the store, yanking on his gray hair and looking like he is ready to cry. It happened two weeks after Frankie got out on bail. Someone had busted out the windows and stole everything they could from my dad. All that was left in the store was the spray painted graffiti against the front window that said, "Nazi shit fuck skinhead store!"

The only way I could calm down was to attach to something I knew was real and wouldn't hurt me. I lay in bed and smelled the plastic and corn. That's how I knew I was home. Marco sat up, his curly Puerto Rican hair sticking up like a cotton ball and his round cheeks flushed because somehow, while thinking about all this, I started screaming. He pulled the covers off me and yelled, "Sit up! Sit up!" I was shaking and couldn't breathe and my eyes were closed, but I was still screaming.

"Fucking stop! Just calm down!" He patted me on the back. I opened my eyes and I felt like everything was on fire, even Marco. I wanted to hit him because I didn't know what we were doing with ourselves since I'd dropped outta school.

Marco just kept patting me on the back and said, "You're burning up." I was all sweat beads and soaked sheets. I thought I loved him, but I didn't love Humboldt Park or our home. He rubbed my back, "I'ma open a window," and he got out of bed. "Just calm down. You need to calm down." The room spun. There wasn't no reason to calm down. Because it was all shit.

* * *

Marco was making us dinner, and I was sitting on our couch in our living room, which wasn't much more than the milk crates filled with Marco's books and CDs. I tapped my foot on the hardwood floor and could hear whatever Marco was making sizzle on the stove and his knee bump into it as he said, "Let's just chill out tonight."

But my foot was tapping, and I didn't know how much longer I was gonna be able to sit in our apartment. The longer I sat still, the more I thought about Frankie and how he left me with the dead guy and was now leaving me with Chicago. I started to feel my chest tighten and my eyes well up, and the only way to stop myself from crying was to keep my foot tapping and get myself out of the apartment.

I reached over the couch for the phone and called our friend Jose, the lead singer of Madre De La Muerte, and said, "You wanna get drunk and fuck shit up?"

"Whatd' you mean?" Jose's voice echoed Pilsen, but I was all the way west, looking out on Washtenaw Avenue. Cars were parked on top of each other, and people sat on their stoops. Even though it was eleven o'clock at night, some of the kids were playing football in the middle of the street and riding around on their bikes. I held the phone closer. Behind me were piles of shoes and random clothes that led to the kitchen where Marco was making quesadillas. "You. Know. Like. Fuck. Some. Shit. Up," I said.

Before I go on I gotta point out I knew what I was doing. Most of the messed-up situations I end up in, I know what I'm getting myself into. I knew it the night at Belmont Harbor and when I moved in with Marco right when I turned seventeen. So when I got off the phone with Jose, I knew exactly what I was getting myself into.

Jose lived with the three other members of Madre De La Muerte, along with his brother's band Chupar, in this four-bedroom red-brick two-flat on Cermak. On their street, all the houses stuck together like Velcro. The porch was on crutches. The front window was boarded up with cardboard. When I walked up the steps, all these kids were sitting and smoking and drinking forties, and the music was boom-booming out of the front door that kept opening and closing as the porch expanded and deflated with people.

Inside the house, people were packed like firewood. It was sweaty, and girls had makeup smeared on their cheeks, and people were standing on chairs drumming on the ceiling. But I didn't know a single person, because ever since I had dropped out and moved in with Marco, I didn't have my friends anymore, I just had his.

Looking back on it all, I could have turned around and gone back home. But at the time, I think I was looking for anything to do so I didn't have to think about Frankie. Because if I thought about him and everything that happened, then I'd have to start to feel something about it. And it was just easier to ignore it.

I kept pushing through all the girls in them tight jeans and the boys in their black shirts until I got into the kitchen and saw Jose. He was tall and had a mole on his cheek, and every time he smiled it looked like the mole was double-dutching over his cheekbone. But before I could twist toward him, this blond chick from my earth science class at Lane Tech came up to me and asked, "What happened to you? You drop out or something?" I felt my skin burn and brushed passed her saying, "Nah, man. I just stopped going."

I wanted to turn around because I was surrounded by all these people who graduated high school and had plans for their lives, and I could barely pay my rent. But I kept going until I was standing next to Jose. I didn't have anything to do but smile. He passed me a bottle of E&J and I was all like, "Man, really? That shit's ghetto." But he didn't say nothing. He just smiled at me with his roasted almond skin and mop hair, and I kept eyeing him up and down. Not because I wanted to fuck him, but because I didn't wanna have to talk to all those people I knew that got to graduate from high school.

The music screamed off the kitchen tiles. I couldn't stand it and started pounding that bottle, and Jose slapped hands with some guy passing through. Every time someone walked by me, I had to suck my stomach in and stand on my toes. The refrigerator opened, and when it did, everyone thought it was a cop with his flashlight busting the party. There were so many people crowded together. Even the ones I knew felt like strangers.

Jose leaned over and asked, "You wanna snort some cheap-ass speed?" And I started to think about all the crack heads that hung around Belmont and Clark. They were always sitting on the curb in the Dunkin Donuts parking lot, or coming into the store and getting kicked out because they'd never have any money and always stole. My mind was all wrapped up in that and how Frankie would always put his arm around my shoulder and slap my head whenever we passed one, laughing, "Megan. If you end up smokin' crack and shittin' your pants, I'll kill ya."

But I just wanted to get away from the party and all them people with their questions. And I wanted to get away from Marco and his "just re-lax, bay-bey" bullshit. I wanted nothing to do with Chicago. That's probably the reason I snorted that shit that smelled like gasoline right off his dresser in his bedroom.

I started blowing him. It was dark in his room, and he lay on his mattress, and I pulled his jeans down to his skinny–ass kneecaps. People laughed in the living room. Someone put Naked Raygun on. Speed felt like an ocean. I pressed my fingernails into Jose's thighs. He gasped and his hand pushed down on my head. I pulled back. I wanted to get shoved on the wall. Someone outside of the bedroom yelled, "Aw hell nah. If that girl's pukin' she best get outside."

I was on top and couldn't feel nothing, but Jose's hip bones bit the inside of my thighs and the speed trickled and waltzed right outta my thrusts. My toes ticked his kneecaps. I kept my palms flat on the white wall ahead of me. Jose slapped my ass with his left hand and I slammed into him harder. When the spot on the wall became warm I slid my palm over. Jose grabbed my hips. Naked Raygun vibrated through the springs of the mattress. My hair fell like a lampshade. I wanted him to slap me again, but all he did was push his thumbs into my hips, throw me sideways, and tuck me under him. "How's it feel to fuck a real Mexican?" he grunted onto my neck. And that shit made me so sad. I moaned and thought about Marco and how he ain't never slapped me like I asked. He'd always say, "man—that's kinda fucked up, right?" and just slapped me the only way he knew. I bit Jose's neck for saying something like that. A girl giggled outside his room. I was face deep in Jose's pillow that smelled like drool and maple syrup and all I wanted was for Marco to hug me. Jose slapped the side of my thigh. Somebody else hollered, "Hey! Isn't that Marco's girlfriend in there with Jose?"

Jose pulled my ass up and tucked himself inside of me. Naked Raygun sweated in my ears. My forehead skidded on the pillow. "Harder!" I screamed. And the bitch that he was came, collapsed, and said, "Ahhhh sheeeet—I'm so fucked up."

I woke up in the afternoon, and by the time I made it back to my part of the city it was almost nine o'clock at night. I walked down North Avenue for as long as I could because I couldn't handle going back to the apartment and the pollution and horns, and traffic was more comforting than having to face Marco. When I got on Washtenaw the streetlamps were on and the sun was down and the neighborhood kids were playing tag.

I walked into the apartment. Marco was sitting on the couch that faced the window and turned around when he heard me walk in. I know all he saw were the dark circles under my eyes and my knotty black hair and our dirty-ass apartment. This place didn't belong to us anymore.

"I heard what you did," he said. He had them red eyes people get when shit's too messed up to cry over. I'd never seen him like that, and I felt it all the way into my gut. I thought he would hit me if I cried, so I didn't. I just bit my lip and walked into the bathroom to take a shower.

When I got outta the shower, the living room and the bedroom were dark and empty. I thought Marco had left me. I walked into the kitchen, which wasn't much more than a stove, refrigerator, and sink, and saw Marco laying on the ground, and that's how I knew it was gonna be bad. When Marco still lived at home, whenever things got bad for him and his moms, he'd lie on the kitchen floor with his fist all clenched up and listen to her cook, and watch for when his dad would come home.

I walked over to him in my towel and looked down. He closed his eyes. Looking back, I think that's the only thing that stopped him from jumping up and beating on me like his dad used to beat his mom. I got on my knees, held the towel to my chest, and leaned over him. My wet hair dripped a trail on his gray T-shirt. I kissed his forehead, but he didn't open his eyes or anything. He just reached up and grabbed my shoulder, pulling me into him.

Before I knew it we were naked and fucking. He was on top and the hardwood floor stung my back. It was silent except for the police siren blasting outside, and even that felt silent because Humboldt Park always had police sirens. He had my legs around his neck, and bent me forward as he said, "Turn the fuck over." He sounded like his dad. I couldn't recognize any of his movements or rhythm and I didn't know if that was because I'd changed or if he'd changed or if we had changed each other and that made me start to cry. My knees stung from the wood and my wrists stretched from the weight and I cried and Marco pushed into me harder as he slapped my ass just like Jose. I collapsed onto the floor but Marco kept going. He pulled my hips up and closer to him. I turned my head sideways. The bones in my neck cracked with each of his thrusts. The floor was littered with cigarettes friends had trashed during our last house party and my new black Doc Martens that I'd gotten to replace the ones I left at Belmont Harbor, were kicked over. I bit my lip so I had a reason to fake a moan, but Marco knew and slapped my thigh real hard for even trying to lie to him again. And I let him. I would have let him slap me in the face over and over and yell at me until my eardrums turned themselves right side out.

The worst part of all of it wasn't that Marco was fucking the history of

Jose out of me. It was watching him fall asleep naked on the kitchen floor holding me, and knowing that when he woke up the next day, all my shit would be gone.

I could have just packed my stuff up and crawled back to my parents. Except it didn't seem like an option. It didn't feel like I could ever go back to them. And if I tried to crash at a friend's, it would have been one of Marco's friends, and I wouldn't be able to stay all that long when they realized what I did to him.

So I ended up taking a room at this gross crack hotel at Fullerton and Pulaski called the Diplomat. I didn't have to think much about it, which was fine by me, because it meant I didn't have to feel much. The Diplomat had always been there. Since my old best friend Monica and I were thirteen, we'd always joke about running away and living there. I guess I managed to do that. It was a tall gray building and the sign flashed *hotel* amongst the streetlights and cars and congestion of Fullerton. It was next door to a gas station that locked the door at 11:00p.m. and forced all of the customers to pay through a bulletproof drawer. That's all there had ever been to that part of Fullerton. The rest of the street was deserted with empty storefronts.

The front entrance of the Diplomat was a long yellowed hallway that echoed like the subway. The night I walked in with my hair still damp, I was shaking, and I didn't want anybody to know I was shaking because that's asking for someone to fuck with you. But walking down that hallway just made me shake more until I hit the lobby, which was a white box with some fold-up chairs and a guy behind a desk.

When I checked in, the man behind the desk squinted at me like he was trying to see through me and then handed me my keys. I'm not gonna lie; I didn't have a fucking clue what I was doing. For some reason, I just kept going and going and ended up with a bunch of hookers and crack heads in this hotel. I'd never want to admit it, but I was starting to freak out. I felt like I was always screaming in my head. But the part that was really scary was realizing that, for the first time in my life, I was completely on my own.

I'd go to work at this neon-colored smoothie shop in Old Town, and every day the stupid-ass manager would catch me making a mistake and shake his head and say, "One more mess up, Megan, and you're gone." It'd take me almost an hour to get back to the Diplomat because I'd have to take the train to the bus and the bus to Pulaski. That was the worst part of those days. I didn't have anything to distract me, and I'd be sitting on the bus all covered in strawberries and smoothie mix, and I'd start to feel a buzz through my chest. Then the buzz would be in my gut, and I'd think about Marco and his red eyes, and then I'd bite my lip to feel something other than the memories.

I'd race past all the freaks and bums hanging out in the long yellow hallway and in the lobby, and then I'd push up these metal stairs, down another hallway that sounded like the inside of an airplane, and rush into my room. I wouldn't ever turn the lights on. I didn't wanna see the stains in the gray carpet or the holes in the window drapes. I didn't want to see how small and moldy the room was. I'd just lie in my bed that smelled like bleach.

The sounds would drive me crazy. The hallways echoed screams. The rooms were filled with people getting high, fucked, slapped, raped, or killed, but nobody cared. I'd lie in my twin bed with the covers up to my shoulders and stare at the ceiling that looked like rotten milk. I'd try not to think about anything, but my mind would always go off about Frankie or Marco and how all this was Chicago's fault. Chicago was bullshit. Then somebody would scream and it'd make me want to scream even louder and run back to Marco. Except I knew I'd never go back to him or Belmont and Clark.

On the fourth night at the Diplomat, some motherfucker broke into my room, crawled into my bed, and put his hand over my mouth. When it was happening I didn't have much time to react, but later on, I realized I knew who the guy was. Every day I'd walk past this group of guys that hung in the stairwell that smelled like piss. He was tall and black and had a jaw that was thick like an iceberg. I came up to his chest and he'd look down on me, as I'd climb up them stairs, slowly getting taller than him.

"Hey gurrrrl." He'd put his hands between the metal bars in the stairs. "How much for dat ass?" And I wouldn't react or anything. I'd just bolt for my room and jump into my bed with my clothes still on.

He kicked in the door. The only reason why I even knew that's how he did it was because I recognized how it sounded. After Mom and Dad kicked Frankie outta the house for being a bum, they changed the locks. One night, I fell asleep on the couch watching TV and started hearing that crack-crack coming from the door until it popped back on its springs, and Frankie stumbled into the living room, all drunk.

That's exactly what it sounded like except I knew that shit wasn't Frankie. I sat up and leaned over my covers. The room was dark, but I saw this tall shadow walk toward the bed. He kneeled and the twin mattress almost capsized. I couldn't move because the bed was against the wall. He punched me in the face and I slid back into the mattress. He put his hand over my mouth and I yelped, and all I wanted was to be sitting on my mom's lap, her blond hair sprinkling lavender in the air. He turned me over on my side so that I faced the wall. But he didn't need to do that. If I screamed nobody woulda cared. My back was to him and I felt his hand slip under my shirt and over my freckles. He rubbed his body up on my spine and ass like I was a slide. I bit the wrinkles in his palm and he gripped on my mouth harder. His fingertips to wrist covered my entire face. He was hard and the only thing that separated us was our clothes. I felt like I was gonna die. I wanted Dad to come and get me outta there or for Marco to show up with his brother's car. I wanted Frankie to kill this motherfucker—not the Korean man.

I kicked my Doc Marten into his kneecap. He let go of my mouth and punched me in the back of my head and kept grinding on my back, his jeans tugging on my T-shirt. I screamed and my screams collided with all the screams in the hotel. Then he punched me again and I stopped. I stopped moving. I wanted to holler in his old waxed-up ear, "And what bitch? That all you got?" But, really, I was too scared to say anything.

He stopped grinding and I felt the weight in the mattress shift. The only thing I moved was my eyes. I looked to my right and watched him lie on his back like we were a couple in love going to bed. I stopped breathing and listened to him breathe. I heard him unzip his jeans and all I was thinking was, oh god—oh god—oh god. And then he stuck his hand down his pants. I still had my shirt and jeans on, and nothing was ripped, but I couldn't feel anything against my skin. I heard the fucker breathe harder. His shoulder moved up and down. Up and down. I felt like my insides were in a washing machine. I couldn't believe the sick fuck broke into my room and gave me a black eye, just so he could jerk off next to me.

I counted to ten and choked on my spit because I forgot how to swallow. And then he gasped, exhaled, zipped up his pants, and walked out of the room with a swagger. I ran out of there just like I ran outta all the places I'm from.

When Frankie and me were kids, Dad used to take us with him to the Burnside Tavern on the way home from work. It was right across the street from Chaos and everyone around Belmont and Clark hung out there. The Cubs game would play from this cereal box-sized TV that was duct taped to the ceiling. Pitches and foul balls and cheers flashed all over the bar and stools and the jukebox. Frankie and I sat on the stools and spun like flying saucers. Dad wasn't much of a drinker, but if he sat in the Burnside long enough, he could find out what was happening with cops, skinheads, trannies, and homeless teens who stood on the corner with fishbowl eyes that said, "For the right price you can get me to do whatever you want."

When Frankie got older, he always hung out at the Burnside and would sneak me in. But I felt weird because that's around the time I started noticing a change in Frankie. He was mean and angry and always looking for a fight, so he found himself some people that were just like him to get drunk with. All his friends were like that. Except for Paul, who was the main bartender and one of the only skinheads Frankie knew that wasn't a dumb ass. I think it was because he was almost ten years older than Frankie and Chris.

Paul was the only friend Frankie had that I felt I could trust. Even when all the trial shit was going on and the cops were questioning every skinhead they could find, he told me, "Whatever you need Megan—I gotchu."

That's where I ran. I was on Fullerton, and when I hit Clark I had nowhere to go except Belmont. I stopped running at the corner and stood under the ten-foot-tall Dunkin Donuts sign. The parking lot was empty except for all these trannies snapping their lips and swinging around the sidewalk, looking at me like I was up on their territory. But even at 3:00 a.m. this parking lot and Clark Street, and the porn rental store across Belmont, felt like they belonged to me. Even the dumpsters in the back corner of the parking lot were mine. I wanted to be like, "Bitch, please—this shit belongs to me." But then I saw, through the streetlights, the Chaos sign sway on Clark Street and couldn't believe I'd ended up back at Belmont and Clark.

When I walked into the Burnside, Paul was behind the bar with his back turned to the front door. But I knew it was him, even in the dark. Paul was the skinniest skinhead I'd ever met in my life. Behind the bar that was covered with ashtrays and glass bottles and broken straws, he looked like a lollipop.

I heard a bunch of beer bottles crash into a trash can. "Get the fuck out—we closed twenty minutes ago." He tossed more beer bottles but I didn't move. I wasn't going anywhere. Then, he turned around, drying his hands on a white dish towel, and said, "Holy shit." He dropped the rag onto the bar and got this big old goofy-ass smile, his crooked teeth bright amongst the fluorescent beer ads hammered to the black walls.

"Megan! What the fuck happened to your face?" He walked around the bar and toward me with his arms all open like he was about to hug an army.

And I was so confused because everything that had just happened felt like a lie. For a second, I thought I was still living with Marco. I wanted to ask him what he meant by my face because Marco never left bruises people could see. But then I remembered the black guy and the sound of him jerking off and his hard-on rubbing up against me. And then, I threw up. The chunks hit the ground like a thunderstorm.

Paul mopped and I talked. I sat on a stool holding a plastic grocery bag filled with ice to my eye and told him about Marco and Jose and how I didn't want to go home. "I was staying at this crack hotel and working," I said, "and figured I'd be able to get my own place, but this motherfucker broke in and rubbed up all on me."

Paul stopped mopping. "Wait. What the fuck?" he said. "He raped you?"

"Nah. That shit wasn't rape. The fucker just jerked off next to me." And the part that still freaks me out to this day is when I said that to Paul, I didn't feel anything about it. I wouldn't let myself.

"I'm gonna kill him," Paul said. "I'm gonna fucking kill him."

Paul drove me back to the hotel in his red pickup. I had to sniffle to stop myself from starting to cry. He'd already seen me puke with a black eye. I couldn't let him or anybody see me crying. Blind Willie Johnson played over the radio, and Fullerton Avenue felt like a death march. The closer he got to the hotel, the harder it was not to throw up again or burst out in tears. Stoplights were heartbeats. He parked in front of the hotel, and I thought I was gonna pass out when he said, "Get out."

"What?" I held onto my seat belt. "You're gonna leave me here?"

"Hell no! You crazy?" He opened his door and stepped onto Fullerton Avenue. At four in the morning it was nothing but red lights and stop signs. "But I'ma beat this motherfucker's ass."

Paul dragged me by the elbow to the hotel, telling me, "I'ma break into every motherfucking room till we find him, and then I'ma beat him to death."

Except he didn't need to do all that. When we walked into the piss-colored lobby, the guy was leaning against the counter talking to the man on duty. The minute he saw me with Paul, he ran toward the yellow hallway. Paul grabbed the back of his collar and popped his ass on the ground. I heard the man's head crack like an egg. The guy behind the counter yelled, "Outside with that shit!" and Paul grabbed the guy by his arm and dragged him down the hallway and onto Fullerton like he was a dead dog.

Paul pounded into him. When his fists got tired he started kicking him until he was in the gutter. The fucker didn't even try to fight back. People came out of the hotel. And then I finally let myself scream. On top of the kicking and grunting and the gasps of the people watching, I screamed so loud I had to have woken up Logan Square, Hermosa, and probably Humboldt Park. The first time I watched someone get beat to death, I didn't know what to expect or how to react. And now, all I wanted to do was scream until my lungs were on the ground, next to the motherfucker.

When Paul finished, the guy was a bag of potatoes. But he was still alive and breathing. Paul spit on his forehead before taking one last kick to the guy's ribs. The fucker moaned and that moan got caught in the gutters. It was the same moan I heard as he jerked off. Everybody watched until Paul hollered at me, "Get all yo' shit 'cause you ain't coming back here ever again."

We drove. We didn't talk. We just drove. I opened the window to feel the breeze on my swollen face. All I wanted was ice on my eye and to be sixteen again, lying on my parents' couch and watching TV with my dad. But we were still on Fullerton, until we hit the highway. On the highway, the Sears Tower and downtown looked like they were built out of cardboard boxes. I hadn't seen them from the highway in forever, but they still looked the same. Knowing that made me feel safe.

I always thought it was my brother and Belmont and Clark that would keep me safe, but I was realizing all Frankie cared about was himself. For a while I believed Marco would keep me safe, but I was destroying him. The only thing I could trust was the stability of the buildings and streets in this city.

The sun came up and I could still taste the vomit between my teeth. We kept driving until we were in Bridgeport and parked in front of the old skin house where Frankie and Paul and a bunch others lived.

"I'll carry your stuff in," he said. "Just go put some more ice on that eye."

"Wait." I felt like my nerves were being electrocuted. Every sound, even the keys clenched in his fist, made my spine ache. "In there?" I looked over at the skin house. It wasn't much other then a four-flat graystone. The Chicago flag hung like dirty laundry from the porch. Frankie and Chris and everybody I'd ever known circulated through that house like white blood cells. And I didn't want to have anything to do with it because it was all selfish bullshit. Except, sitting in Paul's car, I knew I had no other option than that house.

"Yeah." He turned the car off and opened his door. "You got somewhere else you wanna go?"

"Uh. No," I said.

"So then this be your best option, huh?" He jumped out of the car and slammed his door shut.

I dropped all my stuff in the empty bedroom that was right outside the living room covered in crushed Budweiser cans. All I wanted to do was sleep so I wouldn't have to feel anything. Not even the pulse in the eye. The room could barely fit a twin mattress, and in the corner were some boxes that didn't belong to me. I sat on the mattress and leaned my head against an Agnostic Front poster Scotch-taped to the wall.

Paul tapped on the doorframe and said, "You good?" He had dark circles around his eyes and scratched the top of his bald head.

"Yeah," I said. "Thanks, by the way, for cleaning up my barf, or whatever."

Paul smiled. "Just get some rest." And he stood there, his head jumping up and down like a fly, looking at every chipped spot on the white walls. "You know, this was Frankie's old room, and all them boxes are his."

"Yeah, that's what I figured," I said, unlacing my boots.

"Well, since he's locked up, I guess that stuff belongs to you. We's were just gonna toss it." He stretched his hand over the frame, then stepped back and pulled the door shut.

I didn't want any of his shit to belong to me. I didn't want Frankie to be my brother anymore. I crawled onto his old mattress. I didn't know what I would do tomorrow or the day after that but I couldn't even think about it. The only thing I could do was try to fall asleep.

Bottom of Lake Michigan

Jon Natzke

DOWN ALONG THE SLICK BROWN BOTTOM OF LAKE MICHIGAN IS A MENAGERIE of splendid broken things. It runs from Chicago to the tip of Michigan in a spill of debris and garbage, like a murky, man-made coral reef. Refrigerators that stopped cooling, ovens with the doors broken off, cracked ceramic sinks, cars from across the past century, some turned over, some crushed, some half buried, all with shattered headlights and algae-covered front bumpers. There are parts of buildings, naked I-beams covered in copper rust, windows unbroken but smeared black from a life at the bottom, and thousands of bricks—like streets—lining it all in between. There are things that only the fish know about: wristwatches, wedding rings in velvet boxes, unsent letters, someone's father's favorite hat, beer bottles, dolls, maybe a body or two. Maybe more than two. When something new is added to these secret piles, the fish all crowd around it in a big circle, thinking about its significance, wondering if it meant anything to anyone, if it was special. Then one of the fish will get close to the object like he might eulogize the fallen piece of mankind. The reverend fish will stop right next to it, taking his time watching the object, as all the other fish watch him watch the object. Then, when he's good and ready, he will try to eat the object, and all the other fish will leave, because the reverend went and ruined the moment again.

And farther out there is a war going on, not quite in the center, but in the next ring out, past the garbage city that the smaller fish live in, where the larger fish swim and eat what they want; at least they used to, until all the Asian carp moved in. At first it was only one or two Asian carp and the native fish were like, "OK cool, we have Oriental neighbors, which means we're kind of worldly by association." Then the Asian carp told all its relatives back home about how nice it was in Lake Michigan, and they all came over the next year, and the same thing happened the next year, and the year after that, and all the old whitefish thought that maybe they should leave the middle ring because "it was sure getting yellow around here." All the bass and walleye would meet at social clubs in the trunks of Model Ts and talk about how the middle ring needed more night patrolfish, and that the Asian Quarter was so filthy. Most of the whitefish migrated out to the burbs, Green Bay, and Lake Winnebago, and some even to Lake Huron, but all those fish would ever do was talk about how much nicer Lake Michigan was.

Then, even farther, way out in the center of the teardrop bay, there is something, all by itself. It has been there forever, and sleeps as diesel barges and tankers break overhead. The great thing sleeps for years, sometimes close to a century. It is an old thing; in the times of Columbus, when it roamed the oceans, it had been called a sea monster, and in the times before that it had swum the coasts of developing nations, and some had called it a god. The thing was neither; it had not created nor destroyed much of anything. It had simply been there longer than anything else. When man had grown large and powerful, the old thing grew curious and crept through the channels and inlets to where it is now, in the center of the lake. Every once in a great while it will wake and stand from the bottom, its chest and head emerging from the waters. No one has seen the old thing for quite some time, as it comes up at night, and its skin is as gray as the murk it sleeps in. The only thing that sailors talk about are its eyes: lights in the center of the lake, that rotate unnervingly slow, too high up, higher than any lighthouse ever seen. The thing will look at the land around it and see perfectly every aspect of man, every building, every home, from Pacific to Atlantic; it can spy it all with its yellow eyes that crackle with light from the inside. When it finishes surveying it will take one suck of air, which shifts the direction of the clouds, before slipping back down to its resting place at the bottom, where even it won't know when it will wake again.

Friends for Sale

Mason Todd Johnson

WHEN WE SHOWED UP AT DANNY'S HOUSE, WE WERE SURPRISED BY THE FOR SALE sign firmly planted into his overgrown front lawn. Both of us silently stared at it, not really sayin' a goddamn thing. I interrupted the thought going through our heads, both of our heads, I know it, the thought that beat like a snare—*this is a mistake, this is a mistake, this is a mistake*—and asked, "Are you moving?"

"No."

Danny didn't look too confident with his answer. He just kept staring at the red aluminum sign as it rocked back and forth with the cool pre-summer wind, his chubby face dropping, eyebrows and mouth and cheeks and all of it, as if it might all melt right off. We were nearing the end of eighth grade, had been friends for almost two whole grades at that point, had been some of the only friends we'd ever had, really. In school at least, the first and probably the last, or so we assumed. We needed each other.

We hadn't changed much since we had met. I was taller, still lanky, my hair still brown, wavy, and covering my eyes. I was supposed to wear glasses that would rest on my small nose, but I never did. I preferred to walk around in a blurry world. I worried less when I couldn't see the expressions on everybody's faces; I cared less about the stares I might be getting. I was less paranoid without glasses. Danny was still fat, but he had grown a little taller, was less round, nearing chubby. But he was still fat. His head was shaved now, no more bangs above his round cheeks. His eyes were slits, seemingly forced together by his face's roundness, and a line of freckles traveled from the left side of his face, over his nose, to the right.

We waited for his mom to come home, and then Danny had a talk with her in their small, spotless kitchen as I sat downstairs in their carpeted basement, holding a Nintendo controller but trying desperately to hear their mumbled conversation as their voices traveled down the narrow, spiraling staircase like a slow-moving freight train of words. I couldn't make out shit. Danny and his mom were one and the same, two shy people who just talked too damn quiet. She was a big, bulky woman who would have been a good female wrestler, but she still talked so quiet, just like her son. As far as I could figure they rarely talked, living in the house alone together, avoiding each other like strange roommates, hugging the white hallway walls as they passed each other, afraid they might touch.

The conversation was over. Danny's steps hit the stairs and then he appeared moments later, walking past me and sitting down on the floor, grabbing a game controller.

"Danny," I said in mock salutation, trying to sound like nothing was wrong.

"Nathan," he returned with a nod, as his eyes were fixed on the TV.

"Are you moving?" I asked.

"Yeah," he said, expressionless, his voice monotone.

"Where?"

"Arizona," he said.

"Oh."

And that was kinda that. It wasn't in Danny's nature to put up a fight. Not directly. He couldn't talk to his mother, not about anything; he couldn't really talk to anyone except for me, but he didn't even have to because somehow I usually just understood. He didn't have to say he didn't want to move. I knew. I could feel it.

He did tell me though, walking home with me later that night, which wasn't usual, but I don't think he could stand to sit at home alone with what was going around in his head. And as we walked through the concrete pathway of the new plastic park, the sky a dark blue, just barely night, he let it out with just a couple words.

"It's not fair," he said. "I don't want to move."

And I understood. There was a lot more to it than that. What wasn't fair was the fact that he hated it here. He hated everyone. He hated his mom and his drunk dad and the kids at school and the teachers, and he had always hated them. He hated the goddamn Chicago humidity in the summers and the Chicago winters that didn't fucking end till April. He had hated all of it for his entire life, but now there was me. Now he had finally made one friend, found one person he did like, and it was over. It was going to fall apart. We both knew he was going to go from having one friend to having no friends again and that was the worst thing we could think of. And like I said before, he couldn't talk to his mom about it. It wasn't in his nature. He had to fight back in his own way.

The next day after school we ended up back at Danny's white, two-story house, as usual. We stood on the sidewalk staring at the aberration we knew as the For Sale sign as if we expected it to be gone, magically, mysteriously. Danny slipped his bag from his shoulders, letting it slide down onto the concrete, and then walked to the far end of his yard opposite the white aluminum post that held the red sign. Then Danny did more physical activity than I had ever seen him commit. With a running start, his round body lumbering up and down with each step, Danny charged the post, jumped into the air, turned sideways with the agility a fat kid shouldn't possess, and he kicked the post with both of his feet at the same time. The thing stood strong as Danny's body plummeted to the grass. Danny landed on his side hard, his face turning red immediately, the air escaping his lungs for all it was worth. He stared up at the sky, gasping at first, then slowly regaining his breath and just lying there. I stood on the sidewalk, nervously playing with the straps of my bookbag. He eventually got up as if nothing had happened, and we went inside and ate some Pizza Bagels.

The next day we got to Danny's house after school and found ourselves staring open-mouthed at the sign yet again. And yet again he let his bag slip to the ground and kicked the For Sale sign with all his might.

Nothing.

We went on like that for weeks. You wouldn't imagine a For Sale sign could take such a beating, day after day, but clearly the people who build For Sale signs anticipated this. There may have been angry pre-teens all over the nation kicking the damn things, who knows, but those fuckers were strong.

Eventually, after the Chicago weather became humid, hot water hanging in the air, and school had ended, we found ourselves exhausted and standing in front of the For Sale sign.

"I don't think this is doing anything," I said, leaning forward, hands on my knees and panting.

Danny, similarly bent over, looked up and met my eyes with his. He didn't need to say anything; everything that needed to be said was in his eyes, and it was agreed: *we needed to find a new way to deal with this, to deal with the move.*

So we pretended like he wasn't moving. We didn't talk about this, it just happened. We went back to being us, and we didn't need to agree on what we were doing or thinking; we just did, and it worked out.

Over the coming weeks, Danny's house slowly filled with boxes stacked up everywhere in crooked towers, his front room resembling a skewed city of leaning skyscrapers. His room was still perfectly fine to sleep in, but in an attempt to ignore the whole process of moving, he had his mom drag their pop-up trailer out of the garage and into the driveway, which was where we'd sleep almost every night. Not being in school anymore, we had no reason to not be together all the time, and my parents, well, I gotta give them credit 'cause I guess they understood. I think Danny didn't want to sleep in his room because he didn't want to sleep in the house, and he didn't want to sleep in the house because his mom was there, constantly reminding him with her packing that they were moving, and he was so angry at her, angry at himself, because he couldn't say *I don't want to fucking move.*

Man, he could be a real pussy.

Our nights were pretty boring; we didn't do shit. The pop-up trailer, it's not big. It starts off as a small rectangle you're supposed to drag behind your car. When you want to go in you wind up the roof, basically a large, green canvas that extends on either side. Even at fourteen I had to bow my head as I stood inside the thing, but I was pretty tall for a fourteen-year-old. Danny and I would lie on one of the beds as we watched movies on a little, gray television and play board games: *Star Wars*-themed Monopoly and Risk, which isn't fun with two people. The bed was this itchy material, somehow itchy even when covered with a sheet, that felt like thin carpeting on a floor instead of a bed. We rarely did anything with ourselves that included activity. On occasion we'd hear a car horn honking and would walk outside to see my dad in his black SUV, his chubby, goofy face smiling at us. My dad was like me once, thin and lanky with shaggy brown hair, but then he got fat. A huge stomach. Gigantic. But his arms and legs stayed thin, so he was an odd-shaped guy, like an egg with paperclips for appendages.

And his hair, it had started to turn gray early on, so it was just messy patches of gray and brown. We'd walk up to his car and he'd have two 7-Eleven Slurpees for us, both grape flavored; he knew we loved Slurpees. He'd hand 'em over then speed off real fast after saying, "See you girls later," trying to seem cool. It's not that he wanted to make fun of us; he just thought that's what teenagers did with each other, and he wanted, more than anything, to seem like a friend those months before Danny moved. So most nights that's what we'd do; we'd lie on an uncomfortable bed in a cramped trailer watching movies and drinking Slurpees.

And then everything changed. Danny wasn't content to just sit around in a camper anymore; he wanted to do *something*. Anything. So we raided his mom's medicine cabinet. Those who wondered how a woman could be so catatonic would find their answers there. Her cabinet was filled with orange bottles that were labeled with confusing words, and even though we had no idea what any of this was, we knew that no one person could possibly be prescribed all of this. Medications named clonazepam and lorazepam and hydrocodone and paracetamol and sertraline and duloxitine and many other names that had similar endings. Danny's mom, it occurred to us, was some sort of prescription junky. I think it was this realization that made what came next seem acceptable.

Danny opened a few of the bottles and took two pills from each, shoving five pills into my hand, and keeping a handful for himself. His mouth open wide, he threw the pills into the back of his throat, tilting his head back, swallowing each and every one. Leaning down and taking a drink of water from the faucet, I followed suit, having to force the pills into my belly as they tried to stick to my throat. Taking random pills would not have typically been something we did, but we were desperate for change we could *control*. Danny wanted to control the world around him as it hurricaned out of his grasp, and the only way to do that was to do something completely retarded.

We could do retarded. I followed Danny outside, right past the trailer and right to my house as the summer sun set and the streets started to cool in the night. We didn't feel any different as we walked through the gate of my backyard, behind the yellow, three-story house and down the stairs to the back door of the basement, which was rarely locked. Before walking through it I looked at Danny, knowing the pills hadn't done anything to me yet, wondering if they had started to hit him, and nervous about the fact that we were seemingly sneaking into my home. A home we could just walk through the front door of. The majority of the time, Danny and I were on the same level, knowing exactly what the other was thinking, but at this moment I had no idea. Looking at him nervously, cautiously, I asked, "What are we doing?"

"Doesn't your mom keep the beer in the basement?" he asked awkwardly, as if he was in a conversation with someone else. A conversation which made sense.

"Yes."

And that was that. He turned the knob on the door, pushed it open, and we stepped inside. We were immediately hit with the smell of cat shit and laundry detergent as we walked into the laundry room, which was, by the way, where the kitty litter box was. We walked past it, overflowing with little, fun-size candy-bar-like kitty shit, and made our way towards the fridge, stepping past the washer and dryer and over piles of dirty clothes on the way. The laundry room was always a disaster, a place where many shirts, usually your favorite, were lost forever.

We walked back to Danny's house with bottles of Miller Lite shoved down our pants, so many of them that we practically waddled, luckily seen by no one. Back in his pop-up, we drank the bottles of Miller Lite as fast as possible, cringing at the first sip of watered-down, crap beer.

Lying back on that uncomfortable bed, our heads resting at a painful angle against the tarp-like wall of the pop-up and bad beer refusing to settle in our stomachs, the assortment of pills we took started to come to life. I started to feel . . . stoic. Like a hero. I felt like I should stand tall, my chest out. I felt like I should put my foot up on things and pose. That I should turn my neck slowly and scan crowds with a stern face, telling people with my eyes that I was somethin', really somethin', and I was watching them. I didn't do any of that. I just lay there, but I felt like doing that. I felt like I was doing that.

Danny just laughed a lot. Short bursts out of nowhere, like a sprinkler suddenly starting then stopping.

We lay back on complete opposite ends of the bed, our heads still on that tarp behind us, trying to watch *The Simpsons*, but it was blurry with snow because the rabbit-ear antennas just plain sucked. It didn't really matter, though. We had a new game. Danny would laugh that laugh, randomly, going from straight faced to laughing instantly, "Hehehehehehehehe," and then he'd stop almost as soon as he started.

The moment he started, I'd just reach over with my right hand and start pawing at him in an attempt to shut him up. With an open hand, I'd come down and almost slap his shoulder, but then I'd slide my hand down the length of his arm, and I'd do this once, twice, three times, until he stopped.

"Heehehehehehehe," he'd laugh, then BAM, my hand would be out, pawing, sliding down his arm.

And, for some reason, each time we'd do this, we'd inch closer to each other. Just a little bit at time, scooting our butts slowly along that camper bed. Every time I inched closer, the beer and the pills made it seem like I was moving in slow motion, but the rest of the world was moving at super speeds. It was like it was going as I was coming, or I was coming as it was going, but nothing matched up, not me or anything else, and before I knew it we were touching, me and Danny; we were touching, sitting so close our shoulders were practically one, my skinny arms digging into his chubby body.

"Hehehehehehehehe," he giggled.

He was so close; pawing at his arm to shut him up just wouldn't work. I found myself turning towards him and pawing at his head, slapping the top of his head, his short hair feeling scratchy as I slid my hand down his forehead and nose and mouth.

I did this three times, with a short burst of laughing lasting a matter of seconds before he started to laugh without stopping. He just kept going, "Hehehehe," his laughter bouncing its way throughout the camper, sounding as if it were coming from outside, from the trees and the suburban homes around the camper, as if the neighborhood was surrounding us, all laughing in unison, and I just kept slapping my hand down on his head, sliding it down his face, over and over and over, until finally I just kept my hand near his mouth, trying to cover his mouth up with my palm. By this time I was sitting on the bed on my knees, facing him, as he lay back. And I just kept my hand there, twisting it on his laughing mouth, staring at his chubby face as he laughed so hard his eyes were squeezed shut. Spittle formed on my hand and it was warm and it was wet and I wanted it to be there forever, this warm, wet feeling.

He stopped laughing. He was too busy licking my hand. His tongue was out, circling my palm, his eyes still closed, relaxed; he looked like he could be sleeping. Soon he was kissing my hand, smacking sounds replacing the laughing from before. He held my hand in his right hand. He turned my hand as he kissed it; he turned his own head. Puckering and kissing, puckering and kissing. He just kept kissing my hand.

Then he wasn't kissing my hand. My hand was gone and the gap that was between us, the foot or two, was closed by our lips, and then *we* were kissing. No longer were his lips on my hand, but his lips were on my lips. My eyes were open, wide, watching his closed eyes as our heads turned and then separated, sour tastes of our mouths combining into one. We clumsily moved our heads fervently, having never really learned how to kiss; this was the first time either of us had ever kissed anyone. And then my eyes were closed too, and we just kept kissing, violently almost, so inexperienced that it hurt as our lips twisted, as our heads moved away slightly, just to crack back into each other, just to smack our teeth together with a *clank* sound.

I don't know how long we kissed. I don't know when we stopped. I don't know when we fell asleep. All I know is that we woke up the next morning, the television still on, snow on the screen, and buzzing and screeching. We were entangled together, our arms and legs together like twisty-ties, fully dressed. We both woke up at the same time and sat up, looking at each other confused. I reached up and felt my face to find that I had a fat lip, swollen a little, it hurt. Danny's lips were both red, just a little, as he stared at me, confused.

I walked home feeling absolutely nothing, not dread about my best friend leaving, not dread of the prospect of having no friends at school again. Nothing. I think Danny probably felt the same way.

We didn't see each other for two weeks. We mutually avoided each other, too busy feeling nothing to attempt to contact one another. My parents assumed that Danny had just moved; they were surprised they didn't get to say good-bye, but not too surprised because, after all, it was Danny and he was a quiet motherfucker.

My mom, seeing me slumped on the couch and watching daytime cartoons, would just kind of half smile and say, "Oh, baby," as she came and sat next to me, a strong hand on my knee.

Her short, chubby body would just sort of sit there, emanating mom energy, until I shook her hand off with one movement of my leg and got up, muttering, "Jeez," and hiding in my room with my *Robotech* books.

And then my mom ran into Danny's mom at the 7-Eleven near our house. I don't know what they said to each other, but she came home *pissed off*.

She stormed through the front door as I lay on the couch watching *Total Request Live* on MTV. Raising my head, I saw her pass the threshold of the doorway and immediately knew by her red, cringing face that I was in trouble.

"What," she asked, "the hell . . . are you doing?"

I didn't get a chance to answer. Her hands exploded in a fury of angry motions as she stood in front of the stairs, "Why are you not with your best friend who is," and at this point her voice became eardrum-shatteringly loud, "MOVING TOMORROW?"

I looked everywhere but at her. I looked at our carpeted floor, covered in cat and dog toys, at the cluttered coffee table covered in magazines and old pop cans. I looked at the 32-inch TV in front of me, at the white walls and the white ceiling, but not looking at her didn't make her disappear.

"Well?" she demanded.

Still not looking at her I said, quietly, "There's nothing to do . . ."

"Get out!" she yelled.

I looked up at her, confused, and saw that she was pointing out the open, wooden front door.

"Get out!" she repeated, louder, and I knew I had no choice.

I walked to Danny's, turning a five minute walk into a fifteen-minute death march, feeling a weight on my shoulders that had never been there before, as if the sky was collapsing on top of me. I don't know what I was afraid of, but I was afraid.

When I got to Danny's, I saw that the trailer was gone from the driveway. I rang the doorbell and Danny answered, "Oh," he said, "hey."

"Hey."

"What's up?" he asked, avoiding eye contact.

"Want to hang out?" I asked, my hands in my jean pockets, his screen door between us.

"Sure," he said, looking as if he had gotten skinnier the past two weeks, but still, as always, chubby.

We stood there, silently, not saying anything for a solid minute, before he cut the silence, "We can't really hang out here. Everything's packed up and my mom sold the trailer."

"Oh," I said. "Well I guess we can just . . . " I paused for a minute, trying to decide where we could go, having no desire to see my mom at the moment. "I guess we can walk around."

He put on his shoes and came out of his house and we walked down his stairs and across his lawn, both of us silent, looking down, not at each other. As we passed the post that previously, but no longer, held a For Sale sign, I kicked it. Not hard, just a little, my foot bouncing off of it painlessly. It hit the sidewalk. Danny had a small smile on his face. He looked back at me, and it didn't disappear and, well, I knew things were OK. For that moment at least. The sky, it wasn't on my shoulders, it was back where it belonged.

1861, from
"Laying Lincoln Down"

Kurt Kennedy

HARRY LEANED THE BARREL OF HIS RIFLE AGAINST THE BRICK AND BANGED ON THE door to his mother's and Charles Brown's house, loud enough so they could hear it inside but not so loud as to alert the neighbors at this time of night, past the curfew. He knocked a few more times to express his urgency, not wanting to be spotted by one of the patrols. In the amount of time it would take someone to lumber out of bed, make it down the L-shaped staircase and across the parlor to the front door, a man's voice came from the other side of the door.

"Who's that there?" It was a bad idea to open your door without checking the caller after midnight during wartime.

"It's Harry, Charles. Let me in now, please."

Metal sliding and chains jingling and then the door opened.

"Harry. What the hill?" Charles's Southern accent—"hill" for "hell"—came out stronger when he was tired, or had been drinking. "Is eve'thing a'right? 'S the middle of the night."

"No. No." Harry stepped inside after Charles took one small step back from the gap of the door. Charles shut the door and they stood by it in the dark. "It's not all right."

"Well, whatev'r it is, I don't think you should trouble your mother about it now."

"No. I've come to talk to you, Charles . . . I've come to ask your help."

Charles cocked an eyebrow. "With . . . what?"

Harry had always gone out of his way to turn down any assistance from his stepfather. It had something to do with not liking to think of Charles as his stepfather—he was twenty-one years old when his mother married him, after all. It had something to do with the breadwinner status and subsequent pride he'd earned in his nearly ten years supporting his mother and two sisters after his father's death. But mostly, it was because their philosophies and sympathies didn't match up, and so they did what men in such predicaments who are required to be in contact do: they went about their business and exchanged only the basic pleasantries when it was required that they spend time together.

"Now, Charles," Harry began. "The fact that I'm here at the time of night I am should tell you this is urgent and important."

"Uh-huh." Charles was skeptical.

"And you and I have disagreed on some things these last few years but, I think, reached an understanding with each other."

Charles was very skeptical now.

"What I mean is that I think we have—I have—come to accept that, and respect your sympathies. And I wouldn't ask what I'm going to ask without having thought a lot about it . . . and," he slumped his shoulders in resignation, "having nobody else to go to."

Charles understood now. "Your last choace, eh?"

"Charles, a man—a young man—in my regiment died today, and I need you to embalm him so he can be sent home."

Harry watched Charles think for several, long moments. His eyes were beginning to adjust to the pale light coming in the window to the side of the door. Charles stroked his moustache and, as he brought his hand down, Harry thought it looked as if he was grinning.

"Well, Harry." He said 'Harry' almost like 'Hurry' and real slow-like. "My answer is no, . . . and I think you know why."

"Damn it, Charles." Harry began to yell but caught himself and quieted instantaneously, remembering that he had prepared himself for this and that his mother was upstairs. Charles raised his hands to shush him, squinting his face and causing waves in his bald forehead, pale orange from the street-light coming in.

"Charles," said the voice of Catherine Brown from upstairs. It was Harry's mother, who was Charles's second wife as he was her second husband. "Who's down there?" She was apprehensive at even asking the question, possibly giving her presence away to a thief or a vandalizing North or South supporter—both could take issue with their household—but she had heard Charles called by name and had heard no commotion.

Charles ran to the base of the stairs. "It's fine, dear. It's your son." A minute or two previous, he would have said "fine" like "fein" but he was coming out of his drowsiness.

"Harry?" she called down, almost frantic. "What's wrong?"

He hurried to the base of the stairs. "It's fine, Mother. I've come to talk to Charles."

No reply came back, and the ceiling above the men creaked and continued to creak.

"Well, you gone on and done it," Charles said to Harry, then put his arms up and began to walk away, past Harry, toward the dining room, knowing that his wife was awakened and on her way downstairs. "Hell, 's just as well. She'd prolly be just as mad if she knew you came and I hadn't waked her."

"Charles, please." Harry followed him briefly into the hallway that led back to the kitchen, and then to the right, through the wide entryway with embossed wood trim—only barely visible in the darkness of the hour—that led into the dining room. "This man . . . hell, not a man, a boy . . . nineteen years old . . . he's dead. He needs to make it home properly."

Charles said nothing, just pulled out one of the dining table chairs and sat down. The moonlight and streetlights through the large window in the room at the back of the house created more light than in the parlor. The stairs creaked.

"Charles, please understand." Harry raised his voice and anger came through in his pleading. "The army has made no provisions to embalm soldiers. They won't return an unembalmed man home." Charles quickly smirked and laughed, like it made perfect sense that the Yankee army would not even take the time to think about how to care for their soldiers, but he still said nothing. "This boy's family lives in northwestern Pennsylvania, Charles. Even if they would send him, there's no chance of him making it without the embalming."

"Harry, you're fine?" his mother asked from behind him, standing in the entryway.

He turned. "Yes, Mother," he said calmly, consciously toning down his passion, "I'm fine. I came to speak to Charles." He acted as if he was a boy and had just been caught in some disapproved-of act.

"Yes, I heard you say something about someone needing to be embalmed. And?" She tightened the belt of her robe. She wanted to embrace him, but the sight of him in his uniform also made her feel she must be disapproving, so she stayed in the entryway, her hair let down from its usual bun. It was dark brown, graying at the scalp, but this could not be seen in the dimness.

"And . . . what, Mother?"

"What is this about?" She looked up from her waist and let go of the belt. "Who has passed?"

Harry stood up fully and turned to face his mother directly. "A young man in my regiment. David Schull. Pneumonia. He needs to be embalmed in order to be sent home."

She glanced down, and to the side, and breathed out. Then she crossed her arms, craned her head back up, tilted it to the right, and peered around Harry. "And Charles, you won't perform it, I gather?"

"I will not," he said calmly and confidently from his seat. "It's unfort'-nate but not my fault the Yankee army won't take care their own."

"Charles," Harry said, resigned, as he turned back toward the table and grabbed the back of a chair. "I'm begging you. This is me begging you."

"Goddamn it." Charles pounded his fist on the table. He stood up, shooting the chair out behind him, and began leaving the room, not pushing the chair back in. "No. That's final."

"Damn you, Charles." Harry took a step toward him.

"Charles." Catherine raised her voice when she said her husband's name; both he and her son stopped their motions. "If my son—"

"No, dear, please," he interrupted.

"IF MY SON," she shot back, "needed that done for him, God forbid, you certainly would not leave him be, would you Charles?"

"Of course not, Catherine." The Georgia drawl was completely gone from his voice.

"That boy deserves to go home to his family. I want you to help my son."

Charles fidgeted where he stood and began to speak several times, but never even got his mouth opened. Catherine stared at him.

"All right. I'll help him. But I will *not*, not now, not ever, lay my hands on a Yankee soldier. Harry, I'll give you the supplies and tell you what to do.

I mean," Charles smirked as he said this and slipped back into his accent, "le's hope you didn't throw out eve'thing you learned when you threw away your future." Harry's bitter stare after this comment showed his irritation, but he made no move or said anything since he was, essentially, getting what he wanted.

Charles's face became stern again. "But that's ma offer. That's the best I'll give y'all on this." He began walking out of the dining room again. Catherine and Harry said nothing.

Charles passed by his wife in the entryway and, without stopping or turning his head, said, "Well you gonna come with me so I can show you how to embalm this boy or not?" The wood creaked under his feet as he continued into the living room.

Catherine looked at Harry and nodded her head yes.

Harry stepped past her and followed Charles.

An hour later, with a black leather bag of embalming supplies under his right arm and his rifle in his left hand, Harry came out of the front door of his mother's and Charles's house and cautiously peeked out into G Street, to his left and down the lantern-lit, dirt street walled by side-by-side, two-to-three-story brick homes, and then to his right, to the T intersection of twelfth and G. He saw no one.

"Good-bye, Mother." He turned around and kissed her on the cheek. She grabbed the back of his neck, pulled him closer, and kissed his cheek at the same time. The brim of his infantryman hat tapped her forehead and knocked the hat up and to the side on his head. They smiled at this but didn't laugh. He leaned his rifle against his torso for a moment and readjusted the hat. "Thank you for convincing Charles."

"Hush. Go take care of the boy. But, Harry . . . think about it. You're sneaking around in the middle of the night to see that someone goes home properly." She looked him in the eye. "You're meant for something other than soldiering."

He said nothing. He smiled quickly and turned. He stepped out onto the small concrete porch and down the two steps into the street. Catherine latched the door behind him. He crossed the street and, when he reached the T intersection, backed against the wall. He stood there for a moment and listened for the sound of feet or hooves on twelfth. Nothing. He peered around the corner. Nothing. Everything was clear. He turned around the corner of the brick home he was leaning against and onto twelfth. He walked on the dirt road and not the cobbled sidewalk, to muffle the steps of his army boots. He felt the bag under his arm and went over the steps again in his head: thigh incision, femoral artery, incision in femoral artery, insert tube, pump in zinc chloride, pump for at least one minute after solution is emptied, suture.

"Halt right where you are!" a voice boomed at him from behind just as he was about to turn down F. "Drop your rifle to the ground immediately."

Harry did so. The wood and the metal slapped against the dry dirt.

"Turn around."

Harry extended his open palms and forearms to his sides and turned around. It was a fellow soldier—too far away to see any indications of rank on his uniform—on horseback, pointing his rifle at him. The soldier noticed the something under Harry's arm.

"Drop what's under your arm."

"I can't do that, sir." Harry was pretty sure an officer wouldn't be patrolling on the graveyard shift but figured the situation garnered a sir.

"I said drop it, soldier."

"Look, friend, there's a glass container in this bag that cannot break. I can *set* it down for you if you'll let me."

The soldier thought for a few moments behind his horse and his gun. "Do it."

Harry did it, slowly, then stood back up slowly, putting his arms up above his head now that he didn't have to clasp the bag. The soldier nudged his horse's belly with his boot and the pair began to move forward. The soldier did not take his rifle off his target.

"What's your business out here this time of night, soldier?"

"Look, I'm with you. I'm in the Union Army."

"Then you should be able to spout right off what your business is."

"I was at my family home. Now I'm returning to camp."

"Who you with?"

"Pennsylvania volunteers. Twentieth regiment. F Company."

"Where y'all stationed at?"

"At the Executive Mansion—" As Harry answered, he turned back and to his right, in the direction of the Executive Mansion.

"Whoa. Whoa. Don't you move!" The horse jittered and snorted, sensing the nervousness of its rider. Harry straightened up immediately.

"I just need to make it back to camp to help a friend. Another soldier."

"If you got business outside your camp, then you got a pass from your commander. Let's see it."

Harry stood there. "Look, I don't have that. A friend died in camp today. In this bag are the supplies I need to embalm him so he can be sent home. I don't have a pass from the army for my errand because they don't know I'm on it."

"So, maybe you're not a spy. Maybe you're a deserter. I'm supposed to shoot those, too."

"Friend. The army will not embalm this man. They will not ship him home if he is not embalmed. They won't do it for any of us, unless we take care of it ourselves. They expect you to arrange your own death. If I don't embalm this soldier, he doesn't go home to his family. He goes in the ground somewhere around here, hundreds of miles from his home, maybe in a box, maybe not. Perhaps the army is refusing us coffins as well. I don't know."

The soldier raised his head up and pointed his rifle downward a couple of inches, but didn't aim it away. Harry lowered his arms a couple of inches.

"Let me see your identification."

Harry slowly brought his arms down, reached into the breast pocket of his navy blue coat, pulled the papers out, and held them up. The patroller brought his rifle to his side, leaned down from his horse, and grabbed them. He studied them for a few moments. Then he lowered them and eyed Harry up and down.

"So, we really can't go home unless we make arrangements before the fact?"

"That's right." Harry stood with his arms at his side. "Or the family."

"Who wants to put that thought on them?"

"Can't say. There are some who would."

The patroller handed Harry's papers back to him, then extended his hand to him. "Come on. I'll take you back to your camp."

Harry put his papers back in his coat, picked up his rifle and bag, placed them in the same arm, grabbed the man's hand, and mounted the horse. That started the horse moving.

"Get you back there so you can take care of your man," the soldier said.

Keene held up a lantern and stood over Harry, who bent over the body of David Schull, ready to make an incision in the boy's leg. While Harry had been procuring the supplies, Keene had washed the body, laid it out on the cot in the middle of the operating tent, and draped the groin, so when Harry got back all he had to do was slowly walk up to the tent, like some kind of Indian medicine man or priest bringing the sacrificing tools to a sacred yet macabre ceremony. Harry brought the scalpel to the skin on the inside of Schull's left thigh. He paused and inhaled deeply.

"It's all right, son. Just use a steady hand," Keene said reassuringly.

"I know how to make an incision, thank you, Doctor," Harry said, annoyed. He got focused again and brought the incisor back to Schull's leg. "Could you lower the lantern some, Doctor?" He pierced the skin in the middle of the boy's inner thigh and slowly, finely, and with his eyes just inches away, began to finesse the scalpel across, in the direction of the knee. It felt different from cutting into the one hog he had dissected at Penn. This was softer—the knife glided easier. When the cut was an inch and a half in length, Harry realized that it was twice as long as it needed to be. He stopped, then panicked. His shoulder twitched. He pulled the incisor out and set it on the ground, calmly, to show Keene that he had the procedure under control. They peered at each other. Harry hoped the doctor didn't notice his concern. His face seemed questioning—"Why are you looking at me and not tending to the job?"—but gave no indication that he noticed or was concerned about the length of the incision.

Harry placed his forefinger and thumb into the incision and began to probe for the large femoral artery. He felt an assortment of wet strings— veins and nerves. As he shuffled them through his two fingers to determine which was the largest, blood began to ooze out of the cut. It ran down the leg and began to soak the canvas of the cot, forming a stain that slowly spread out from itself.

"The femoral's the biggest," Keene said. "The rest's just veins and nerves."

"Yes, Doctor. I know the femoral artery."

"Then you must grab hold of it."

Harry strained, like reaching for something under a sofa and just needing to stretch a nudge farther.

"There," he was relieved. "I've got it." He kept hold of it but basked in his small accomplishment for several moments, and focused on the speed with which the next step needed to be conducted. Another incision had to be made in the artery itself, and the tube for pumping in the embalming solution needed to be inserted quickly to prevent too much blood from escaping. Too much already was causing drops of blood from the saturated cot to begin dripping onto the dirt on the ground underneath it. He picked the incisor up again with his free hand and brought it close to the leg. "Doctor, as soon as I make this cut, I'm going to need the rubber tube.

Please have that ready to hand to me."

The doctor picked up the tube from the laid-out supplies on the ground next to the supply bag.

"Bring the lantern back down, please." Harry pulled on the artery gently and popped it out of the slit in the skin, so it was visible. When he did this, a quick wave of blood came out of the cut, adding to the already-established flow. Dripping from the cot, it pooled up between Schull's legs.

"Damn it," Harry said. "There's too much blood coming out. The body's not supposed to be bled for this process."

"It's too late," Keene said. "He's losing too much now. Must've nicked him when you twitched. You're going to have to let him bleed out."

"What if the solution doesn't take?"

"Harry, you've got no choice. Now, here." Keene took his lantern away for a moment, rummaged in a corner of the tent, and turned around with a shallow tin pan. He placed it under the cot and the blood drops immediately began pinging into it. He grabbed the incisor from Harry, reached under the cot, and slit it between the legs. The pool of blood gushed through and slapped into the pan, and continued a steady flow.

They sat on the ground with their legs crossed, on both sides of Schull. The bleeding man, for the most part, blocked their view of each other, so they talked through and around him.

"How do you know how to do this, Doctor?"

"I was the undertaker in my town," he said, "just till a couple months ago. Had been for years. When the war broke out, I figured it was time for me to get on the right side of the dying. Try to help people live." He reached up and shook Schull's thigh, and more blood poured from the incision.

"Hmph." Harry laughed to himself.

"What is it there?"

"You remind me of a teacher of mine." He stared at the pool of blood in the pan as he said this.

"I tell you I worry, Harry." He paused. "Everyone is itching for this thing to start. But when it starts, that's it. There's no going back. There'll be a lot of times when men can live, or they can die. And, I'm afraid I won't be able to help them."

"You're a good doctor, Mr. Keene. You're a good man. You'll help them. You will." Harry caught himself. "You'll help . . . us." The reality of his position struck him right then much more profoundly than it had before: his uniform, this way of life, that he might die, or have to kill. That scared him more than dying himself—being on the wrong side of the dying, the certain, inevitable dying. Keene continued saying things, but Harry didn't listen to the words.

"He's ready," Keene said as he peered his head over Schull's body.

"What?" Harry saw his head but hadn't been listening.

"He's bled out. You can put in the fluid."

"Already?"

"Don't take too awful long."

Harry got to his knees and waddled a few paces to the side of the cot. Keene held up the lantern in one hand and the incisor in the other. Harry took it from him. Keene bent down and came up with the rubber tube.

"Are you ready, Doctor?"

Keene nodded.

Harry leaned in to look at the incision he had made a dozen minutes ago in his friend's leg. He reached in and found the femoral artery with more ease than before. He pulled it out to be able to see it. A bit of blood covered it from the soaking before, but there was nothing left to run out. He brought the incisor and, very slowly, with his fingertips nearly gripping the blade— fingers ignoring the shaft of the incisor—he carefully cut a half-inch down the artery. A few pin point-sized drops of blood popped out of the cut. He grabbed the thin tube from Keene. He brought the end next to the vein—it was twice the diameter. He held it perpendicular to the femoral, slipped it in the slit, and began to move it up, toward the groin.

"No, no," Keene said. "Put it in facing down, toward the feet."

"But won't—"

"Just do it."

Harry did. He held the rubber tube perpendicular to the artery and slipped it downward. The artery tore, extending the incision by an inch and popping the tube out. He looked at Keene.

"Now do it through the upper part," the doctor said.

He slid it through the upper tip of the incision. It stretched out the artery from the inside, like a snake that had just swallowed something, but this time he massaged it through from the outside, with his other hand. An inch and a half of the tube made it in securely. Harry grabbed the bottle of solution from the ground and attached it to the opposite end of the tube. He pumped the rubber bulb on the spout and the zinc chloride began moving through the body of David Schull.

Reign Dance

D. Jeffers

I

THE LITTLE COUNTRY ROAD WAS LINED WITH NEARLY IDENTICAL HOUSES, EACH one positioned about ninety feet from the next, reaching down one side, around the cul-de-sac, and up the opposite side. Fresh green lawns sat squarely in front of each house, and spacious backyards without fences merged, leaving only clotheslines to distinguish the properties. The maple trees and sprouts of wild shrubbery littered between homes provided little shade as Jimmy raised one straight leg, then the other, carefully lifting his feet from the ground to the sky, kicking up plumes of dust on the dirt road in front of his house. His hands were tucked so far in his pockets that his jeans had begun to lower and his belt tightened over his rear end. His head hung low while he watched dispersing dust particles vanish and reappear again, letting the summer sun tan the back of his neck.

The air was heavy with moisture that day, making it hard to breathe and signaling an oncoming storm. Sweat had collected under Jimmy's hairless armpits and the small circular stains on his red-striped shirt were enlarging. Jimmy continued to shift dirt around on the road with his feet, humming before finally singing to himself under his breath, "Speed of lightning, roar of thunder. Fighting all who rob or plunder. Underdog. Underdog!"

The sun glinted off the front windows of his home in the heart of the cul-de-sac, and shone down relentlessly on rooftops. Inside, Jimmy's mother pulled back solid lavender curtains and peeked out of the living-room window, checking on Jimmy and impatiently waiting for her husband to return home. She walked back into her modest little kitchen, used her hand to slide potato peels off the counter into a bag, and tossed the bag into the garbage can beneath her without looking. She wiped her hands on her flowery pink apron while letting out a sigh of frustration, thinking about the cold hamburgers and French fries they would be eating for lunch.

The stillness of the air outside was broken by a rattling up the road. Jimmy snapped his concentration and looked for the approaching sound. He could see his father's new, brazen red pickup truck coming down the road with its wheels kicking up dust behind it. It looked like a bullet when it sped past houses, its hood glistening in the sun. His dad honked at Jimmy as he pulled into the driveway with ease, showing off the smoothness of the steering and his driving skill. He opened the door in one quick motion, slid out smoothly, and, without turning off the engine or shutting the door behind him, walked around the tail end of the truck to see Jimmy running toward him.

"Paw!" Jimmy was running as fast as his feet could carry him into his father's open arms. His father stooped and grimaced as he rested on a knee; small, jagged pebbles pierced and stained his slacks. He stuck his hand out over Jimmy as he approached and placed it on top of his head, stopping Jimmy in his tracks as he panted and sweated profusely.

With a loving tap on the head, the father said, "I tole you 'bout playin' in the road. You're gonna git yourself kilt."

"Yes, Paw." Jimmy's nose was tickled by an extraordinarily sweet smell, like candy apples at the state fair or fresh honey.

"You know what God say to do to disobedient children, right?"

"Yes, Paw. Sorry, Paw." Jimmy's eyes shifted from his shoes to his father's gray felt hat, and back to his shoes, trying to hold back a sneeze.

The father let out a small, nervous chuckle and used Jimmy's head for support while regaining his balance. He tapped Jimmy on the head once again with the palm of his hand and said with bass resonating in his voice, "Git on in the house."

Jimmy ran to the house while his father closed the truck door and trailed behind. Jimmy halted in the doorway and let the smell of food drift up his nostrils from the kitchen. He hadn't noticed how hungry he was until then. His mother redirected her attention from the radio perched on the windowsill playing love songs, to her son posing in the doorway. With a blank, glassy stare, she used her head to motion toward the dining room.

"Food's on the table, sweetie."

Jimmy moved along quickly to the dining-room table to see two plates resting on it, one at his usual seat and the other at his mother's. As he pulled out his chair to take a seat he heard his father come into the house with heavy steps and a low-pitched grumble of greeting, followed by a bothersome silence. The mother and father looked at each other, studying each other as if they were strangers. The mother removed her apron and stepped past the father hastily without saying a word. The father could only remove his hat and move slowly into the dining room.

The father sat and watched his family eat lunch, looking first at Jimmy, and then at his wife, noticing that prayers had been skipped. He cleared his throat and grumbled half-heartedly to no one in particular, "The church sure keeps me busy." His reply was followed by a deafening silence. The only audible sound was Jimmy chewing away at his burger. He started up again, "And I sure am hungry."

His wife bit into a fry and looked her husband up and down with an icy glare, searching all over him, smelling the same sweet fragrance Jimmy sensed as it drifted to her side of the table. Jimmy paid no attention to his parents' uncomfortable exchange; he was in enough trouble with his father already. He concentrated on his burger. His mother broke the dead air.

"Why doesn't *she* cook for you?"

The father's eyes widened at the remark. He fumbled with his hat on his knee, searching on the floor for the words to say. He found them in the back of his mind and stammered, "Catherine, it ain't what you're thinkin'."

Catherine let a sly, thin smirk grow on her face, and her voice became misleadingly pleasant. "Jimmy, step out while me and your paw talk."

"Can I go back outside and play?"

Catherine nodded her head, shaking loose a blond strand of hair. His father interjected, keeping his eyes locked on his wife's. "Stay off that front road," he said, as Jimmy stood from his seat, hamburger in hand.

Jimmy strolled around the back of the house with his burger in hand, stepping in the green, plush backyard and leaving visible footprints in the carpet-like grass. He adventured, stepping out of the shade provided by the house and into the sweltering daylight, daring to march under the clothesline with socks and underwear hanging loosely from it. He used one hand to hold the burger while he ate and walked, the other casually swatted at mosquitoes from time to time. He noticed an unusual protrusion in the earth of the backyard, poking between one of the poles of the clothesline and the sapling at the far reaches of the yard. He walked over to it, stood over the little hill examining it, taking note of the black ants parading in and out of the top of it. Jimmy gazed admiringly at the hill with amazed little eyes while the noon sun heated the spot on his head his father had jostled only moments earlier. He watched the ants, and a smile grew over his face.

Jimmy dropped to a knee and gave the little ants a piece of bread, and within no time, droves of ants spilled from the top of the hill and circled around, nibbling and stealing away small bites for themselves. All of the ants, maybe hundreds of them, worked as a single solitary unit, carrying food and building their own little Utopia.

The ants reminded him of Sunday sermons, where he would watch his father stand behind the lectern and rattle on about the selfish ways of people and how everyone took more than what was necessary. Jimmy burst into a hysterical, childish laughter, thinking that ants were much better people than most people. He dropped the rest of his burger and let a thought interrupt his laughter: who did the ants pray to at night? Jimmy lay on his stomach, resting on his elbows and placing his head in his hands, getting a better view of the hill.

"Don't worry, little fellas. I'll be your God."

Jimmy lay in the backyard until the sun had begun to set, watching the ants come out of the hill, crawl around and over the dissolving burger, and return back to the hill. It was fascinating. Jimmy's ears perked up when he heard his father's truck engine revving in the driveway and his mother's voice shouting, "James! Come in! Dinner's ready!" Jimmy gave one last longing look at the ant hill and the dwindling number of ants, and got up and ran around to the front of the house. In the distance down the road, Jimmy could see the bright red taillights of his father's truck. He stood paralyzed for a moment, watching the truck pull off before he walked into the house and took a seat at the dining room table with his mother.

"Hey, Maw. Where's Paw goin'?"

Jimmy noticed that his mother's eyes were wet, as if she had been crying. She responded with all of the resilience she could muster, "He had to take care uh some business. He'll be in tomorrow." Jimmy nodded, relieved that he had dodged his father's spanking for playing on the road. They ate their food silently while listening to their television set play *Gunsmoke* in the living room. Jimmy went to bed that night with visions of ants crawling. It would be the first night of many.

Jimmy awoke the next morning eager to get outside to check on his ants. He hurried, bathed, combed his hair with the ducktailed part right down the middle of his head that his mother liked, and powered through his breakfast, eating almost everything. Jimmy excused himself from the table with a piece of buttered toast in hand. Before he left for outside, Jimmy stopped in his tracks and turned to ask his mother, "When is Paw coming back?"

"He'll be in by dinnertime."

Jimmy looked at her face; the worry that usually creased her forehead had seemingly faded overnight, and with that, Jimmy was suddenly relieved. He stepped out the front door, glanced down the road and saw Phillip, the paperboy, on his usual route. Jimmy waved at him maniacally, biting into his toast, forgetting that he intended to feed it to the ants.

Phillip saw a pair of arms waving in the air from a distance and recognized that they belonged to Jimmy, the preacher's boy. Without breaking his stride, he made his way toward Jimmy, throwing newspapers side-armed onto people's front porches. By the time he got to Jimmy, he saw that he had half a piece of toast in his hand. He looked down at him, puzzled, raising an eyebrow, and asking, "What's your bag, man? You're going crazy over here."

Phillip was a tall, lean kid who, at only twelve years old, could have been mistaken for a small high school student. Jimmy looked up at him, craning his neck and said, "I found something neat yesterday." With that, he stood confidently, folding his arms across his chest with the toast peeking out from under his armpit.

"Oh yeah. What is it?" Phillip's voice cracked, going from a smooth baritone to a squeak.

"Ants. And I'm their God."

Phillip looked at the preacher's kid with utter bewilderment in his eyes. He adjusted the bag slung around his shoulder, pulled out a newspaper, and shoved it into Jimmy's crossed arms. Unenthused by Jimmy's discovery, he offered a half-hearted, "That's pretty far out," hiding the sarcasm in his voice.

"You wanna see it? It's just around back."

Phillip ran his fingers through his sandy brown hair once and said, "Nah. I have to cut out. Have a lotta work to do. Maybe next time."

Jimmy nodded his head understandingly. "Sure."

"Easy."

"Bye." Jimmy watched Phillip return to his route, throwing rolled up newspapers with black letters sprawled across the front. He turned to run to the backyard to check on the ants, dropping the daily newspaper on the front steps along the way. The morning air was a bit chilly for that time of year; the humidity still hung in the air from the previous day. When he turned the corner he could see the little hill, untouched and as remarkable as he remembered it. The grass was covered with droplets of dew, and it glistened and sprayed as Jimmy's feet moved through the cropped blades of grass. His running slowed to a march as he passed the clothesline and went straight to the hill, expecting to see ants making their way back and forth across the top like yesterday. He saw them, but didn't see the entirety of the burger; the buns had evaporated into thin air, leaving only moistened beef and partially moldy cheese on the lawn. The outcome painted a grin across his face as he dropped the remnants of the buttered toast where the burger once was.

Jimmy lay on the ground quickly without thinking about the dampness of the grass at all. He looked at the toast, which was getting wet lying in the grass, and the ant hill, measuring the distance in between with his forearm. The small protuberance, made of brown dirt and shaped into a perfect cone shape, was speckled with ant footprints and the dew of the morning; it seemed to be an impossible brown, different from the usual brown of the backyard.

"Youse fellas are mighty smart. I'm gonna protect y'all, and feed y'all all the bread I can get ahold of."

Jimmy watched for hours, occasionally peering into the dark hole at the top of the hill. He gave them more bread from a half-eaten lunch, and poured a small puddle of water next to the hill. In hours it seemed like the ants had multiplied, going from four or five sprawled on the side of the hill to hundreds, thousands by Jimmy's count, crawling and advancing, pinching off pieces of toast, or Wonder Bread, or buns, and ducking away in the hill. The beef from yesterday had even begun to vanish slowly, either by decomposition or the ants' hunger. The ant God watched his discovery uncoil and flourish right before his wide little eyes, his pride surging as if he had created them himself.

Soon the sun was setting, hiding behind the horizon and spraying a brilliant orange glow across the backyard. A single ray of light shone through the branches of their maple sapling on the ant hill, seemingly deliberately, illuminating the hundreds of thousands of ants, crawling in every direction, over the hill, over the places where food had once been, over the former body of still water that nested mosquitoes for a short time, and over Jimmy's hands. He brought out more food, and let their little feet and antennae tickle his fingers and their mouths nibble gently at his palm. He observed their actions, lifting them to eye level and blowing softly on them, pretending that his breath was a cool breeze. He carried them from one spot to another, letting them crawl in between the blades of grass as if they were forests made specifically for navigation. He let them crawl on dirt, imagining the sands he had seen briefly in *Lawrence of Arabia*. Wherever the ants were, he watched, intervening when trouble and doubt brewed.

The rumble of a motor in the driveway was the only thing that took his attention from the ants. Father was home.

The dinner table had an eerie feeling that night. The father hadn't spoken at all, and the mother's words were directed only to Jimmy. The mother and father avoided eye contact, staring into their plates, bowing their heads listlessly as they began to utter prayers. The father waited for the perfect time to break the silence that had grown into a monster, sometime between the scraping of forks on the plates and the slurping of strings of spaghetti.

"Say, son, whatcha do today?"

Before Jimmy could answer, the mother cleared her throat loudly, as if she didn't want Jimmy to answer his father. Jimmy looked at his mother and father, who still hadn't looked at each other, and said with an air of glee, "I played with my ants out back. They're growing up mighty fast, too."

The father let dismay grow across his face before he could answer, the unnerving silence again growing into a monster. The father looked up at his wife sitting across the table, squinting as if he couldn't get a good look at her in the lighting. He clenched his teeth, and his voice sounded angry as he spat out words. "That's what you let him do all day! Play with ants?"

Jimmy was disheartened by his father's outburst, thinking that his ants were important, and would probably enjoy the spaghetti they were eating. He dropped his head and played with his pasta, twirling the fork and lifting, letting the spaghetti fall off in tight coils of noodle. His mother stayed silent, keeping her composure and a strong demeanor for Jimmy's sake. She took a sip from her glass and kept eating. The father became aggravated by her stubbornness in silence and dropped his fork, reached for the napkin set immediately to his left side, and wiped the corners of his mouth.

"Listen, Jimmy," the father mumbled in a sullen, defeated tone. "I love you. Me and your maw both love you, but things aren't working out."

Jimmy's eyes widened. That moment froze for him like life altering moments tend to do. He didn't know what to expect.

"Me and Maw are splittin' up. Things aren't how they're s'posed to be, you understand. It'll be much better like this," he tried to assure Jimmy.

Jimmy tried to let his father's words soak in, but they didn't register in his brain. He looked from his father to his mother, expecting clarification. His father trudged on through his words, "I won't be around as much, but I'll still come n' see you, and you'll see me on Sundays at the church, and things'll be better. You understand me?"

Jimmy was dumbstruck. He could only utter a single "huh" and let his father's incoherent mumbling resound in his mind. The muscles in his face paralyzed; he could feel his stomach tighten around strands of spaghetti as he choked back tears. His mother watched him, letting the tears Jimmy couldn't release roll down her face. His father reached his hand out to pat Jimmy's head but missed, and ended up with a handful of shoulder that he squeezed consolingly. "Come on, Jim, don't cry."

Jimmy pushed his chair back and fled from the dining room, leaving his parents in their awkwardness; he pushed out of the front door and around the house to the backyard with strong, silent tears streaming down his face, leaving streaks on his cheeks like face paint before a battle. He ran full speed, letting one foot float off of the ground for a split second before the other hit. He ran to his ant hill, and with the precision of a football player kicking a ball, he let the tip of his left shoe kick and collapse the peak of the hill. Almost immediately ants spilled out of the top of the hill like lava spewing from an erupting volcano, the backs of the ants glimmering in the remaining sunlight. He jumped up as high as he could and stomped the ants with both feet, squashing them into their forests, their deserts, their mountain, while his tears watered them all. His shouting rang out on the country road in the front of the house and was the sound of death for his ants for the next hour as earthquakes crumbled their little Utopia. Jimmy's parents were separating.

It's your fault! It's your fault, you stupid ants! You wanted too much, and look what happened. Die! I hate you! You didn't appreciate it. I fed you, and I hate you! My paw is leaving 'cause of you! I hate you! Aaaarghhh!

Jimmy treasured the days when he was God.

Twentieth-Century Dispatch

Oliver Hunt

DEAR PEOPLE OF THE FUTURE—
    Or, if aliens from space take over, Dear Aliens—
    Or, if all that's left are cockroaches, and they can read English, Dear Cockroaches—

This is my own personal time capsule. In it, you should find one Zero bar, one Twix bar, half a pack of watermelon Hubba Bubba, a Marshmallow Peep, an issue of *Swank*, an issue of *Fangoria* with Freddie Krueger on the cover, a pocket knife, a plastic skull, a Chinese star, a blue and turquoise rabbit's foot, a cassette copy of the *Beat Street* soundtrack (Vol. 2), a cassette copy of Whodini's *Escape* album, a beta copy of *Enter the Ninja*, a Clash T-shirt, a pair of checkered Vans, a shotgun shell, a valentine, and a speckled blue pebble. We had to do time capsules as a project at school, but this one is my own.

    To be honest, I think shit like this is pretty gay. By the way, you guys don't mind if I curse, do you? Tough shit if you do. What are you going to do? Spank me? Suspend me? Call my mom? Wash my mouth out with soap?

    Anyway, like I was saying, I think shit like this is pretty gay. Like, with the time capsule project at school, my teacher, Mrs. Lunahan, wouldn't let me put any of my stuff in it. Then she told me she was giving me an F on the project because I didn't participate. I told her I tried to, but any time I tried to give her something for the capsule she'd tell me it was inappropriate. She said it was my job, as a student, to find something appropriate, and it wasn't her fault if I couldn't grasp what was and wasn't right for the capsule. Mrs. Lunahan's a bitch.

You should see some of the shit they put in the class capsule instead: issues of *Time* and *Newsweek*, *Star Wars* and GI Joe toys, barrettes, baby shoes, baby pictures, school pictures, Transformers, Dr. Seuss and Shel Silverstein books, a videotape of the Challenger blowing up . . . I mean, Andrea Murphy got to put a valentine in the time capsule, but when I tried to, Mrs. Lunahan said, "We already have Andrea's valentine. We don't need another one."

So Mrs. Lunahan can suck it, and so can Andrea Murphy, and so can that school. Oh yeah, I guess I should tell you. My name is Louis Trumball, and where you found this used to be some woods in Evanston, Illinois. It might still be. I won't know. Today is May 7, 1986. It's sunny now, but it rained earlier and everything's still wet. The ground is muddy and there are wet leaves, wet grass, and water is dripping from trees and wet grass. It's still kind of cold, too.

I'm fourteen and in the seventh grade at Chute Jr. High. This is my second time going through the seventh grade because I got held back. That's not really normal, but it's kind of normal. Anyway, it's not like I invented it.

The kids here think I'm dumb. I don't care, fuck them. I never liked them, and they never liked me. Even in preschool and kindergarten I had to fight with them all the time just to get a turn on the swing set or the merry-go-round. In kindergarten, my only friend was a girl named Lisa. I don't remember her last name and I don't care. One day, on the playground, she told me she couldn't be my friend anymore because none of the other kids liked me. Except on my birthday, when my mom gave me cupcakes to pass around to the other kids, she said, "I can be Louie's friend today because he has cupcakes." Yeah, maybe I'm supposed to be dumb, and bad, but I figured out all the other kids that day.

I wouldn't want to be like the smart kids, or the kids who are supposed to be smart, anyway. You should see the tests they have to take. They've got, like, a million of those bubbles that they have to scribble in with number-two pencils. And their parents don't let them do *anything*. I used to try to play with Jeffery Morrow, but whenever I went over to his house he'd say, "I can't play. I have about a million pieces of homework that I have to do, or I'm grounded."

I guess it's cool for them that they get to go off to another school, where they work on art projects and stuff. Still, they're always being taken to these places where they're always getting tested for something. Maybe they're being trained to be spies or agents or something. I mean, I'd be just as good at that as they are, but damn if I would want to go through all that. I mean, they get grounded if they get a *B* in a class.

So, yeah, if people think you're dumb they give you simple classes and kind of let you do your own thing. Oh sure, they kind of hover over you, to make sure you're not gonna set their garbage cans on fire (again), but they don't expect anything from you. They just want to pass you down and be done with you. I'm cool with that. Even if I bomb everything in seventh grade again, they'll pass me on to eighth. I'll probably turn sixteen in the eighth grade; then I'll drop out. That's if I even keep going.

I might actually like Chute if it weren't for all the teachers, students, principals and vice principals there. I actually like the light and dark brown and green lockers against the blocky white walls. I even like that the lockers are kind of dented and scratched up. I liked having a locker, too. It felt like I was getting older, that I wasn't a little kid anymore, and that it was my space. I used to put up pictures of RUN DMC and UTFO that I'd cut out of magazines, but I don't do that shit now. I'm not into that anymore, and teachers would walk by and rip it down anyway, telling me it's not my room. Also, I don't really like having a locker anymore.

Maybe Principal Mason should've told John Graham and Jim Cole it's not my room, since they shoved me in and actually closed it on me. I was banging on the door of it, then the class bell went off, so I'd be late anyway. I could see Principal Mason's brown boat shoes through the slits in the locker, and I knocked on it, saying, "Hey! Hey! I'm in here!" I had to call out my combination, so now everybody probably knows it. Mr. Mason opened my locker. His round face and bald head made him look like a snowman usually, but then it was all red, and he screamed at me. His spittle hit my face and he told me I was messing around too much and that I was a terrible student. I tried to tell him I got shoved in there for no reason, but he said I must have done something or said something or anyway it didn't matter. He wasn't excusing me.

So then I had to go to Mrs. Silver's science class. That's another thing I might actually like if it weren't for all the students and Mrs. Silver. I liked the yellow walls of her class with the bulletin boards and all the pictures of the solar system, reptiles, tornadoes, and weird rock formations that look like somebody cut a mountain in half. I thought maybe we'd get to do experiments like in mad scientist movies, with a bunch of test tubes and weird chemicals and stuff. I thought we'd at least get to make our own volcano or something. But it was just Mrs. Silver talking.

I actually might have even liked Mrs. Silver, except for that time she caught me looking between her tits. She cleared her throat, and she had this long, smooth neck that kind of looked like peach ice cream that I imagined sucking on, and she pulled her white sweater vest over her chest while looking directly at me. Tim Barrow caught it and said, "Hey everybody! Louis is checking out Mrs. Silver's tits!" Mrs. Silver got red faced, slammed her pointer against her desk, and sent Tim Barrow out of the room. Tim Barrow said, "It's not my fault Louis is a pervert!" and slammed the door on the way out. Kyle Rowan, who sat a couple of rows back, said "Wow, I thought he was a fag."

I'm totally not a fag. I mean, I only think about chicks when I . . . I just know I'm not, OK? I mean, I wanted to like the girls here. Like, I wanted to like Nikki Sawyer, who looks Mexican and wears these short jean skirts to school with fluorescent green Wham! shirts, even though I think Wham! is really gay. It's funny, then, that Nikki's all into Wham! and she calls me a faggot and tells me her twenty-year-old brother's going to kick my ass because I dared speak to her.

I maybe would have liked Michelle Gold, who has red hair and wears tight jeans with Mötley Crüe T-shirts and a lot of eye makeup and lipstick. She talks about doing it with guys all the time, so I asked her if she'd do it with me and she started screaming, "Gross! Ew! Rape!" She screamed rape just because I asked her, and now her twenty-year-old boyfriend is supposed to beat me up too.

I wanted to like Andrea Murphy. She's got a nice, freckled face and blond hair and wears girly dresses with flowers and white stockings. But she laughed at me about the whole valentine thing. Plus, like all the other girls, she calls me a creep, a loser, and a pervert (and maybe I am a pervert—at least I'm not a fag) and sneers at me and says that all the guys like Jim Cole and John Graham are cool because they beat up on me.

So all these girls probably do it with the guys who fuck with me, and they probably all laugh at me at some make-out party. I don't care.

OK, the stuff in the box. Yeah, I stole the Twix, Zero, and Hubba Bubba. I also stole the *Fangoria*, but I found the *Swank* in the woods as I was coming out here to bury everything else. Yes, I looked through it first. So the fuck what?

The pocket knife was mine when my dad wanted me to be in the Boy Scouts. On my first campout, though, I pulled it on John Graham, who was in my troop, because he knocked me down and took my canteen. I slashed across and cut his jacket open. He got cut a little too, but not too bad. Anyway, I got kicked out of the Scouts and my dad took my knife. I snuck into his room while he was asleep in the living room and took it back. I knew I wasn't going to keep it. I also stole twenty dollars out of my mom's purse, and I sent away for a cherry switchblade, so I don't really need this knife.

The shotgun shell is my dad's. He used to want me to hunt with him, but I hated hunting. I mean, getting up all extra-ass early, on a *Saturday*? To walk around in the mud, and sit in a dark and depressing duck blind, and squawk into a dumb duck call? *Fuck* that. Yeah, my dad's pretty lame, and he's a dick to boot. I'm supposed to be grounded for, like, forever. It's really ridiculous. It's due to my grades, mostly. My dad says he knows I'm not dumb and that I need to get on the stick.

I said, "Sure thing, Dad, I'm gonna get right on that stick." He back-handed me and told me not to get smart with him. He yells at me for being dumb, tells me I'm not dumb, then tells me not to get smart. I'm pretty sure he just likes being mad at me so that he can keep punishing me forever. He still spanks me with his fraternity paddle sometimes, then later I hear him laughing to his friends about it. He says, "Yeah, my boy here thought he'd get a little lippy with me, so I took out my old fraternity paddle and pounded his ass pink."

So whatever. Really, I just pretend to be grounded, but my parents are either working, or off doing something, or fighting—and when they're fighting they never talk about Tommy. They talk about me and what to do with me. My dad tells my mom I'm stupid and spoiled, and my mom tells my dad he rides me too hard, flies off the handle at everything, and is drunk all the time. While they're either working, or going on fishing trips, or out playing bridge or cards, or fighting about me, I go off and do whatever I want.

At night I sneak out. I do it alone, now. I used to sneak out with my friend Carl, but he decided not to be my friend anymore. That asshole. We used to hang out at school every day, and we used to talk on the phone for hours every day after school, but I don't know. The teachers or the other kids or his parents or my parents told him not to hang around me anymore. He told me his mom and dad said I need to be put away somewhere, and that I need help nobody at school can give me, and that the other kids just don't like me.

I knew something was up when he was supposed to meet me at the 7-Eleven on Davis at two. He never showed. I asked him at school what was up, and he said his dad busted him when he was crawling out of his window. He said he was grounded as shit.

That'd be one thing. Except now when I sneak out, I see him coming out of the bowling alley, or the movies, with little fucks like Kenny Roland and Jim Cole. Kenny stands behind me in gym class and calls me white trash, with a white-trash drunk dad and a trashy-whore mom. Jim Cole told me his dad could buy and sell my tweaking, unemployable dad a thousand times over, but that he and my mom weren't worth anything. Carl doesn't even look like he's sneaking out. I see his mom's car coming to pick him and whoever else up when I see him out.

I asked Carl what he was doing with those dicks, and he told me not to try to choose his friends for him. Then he told me he didn't want to hang around me anymore. I told him he was a dick, too, like everybody else, and he said, "Fine, nobody cares what I think anyway." That's cool, you know. Fuck him, too. I don't get cupcakes to pass around anymore, so that's pretty much it for people like Carl. See, I don't need these people. I don't need Carl, or my mom, or my dad, or the teachers at school.

Anyway, back to what's in the capsule. The Clash T-shirt and the Vans belonged to my brother Tommy. The Clash was his favorite band. He used to listen to them all the time. I didn't like them. A couple of years ago, I wanted to be a break-dancer, and The Clash was a dumb, white, English rock band.

Now I miss hearing them coming out of Tommy's room. I miss those big dumb chords and that dumb English singing, so I kept his Clash tape. Sometimes, I listen to it on my Walkman. That's a secret, though, OK? Not like it'll matter by the time you find all this anyway.

Anyway, Tommy hung himself. He was seventeen. I didn't see his body or anything until the wake. I came home from school, and there were all these cops and ambulances parked outside the house. Mom and Dad were sitting on the couch not saying anything, and they looked kind of like people I didn't know.

Sometimes, I go into Tommy's room. It's empty now. I imagine what he looked like hanging in the closet.

His room used to be so messy, with all of his piles of clothes, records, comic books, and skateboards, and with all the posters and pictures of bands and stuff on his wall. Now there's just thumbtack holes and a few pieces of tape still stuck to his walls, and that's it.

I've seen pictures of people hanging before, all drunk looking, with their mouths all crooked and upturned and their eyes all squinty. It's hard to see my brother like that, though, with his big mop of curly blond Harpo Marx hair still springing up around his dead face. He left a note, but my parents never let me read it. It was probably all sloppy and hard to read anyway. He was probably wearing his ripped up jeans and his Damned T-shirt. That was his other favorite band. He probably shit his pants, and there were probably brown splotches on his jeans, but I could never smell anything like that in his room.

At his funeral he just looked asleep, the way they make people look for funerals, except he had kind of a sneer. Like, I hadn't noticed it before, but I guess his face did that when it wasn't smiling or talking or doing anything else.

This is another little secret we have, OK, future people? I read books about ghosts and stuff. When I'm in Tommy's room, sometimes I hope to see him as a ghost. I don't know if he'd be able to talk or anything. I mean, I know this sounds totally gay, but I want to see him as a ghost, because I'm afraid I'll forget what he looks like. My mom went crazy and locked all of his old pictures and stuff away in a trunk, and my dad said, "Fine, I don't give a shit what you do." Sometimes, in his room, I get that weird, hairs-standing-up-on-the-back-of-my-neck feeling, and sometimes, like, I see these little squiggles and stuff out of the corner of my eye. I once thought I'd see what would happen if I went into his room and listened to The Clash. So I took my Walkman with The Clash tape into his room and sat in front of his closet.

I looked over, though, and I saw my mom standing there. She said, "Louie, what are you doing?"

I didn't know what to say, so I didn't say anything.

Now I have to go with Mom and Dad to see a psychologist once a week. She's this weird woman named Dorothy Kind, who kind of looks like a lizard. She asks me a bunch of questions about how I feel about Tommy and my mom and dad and school. I really don't like talking to her. I don't like talking to her, and she tells my mom and dad that I'm avoiding her questions, and then they yell at me. Then they yell at each other. Then I go to school and all the other kids know I have to see a psychologist and they ask, "Have you killed anybody, yet?" and Carl laughs at me like all the other kids do.

So I've got a switchblade coming in the mail, and when it gets here, I'm leaving. I'll have that switchblade in case anybody tries anything, but I'm getting out of this shithole.

So if you people or beings or roaches or whatever of the future find this, just know that my dad's an asshole, my mom is OK, except she's sad and crazy, Carl is a dick, Dorothy Kind is a creepy idiot, Tommy's dead, and Evanston sucks.

Also, those candy bars and stuff might not be very good by the time you find them, so I wouldn't eat them. They're just to have as, like, antiques or something, OK?

Have a nice day,
Louis Trumball, Age 14, Evanston, Illinois, Earth.

They Watch TV in Heaven

Jason D. Smith

TOBY CHARLESTON WOKE UP ON HIS SEVENTH BIRTHDAY AND KNEW EXACTLY what he had to do to bring his mom back down from Heaven. He had heard that TV came from outer space and that Heaven was in outer space, so all he had to do was get on TV and simply show his mom the way back home.

Toby knew that in order to reach space and Heaven, he would have to talk into a camera like newspeople do. He was sure that if he did something interesting enough on camera, his mom would see it in Heaven; she loved TV. Toby remembered watching television with his mom, and how much she liked a guy named Joey Chestnut. Joey Chestnut was—and is—the world champion of competitive hot dog eating. Flipping through the channels, Toby and his mom were startled by the image of a man shoving hot dogs in his mouth as fast as he could. They had never seen anything like it. He would first eat the dogs two at a time, chomping them down into sections and swallowing without chewing. Then he dunked the buns in a big cup of water and stuffed the soggy bread into his mouth. Behind Joey was a busty woman in a bikini, holding a giant flip chart of numbers. She was flipping the pages of the chart and the numbers grew: 27...28...29....Toby was in awe, the crowd chanted, and Toby's mom yelled, "I think I'm in love!"

Toby knew that if he did what Joey did on TV that day, his mom would see it for sure, and she could find her way home. So Toby built a satellite out of cardboard, paper plates, and tin foil. Then a video camera out of a shoebox and a kaleidoscope. He tested it, made sure that it recorded properly, stroked his chin like scientists do, and moved on.

He had asked his friend, Shelly, an Olympic women's volleyball player, for help. She had started showing up out of the blue (like all imaginary friends do) after the Olympics ended in the summer of '08. On hot days she appeared wearing a sporty black swimsuit and wrap-around sunglasses, with a volleyball under one arm. They usually played *Space Pirates* and *Ice Age* animals together, but she was up for a change of pace. Toby knew she would be perfect for the job because she could outrun anybody and fight people off by spiking volleyballs.

Toby's dad had invited the neighbors over for a barbecue in Toby's name. Nobody brought presents, just beer. Ever since Mom left for Heaven two birthdays ago, Toby's birthday became an excuse for his dad to throw a party without any balloons or birthday cake. Toby and Shelly had snuck past the adults huddled around a cooler of beer, swiped a hot dog tray from a picnic table, and made a run for it. Toby instructed Shelly to spike volley balls into the faces of anybody who tried to stop them, even his dad. They ran past the sliding door to the kitchen, into the bushes against the house, and then emerged at the side of the house, where Toby had set up his satellite and camera. There, they were halted by Vince, Toby's testosterone-confused brother. He was in the middle of sitting on the chest of Toby's younger cousin, Patrick, forcing him to eat ladybugs. Around them, bits of tin foil glinted in the harsh summer sun— the satellite and camera were destroyed. "Spike him with volleyballs, Shelly! Spike him!" Toby yelled with tears and rage. His plan was ruined.

Vince got up from Patrick's chest and turned to Toby. Toby held the tray of hot dogs, waiting for his brother to be pelted by a barrage of volleyballs. He imagined hundreds of striped balls smashing into his brother's face, knocking him over, turning his stocky profile into a purple and red lumpy mass. But nothing happened, and Toby looked around to find that Shelly was gone.

"What the hell do you want, Marshmallow?" Vince boomed. He played football, and his barrel chest seemed to amplify his voice like he was talking into an oil drum. Vince looked down at the tray of hot dogs. "Those are the dogs Dad grilled, aren't they?" Toby stood, listless. Patrick got up from the grass while spitting out lady-bug wings, then ran back to the adults while he still had the chance.

"Awww, I'm gonna tell on you!" Vince started to suck in a deep breath, like he was about to blow out candles on a birthday cake. Vince would always tell on Toby by screaming, "DAAAAAAD!" at the top of his lungs.

Dad was like a troll. He liked watching baseball and drinking beer and sitting in his chair, doing what he liked until Toby got himself in trouble. Dad would appear, red in the face, clenching his belt. He would bare his teeth and hunch over, his shoulders hitting the ceiling. If Toby was lucky, he could dart under his dad's tall legs and make a run for it. Toby's dad would always pursue him, turning it into a sick game. Swinging wildly, Dad would use his belt like a whip, smashing lamps and punching holes in the walls, trying to make contact with Toby's skin. Toby always ran to the "sick room," where his mom used to sleep while fighting off the cancer. Dad never stepped foot in Mom's old room, and it was the only place that was safe other than school.

Right before Vince could call for Dad, Toby yelled, "STOP!" He knew his plan was ruined and that Mom wouldn't be home for his birthday. But anything was better than agitating his dad. "Please," Toby said in a defeated tone.

Vince cracked an evil smile. He looked like a snake, or the creepy mailman that liked to watch Toby play in the front yard. "Why?"

"I want to show you something . . . ," Toby had to think quick. ". . . I bet I can do something you can't do."

Vince did not like this; he could do anything that "Tubby Toby" could do. "No way! You're dead meat," Vince said, and started taking a deep breath again.

"No! Please, Vince, please!" Toby said, tugging at the collar of his shirt. He couldn't stand the thought of Dad cornering him again. His arms and chest were still stinging from yesterday. He had only spilled orange juice at breakfast. There was no telling what his reaction would be if Toby was caught with the hot dogs. Toby had to do something, anything. So he plopped down onto the prickly summer grass, tray in his lap, and started eating—just like Joey Chestnut.

Toby grabbed two hot dogs, first eating the dogs, then dipping the buns into a cup of water and shoving the waterlogged bread in his mouth. Another two, and another two, and another. Vince was frozen in awe of the spectacle. Bun oozed out of the corners of Toby's mouth, and Vince laughed out of his barrel chest. Toby felt like he was on stage. He could hear a crowd cheering for him, he could even hear his mom cheering, and he thought maybe she would find her way home, and maybe he could get away from

Vince and his dad, and they could watch TV together like they used to—and the hot dogs were gone. Toby emptied the tray, and he felt nowhere near his mom.

Hulking over Toby, Vince was not sure of what he just saw, but he knew that it was something he couldn't do. Vince grabbed Toby by the collar of his blue-and-white striped shirt, lifted him up from the grass, and wrenched the fabric until Toby's face turned red.

"You're such a loser. Who cares if you can eat a bunch of hot dogs? Everyone knows that lardy little kids like you are good at eating."

And with that said, Vince punched Toby in the stomach. Toby staggered back from Vince's grasp, doubling over and gasping for air. It was too much; Toby could not hold back the tears, or the hot dogs, and puked. Bits of hot dog, bun, and bile first shot, then rolled out of his mouth, dampening the sun-scorched grass, soiling his shirt, and spattering on his tennis shoes. After heaving several times, Toby remembered a time when he was sick and his mom rubbed his back while he puked in the toilet. Something about the cool toilet seat against his cheek and his mom's hands running up and down his spine was comforting.

"Dad's going to kill you!" Vince said, walking back to the adults.

Toby needed to get back to his room. At the side of the house, the basement had a small and narrow window. Toby could open the window and slide feet first on his stomach, squeeze through and drop down into the basement. He knew that this would be the fastest way inside without his dad noticing.

Toby dropped down into the basement.

Winding his way through vine-like tangles of tubes, he felt his mother's old clothes hanging over him like Spanish moss on branches made of metal. He squeezed past the wash pan he used to give her baths with, and snuck past the machine that used to help her breathe. He was afraid that if he bumped into it, it would turn on and start pumping air, alerting his dad. Toby wasn't allowed down here, and his dad only came down when he was drinking. Climbing the stairs of the basement, Toby tripped over a pillow; it reminded him of a time when he was lying in the bed with his mom, right before she left for Heaven. She tickled Toby's pudgy stomach, and stuck her finger in his belly button and called him "Mommy's little munchkin." When Toby got scared, like he was now, he would snake his hand up his shirt, and put his finger in his belly button. He even remembered not to bite one of his fingernails, so that it felt like his mom's finger poking him.

In his room, Toby took his soiled shirt off and lay on his bed, shirtless. Rolling onto his back, he listened to the sounds of the barbeque coming through an open window, where his dad could be heard.

"Goddamn it!" the words shot through Toby's window like a rogue baseball. His dad's voice became muffled and inaudible until it rose again, "Toby did what?"

Toby sat up in bed with wide eyes; he could hear his dad come into the house. The sliding glass door was flung open, shaking the walls. A heavy stride could be heard through the kitchen, through the living room, up to the landing to the stairs. "Toby! Get your ass out here!" Before Toby could move, his dad started thundering up the stairs. Sitting up in bed, Toby waited for the door to be breached. He watched the Velcro dart board on his door shudder with every step up the stairs. The door flung open with such force that its handle punched through the wall. Toby thought about clambering out the window, or hiding under his bed. Instead, he just curled up and waited for the belt.

"Everything OK up there, Red?" a voice called from downstairs. Dad froze. Alcohol fumes billowed out of his mouth, and his eyes were wide and made of coal. He could explode any second. Everything about him was combustible.

"Red? Red! Get back down here! There's a beer waiting for ya!"

Red glanced behind him, then back at Toby. "I'll deal with this later. Don't you dare leave this room." He turned and left, slamming the door. Toby sat frozen in his bed, and listened to make sure his dad was heading back to the party. The stairs creaked, a beer was opened, the sliding door closed. Safe.

Toby crawled under his covers and poked at his belly button with his long fingernail. He began to wonder what his mom watched on TV while in Heaven. He imagined her sitting on a couch made of clouds and pictured her brown hair turned a golden blond. She had angel's wings, and they would splay outwards when she stretched her arms during commercials, like she always did when she was here. She ate popcorn out of the bag and ice cream out of the tub, being careful not to dirty her feathers. More than anything, Toby wanted to be there next to his mom, her arm wrapped around his shoulders, away from his dad, watching whatever they watch in Heaven.

Ophelia Drowning

Christa Tillman

PEACE WAS COMING AT LAST, THE HAPPILY EVER AFTER TO A HORROR STORY OF A fairy tale. The end. I was walking to the edge of the lake. The smell of the water, full of algae and life, filled my senses, sweeping through my nostrils to the back of the throat where it lingered in my mouth. The soft mossy ground sank beneath my bare feet; the silky mud oozed between my toes while the hem of my white gown grew brown from the wet earth. I reached the edge of the cold water and shivered with relief. "It will be over soon," I told myself as I waded into the lake. The tide ebbed over my ankles and crept up my calves. I was covered with gooseflesh, my hair standing on end from the chill; I embraced it, letting the water rise over my knees. Weeds from beneath the surface caressed the skin of my legs and tangled around my limbs, urging me forward, entrapping me in the water. I waded deeper into the lake.

The water rose to my waist. The skirt of my dress floated about me, rippling with the weeds, weighing me down. The white fabric was sheer, exposing the silhouette of my breasts; no one was there to see. This was an act of privacy, the most personal act one could undertake.

The deeper I went, the more my hair began to trail in the water, drifting like the stringy weeds. The water had risen to my breasts, consuming my shoulders, devouring my neck.

I deadened from the chill, succumbing to the numbing sensation. I paused, feeling the water at my jawline. The gentle slapping sound of the waves soothed my ears. I closed my eyes to listen. I heard birds singing from the tree-tops while crickets chirped in the grass, and I was so calm I could almost hear the tiny footsteps of marching ants. A frog leapt nearby and plopped heavily beside me in the water, causing ripples that splashed cool water in my mouth. A squirrel rustled through leaves as it leapt from branch to branch.

I opened my eyes. The sunlight reflecting off the surface of the lake blinded me for a moment and then settled into a scattering of diamonds that sparkled on the blue-green water. I took a final look around. The translucent wings and opalescent bodies of a pair of dragonflies glistened brilliantly. Proof that life goes on.

At peace with that knowledge, I leaned back into the embrace of the water until only my face lay above the surface. Taking one deep breath, one last gasp of air, my lungs expanded and I tasted the oxygen before I fully submerged myself.

Like a waning dream, the sun shined down at me through the rippling surface and I marveled at the crystalline light. It forgave me, told me everything would be all right; there would be peace. And in moments there was warmth in the cold waters. I smiled and closed my eyes at last.

El Dios del Rio

Bronwyn Mead

THE BOYS MARCHED IN A SINGLE LINE SOMEWHERE BETWEEN THE OCEAN AND THE river, far enough from both that they couldn't hear the sounds of moving water, and far enough from both that they forgot what depth looked like. Water was something they drank, or something that fell, a burden that made their boots heavy.

They had been taken from their riverside homes and pushed into the straight line. In the light, their boots marched over rain-sodden ground, through crop fields, jungles, and small towns. At night the boys slept on rough blankets thrown over wet grass. Collectively their thoughts rose over the trees, and drifted back to their villages, to their families. In the mornings the harsh and direct words of the recruiters tapped on their backs, and pushed them forward towards the city and towards the military base that would make them men.

Amadahi marched at the end of the line. In the back he didn't have to concentrate on preventing water from pooling into his footsteps. He walked with his hands out, letting his fingertips brush the thick green corn stalks. Each stalk he touched became brighter, stood taller, and pushed its leaves higher. Each tap of his fingertip made the stalks grow. At the front of the line, the other boys would notice this, and so Amadahi marched at the end of it.

Outside of the line, Amadahi kept his hands in his pockets, his fingers pushed against the palms of his hands to keep the water from coming. He could hold it inside him, keep it secret and hidden, but control took energy and focus. It kept him quiet with his chin tucked in, and most people assumed Amadahi was shy.

During the privacy of night he slept on his stomach, his hands pushed into the dirt, letting the water flow from them uninhibited and into the ground. He prayed that by morning the puddle that surrounded him would be soaked deep into the dirt.

Almost there, the collective voice of the line thought. The words rippled through the boys until they reached Amadahi. Almost there. He already missed his mother. He missed the river. He missed the slap, the slap, the slap of cotton T-shirts hitting the rocks on the riverbank, slapping out the smells of men's underarms. The slapping pulled at him, called to his fingers and toes to keep up the beat. The women of his village would kneel in rows along the river's edge every Tuesday and beat the laundry against the rocks, careful not to make holes in the cotton, but hard enough so they smelled clean. They gossiped and laughed and slapped and draped the wet clothes across bushes so they would dry in the sun.

At his bend in the river the water passed slowly, its current held back by partial dams and thick tree roots. It was so slow the water was clear enough to see the gray fish undulating in the liquid, clear enough to see the mangrove roots twisting around each other and snaking themselves down to the wet soil of the river bottom, like arms and legs of an underwater giant.

It was just turning spring and he would miss the red Camucamu berries falling from their branches and floating, swirling across the water's surface the way he imagined snowflakes fell and blew in the wind. He would miss the children with their long sticks dragging in the water, trying to coax a cluster of small fruits close enough to their outstretched hands, to snatch them and toss them into their mouths.

The line stopped. Amadahi lifted his chin from his chest and put his hands in his pockets. In front of him was a deep valley filled with beige buildings with round red roofs and square gray towers that stood taller than any tree he had ever seen. On the other side of the valley was a mountain range. Even at a great distance the mountains felt powerful, old, and unending.

"*Huancayo*," said the line as they marched down into the valley, into the big city. Most of the boys had never seen a city before, having grown up in small wooden huts on stilts along the Amazon River, spending more time in boats fishing than on land. Their knees hurt from walking on solid pavement in military issued boots that were not yet broken in.

In the bright midday light the city looked unreal, too harsh, with lines too straight, and buildings too solid. It went against everything Amadahi had grown up seeing; there were hardly any curves, hardly any movement. He searched for water, a fountain, a pool, a puddle, but the city was bare and hot, the only moisture in the air. He opened his mouth and let the humidity collect on his tongue.

The base was even drier. Their sleeping quarters was a concrete-floored brick building with rows and rows of bunk beds. On each bed, folded and stacked together neatly, there was a training uniform, as well as a towel, a toothbrush, and a razor.

After being served hot food in the cafeteria and permitted a five-minute shower, the line broke apart into thirty eighteen-year-old boys in separate beds, sleeping.

"It's routine, just want to see what your blood type is," said the young nurse as she pulled the thin curtain closed. On the other side of the curtain soldiers waited for their physicals, their shadows and speech waving behind the fabric. She pulled latex gloves onto her short fingers. Her hands were almost paw-like, small and soft looking, and her angular, arched eyebrows reminded Amadahi of the jungle cats that lounged in the trees. Her hair was dark and pulled away from her square face into a thick bun that hit the nape of her neck. She held out her hand. Amadahi took a deep breath and placed his hand in hers and closed his eyes, knowing his dam would be stronger if he didn't watch her.

The nurse tore open an alcohol swab in one quick rip, possibly the millionth alcohol swab she had opened in her lifetime, and cleaned the end of his finger. Usually the nurse counted to three, gave the patients a chance to prepare themselves for the prick, but when she looked up to start counting she was taken aback to see that her patient had his eyes closed. Without looking away from his face, she cleanly stabbed the tip of his middle finger. She was surprised at his movement; at first glance he appeared still, but with her hands wrapped around his she could feel him rocking very slightly. Amadahi could feel her watching him. His eyes opened, and for a small moment their gaze met before angling downward to the blood droplet on his finger between them. Her eyebrows rose higher; the blood on his finger was blue, deep magnetic blue. In his distraction he let a thin stream of water leak from the center of his palm and dribble onto the table.

He could feel the rapids crashing through his veins, the panic rising. In his village his time was spent in the water, setting traps for small crawdads and fishing for food. Even more often than "Amadahi" his people called him "*el niño del rio*," the river boy, for he contributed more fish to the small village than any other man or woman they could remember. Because of this, his constant dripping went unnoticed, for his clothes were always dark and heavy and sopping wet.

"Don't tell," he whispered, shoving both his hands into his pockets. He didn't know what strangers would do to him here, how they would react, where they would send him. Being trained to be a soldier wasn't a choice, but a requirement of all healthy males his age. Boys had to undergo three months of training, physical and academic, in case of war. After three months they would be sent home, but with an oath to their country that in a time of need, a time of battle or crisis, they would serve.

The nurse turned her face away from him. "There's nothing to tell; you're A positive," she replied quickly and quietly, picking a blood type at random, as she threw away her gloves and made a note on his chart.

He didn't wait for her to say more, walking through the curtain without waiting for her to pull it aside.

The nurse sprayed the table down with disinfecting spray and wiped it dry with a paper towel, wondering why she had been so quick to trust and cover for him. When the boy saw his own blood she knew that he had never seen it before, never really known what flowed through his own veins. And his palm, was it sweating? Or did cool water drip from it? She looked at his chart again. "Amadahi," she said out loud.

To her, the boy was so old and so young at the same time, his chart calling him eighteen, barely younger than she, and from a place she had never heard of before. Probably some tiny river village, she thought. The other boys she blood typed that day had been loud and flirtatious toward her, trying to talk her up as she pricked their fingers. This one was quiet and calm, though his body seemed to sway ever so slightly, like a tide. His skin was darker than hers, a trait common of those from rural villages. In her mind she saw the blue blood again, tried to rationalize it with every scientific argument her mind could conjure. The more she tried to explain it to herself, the more familiar the thought became. The boy's blood was blue, as true and honest as the sunrise.

Amadahi walked through the waiting room looking at the floor; the other bodies in the chairs were just blurs. He followed his memory of the building to a lavatory in a secluded hallway. A sudden dark rain hit the hallway windows, a storm churned by his panic. Half an hour earlier the sun was high and bright, no clouds on this side of the mountains, but now the sky was charcoal and thunder bellowed. His wet hands slipped on the door handle and he locked himself inside, immediately placing his palms onto the sink drain. Relief rushed over him and his breath slowed and his muscles unclenched as he let the water flow out of him. He dipped his head down and let it hang between his bent shoulders, calling for the quiet sound of his river, a sound that calmed him. He avoided his face in the mirror, tired of his strange reflection, his close-shaven hair, his nose that was flat and wide, cheekbones square and hard; a face so unlike the people of his village. He had his mother's dark skin, and her large mouth with kind teeth, but there were many features that did not belong to her, ones that he had never been able to match with anybody.

Sarita, his mother, was tall and willowy, but strong. He had her strength too, but his frame was thick and muscular, shorter than most of the boys his age. When he was young he would pry his mother for answers about his father, where he was and what he looked like. Sarita would push her back straighter, look Amadahi in the eye and say, "You look exactly like the man that helped me make you, but he's long gone, *mi hijo*, no use to be waiting." When he asked her about the water her muscles would soften, her face brighten, and she would say, "That's also from the man," saying it so kindly. Sarita never referred to him as "your father" but only "the man." To her, being a father meant rearing, bringing food to the table, teaching a child what's wrong and what's right. So to her he was just a man.

The door handle jiggled. Amadahi took his hands out of the sink and wiped them on his pants. The water had stopped during his meditation.

"Excuse me?" said a female voice, and a hand knocked. Amadahi opened the door to see the young nurse. She looked down the hallway before saying, "May I come in?" Puzzled and nervous, he stood aside and shut the door behind her, trying to push away his discomfort.

She looked at his hands; they lay calm and open against his thighs. "I . . . I won't tell. I don't know why, or what you are, but I won't."

Amadahi just stared. Standing, she was taller than he'd imagined, her eyes only a few inches lower than his, but her body was still small and soft looking. "What is your name?" he said finally, curious and apprehensive at the same time.

"Pilar."

"Amadahi."

"May I see your finger?" she asked, walking closer to him in the small square bathroom.

For a moment he considered walking away, leaving this woman to believe whatever she wanted to believe. He waited for the flight instinct to take over, but it never came; curiosity dominated any fear.

He gave her his hand and she examined his fingertip. She squeezed it lightly, and gave a short quick inhale when a blue droplet formed and grew.

"I didn't know," he answered, "I guessed it was different but never knew for sure." The longing to share himself fully, to be understood by this woman, pulled at him stronger than anything he had felt before.

He rotated his hand so his palm faced upwards and cupped it. As Pilar watched, his palm filled with silvery blue water that reflected the light bulb above them. She dipped her fingers into it, her eyes suddenly growing larger, and she brought her wet fingers to her forehead, chest, and both shoulders.

"My God," she whispered.

Amadahi separated his fingers and the puddle of water splashed on the gray tiles. "I do not think that is what I am."

"But this," she pointed to the water on the floor. "This came from you. Your blood . . . you're not human . . ."

"Stop!" he said, forgetting his shyness. "Stop, I am no god, I am barely a man. I bleed and feel pain and sadness. I am no god."

"Then what are you?" she asked in a serious voice, each word holding equal weight. It was less of a question and more of a plea.

The words hung on his clothes and eyelids, "I don't know."

Rain hit the roof in a melodic beat, the tinkle of drops pouring down its shingles and scattering across the wooden windowsills. Pilar shut each window in rhythm—slam, slam, slam— and as she watched the drops, they grew bigger, from the size of small pebbles to stones. She waited for the thunder to boom, but it didn't come. She only heard the thick raindrops pounding evenly against the windows. It was the kind of rain that made things grow.

An open palm slapped against her door. She opened it tentatively, keeping the brass chain locked so only half of her face peeked out.

"Amadahi," she breathed when she saw his face, dripping and serious. "It's late; why aren't you at the base?"

"May I come in?" he asked in his village's accent, much more sweet and tangy, like the flesh of a papaya, than the way people in the city spoke.

She pushed the door closed and undid the lock. His wet jeans slapped the floor as he walked in and turned to look at her. His eyes reminded Pilar of warm, wet dirt, the kind at the bottom of a river. He was never still, his movements small but deliberate and fluid. Water dripped down his face, along the side of his nose, and into his gray T-shirt, dark and stuck tight to his chest.

"I like your flat," Amadahi said, looking around. On one side, there was a small bathroom behind a door, and on the other, a simple kitchen fit into the curve of the old wall. There was also a wooden desk and dresser, and pushed up against the round windows was her unmade bed. He walked around the room, a trail of water droplets following him on the floor. Pilar stood still, watching him gaze over her things, watching the drops of water that never slowed. She smoothed down her dark, shoulder-length hair, tugged at her white camisole, and straightened her skirt on her hips, trying to busy her small hands.

"Did you bring the rain?" she asked.

He walked toward her and put his palm on her neck. Water dripped from his hand and trickled down her skin in long continuous streams. She inhaled deeply through her open mouth. He placed his other hand in the middle of her back and pulled her close to him. Moisture seeped into her camisole and expanded, the wetness crawling down her spine, spilling into her skirt, drips crisscrossing down her bare thighs, calves, and ankles, and pooling on the hardwood floor. He put his lips to her warm neck. "Yes," he breathed, pulling the straps of her shirt off her shoulder and kissing across her skin. Her arm felt like it had been dipped in warm wax, the feeling coaxing her into a trance. She let herself fold into his warm damp chest and placed her arms around his shoulders. The wetness wrapped itself around her, pulled her in, and merged with her like two hands intertwining their fingers.

Amadahi removed her wet shirt, and pulled her skirt off her hips. On his knees, he hooked his fingers into her underwear and slid them down her thighs, dragging his wet lips down alongside them to her ankles. Constant water flowed from his hands, the puddle around the two expanding, pushing the books and socks and rugs on the floor to the corners of the room with its current. The water level rose.

Pilar's hair began to lift, the straightness she had forced onto it dissipating, and the curls springing up and out from the moisture. He lifted her wet, naked body and put her on the bed before removing his T-shirt and jeans. He seeped into the covers, the linens soaking and warm, and the water level grew, creeping up onto her mattress. Pilar looked at his body, hard and soft at the same time, looked at his hands, the endless flow of water filling her belly button and expanding like a star bursting across her skin. She pulled him by his hair for his lips to meet hers, and she drank from those lips, water rushing out of him and into her mouth, over her face and skin, and she didn't have to breathe, she didn't have to inhale, she just drank.

Their bodies became weightless in the rocking water, and a storm came. It turned the water from crystal to dark blue and pushed them together. He filled her deeply and rocked with the movement of the turbulent waves. Water doesn't follow a pattern, its caps rolling and dipping to a rhythm of its own, and this was the way in which they made love: rolling and dipping, gently flowing, and harshly crashing down again. His hands gripped hard on her hips and her hands gripped hard onto his hair, his neck, his shoulders, his back, scratching and grabbing his skin, biting her own shoulders and tossing her head back and back, pushing her up and up and up the wave until she rippled and peaked and flowed down again with the ebb.

The water kissed the sloping ceiling. Their bodies were floating, suspended in water. Amadahi was weightless and Pilar pushed him down beneath her, holding tightly onto both his hands and wrapping her legs around his hips. He let himself go, arched his spine and let the water take him over, take him into her, until he hit the wave, crushed his chest into itself and squeezed all his muscles at once, again, again, and then let go, bubbles escaping from his lips in a sigh.

For a moment they floated flat on their backs, rode the descending water, riding it down to the bed as the storm calmed and the crystal clear liquid flowed back into Amadahi's hands, until they lay upon the wet linens, beads of moisture dripping off them. Pilar curled herself into his skin, the wetness warm at body temperature so it felt like nothing, felt like being dry. Amadahi looked around the room, books lying open in the inch-deep water, their pages crinkling with dampness, clothes dripping from their hanging places, the sound echoing the outside rain. He pulled himself away from her, folded her arms across her sleeping body, and retrieved his sodden things.

When he left, she awoke to the water growing cold without him, and her skin prickled in tight bumps. She pushed herself into a sitting position, water pooling against her hand when she pressed it into the mattress. The room had shifted; the desk was pulled away from the wall, the items from its surface had drifted into one corner, the chair was on its side, and her dresser had floated to the center of the room. She stepped off her bed, her feet slapping against the puddles on her floor, looking in the drawers for something dry to wrap herself in. There was nothing. She licked the drops from her lips and shivered, trying to piece together the night.

Amadahi was born so close to the bubbling river that some of its blue went into his blood. When Sarita washed their clothes at the river bend, she set her baby in the roots of the mangrove trees so he could play with the fish. She put little worms into his palm and the baby would giggle as the fish nibbled at them, unafraid of his humanness. He was so small, barely bigger than some of the fish, and bare as a banana with its peel off.

The baby would hold his breath and pull his little body down by the thick roots until he was at the murky bottom. There he watched the larger fish, piranhas with big jaws and sharp teeth, swim back and forth. Everyone in the village knew they fed on flesh, but they never bit the baby. They gently slid their slimy scales across his skin and let him pet their tail fins. On the bank Sarita calmly counted to herself, counting the minutes her baby could hold his breath, never quite sure how long because she would lose count and get nervous, calling to him, "Amadahi, Amadahi!" Underwater his name wasn't muffled, but clear, even when he heard it from eight feet down. Up, up the baby would wiggle and kick his little legs, swim until he saw the pink headscarf around his mother's hair. She'd scoop him out of the water into her arms and carry him home in the basket of wet clothes upon her head.

In her heart, Sarita knew about the blue in her baby's blood, the water that filled his soul, but she told no one about the Tuesday afternoons that Amadahi spent under the water. The villagers never asked about the man that put Amadahi inside her, sensing they would never get an answer.

When he was older, he'd go to the Amazon by himself and swim every day, spending hours exploring the mazes created by the mangrove roots, and he always returned with lines and lines of fish. Gently, Amadahi would hold a smooth-scaled fish in between his palms and ask for its gift of food. He never took a fish that asked to return to the water, only taking the ones that were ready. Fish know that the world is a cycle, that one day they will come back to this time and space, but still some fish aren't ready to leave their river. If the fish remained still, showing her readiness, Amadahi would toss her to the riverbank where other fish lay, their mouths agape, saying farewell.

The day Amadahi turned eighteen was only three weeks before the recruiters drove through their village in military vehicles, rounding up the next group of forthcoming soldiers. He had known since he was small that this would happen, but he still wasn't prepared. They placed him inland, so far away from water that he nearly drowned.

Pilar pulled her sheet off her bed and wrapped it around herself, rubbing her arms to get warm. Bits and pieces of the night came back to her: Amadahi, the wave. But much of it was lost and unclear, like a dream.

"Oh no," she said, walking over to the kitchen. She turned the knobs of the stove between her fingers like she was trying to find a radio station, listened to the clicks, and waited for the fire to ignite, but there was none. She lifted the stovetop and smelled two flameless puffs of gas between the elements. Maybe all was not lost. In the back of a kitchen drawer she found a lighter that felt dry between her fingers. With a quick motion, she lit both pilot lights and promptly turned on the oven, holding her hands to its heat and turning around so it warmed her back.

Her eyes fell on a puddle on her floor. It began to shrink, crawling inward like a quiet implosion before disappearing completely. More puddles vanished. She walked across the room to her closet, running her hands over the hanging clothes, and felt no dampness. The tops of her dresser and desk were dry, and her bed linens, just moments before saturated and cold, were now soft and warm. Frantically she searched her flat for something wet, but there was nothing, not even a spot of dampness on the sheet wrapped around her. Her apartment was dry. All the water Amadahi left behind had dried up.

Amadahi walked back to the base through the humid air and his pores soaked it up like sponges. He tipped his chin down, smiling to himself. He didn't want to leave Pilar's bed, but he had snuck out of the bunk unnoticed the night before, and sneaking back inside in the same fashion depended on him getting back before the base woke.

His body felt warm, almost hot. He stopped on the street and cupped his palm, called for water to rise so he could splash his face. It didn't come. He concentrated harder, cupped both palms and stared at them but they stayed dry.

His skin began to wrinkle and hang on his muscles, losing its fullness. Under his lids his eyes felt scratchy, and his mouth, no matter how much he swallowed and moved his tongue, wouldn't moisten. He started walking again, faster this time and with no smile. His skin itched and burned and blistered painfully under his clothes. It felt like his veins were drying out, like his bones were cracking and turning to dust. He lost control of his movements, suddenly so tired and weak that he collapsed, folded mechanically into a dry pile on the side of the road.

"There's nothing more that we can do. He's been hooked up to an IV for over forty-eight hours now with no improvements. It is almost as if his body is rejecting the water. He's dying of extreme dehydration," said a male voice Amadahi didn't recognize. He opened his eyes and in the bright white hospital lights saw a short man in a white coat speaking to one of the recruiters from the base. The recruiter, a large, serious man, approached Amadahi's bed.

"Son," he said in a soft voice that didn't match his unexpressive face, "we're going to send you home."

Amadahi opened his mouth to speak, but couldn't bring the words forth. A blur rushed into the room.

"Nurse," the man said, "help this boy drink."

Pilar nodded her head and put a straw between Amadahi's lips with shaking hands. She didn't need to speak to say that she was frightened, and worried, and confused, and drawn to him so completely. He drank, but the water only moistened his lips for a fraction of a second.

"Home," Amadahi breathed weakly, his throat so dry that the smallest exhalation was painful. He closed his eyes again, tried to conjure up the sounds of his river, the face of his mother, the feeling of Pilar's naked skin, unsure if he would even make it that far.

"I'm going with you."

The next day the men loaded him into the back of a Jeep Wrangler with his nurse at his side and drove through fields and jungles and small villages. They drove until they reached the little one where the water passed so slowly it was as if it had stopped time. The children of the village gathered around the vehicle, their faces pressed up against the windows to see Amadahi, small and weak looking in the backseat. His name passed through each of their mouths and spread through the small village to Sarita. She dropped her things and ran, ran hard on the wet earth to the men and the car and her child.

One of the men in uniform caught her by the shoulders, "Are you his mother?"

"Bring him to the river!" she cried, tears flooding down her cheeks.

"Now! Carry him to the water!"

"Ma'am, he's weak."

"Do it!" she yelled, and pulled out of his grasp. Pilar pushed open the door and pulled Sarita inside, watched as she spread her cool hands over Amadahi's face and forehead.

"I'm drying," he whispered. Sarita kept her hands on his face as the men lifted him easily from the car. Two men carried him, holding up his knees and putting their arms behind his back. Amadahi weakly set his arms around their shoulders, his head bobbing with the walking movements. They set him down at the water's edge and backed up, looking sadly at his crying mother, then got back into the Jeep and drove away. Pilar stood and silently watched, afraid to get too close.

Sarita kneeled next to him. "Go, *mi hijo*, I know you need to go."

Amadahi could feel his heartbeat begin to slow, his temperature decrease. His shaking hands unbuttoned his soldier's jacket and pants. Pilar went to him then, kneeled on the ground and helped him undress, pulling the stiff fabric off his shoulders and removing his pants as he lay still in the grass. Suddenly he pushed himself off the ground and stood. He looked at his mother and she nodded, and then he looked down at Pilar. He kept his eyes linked with hers for a long time and then straightened his arms above his head and dove. Water rushed over his body as he descended. The fish kissed his skin, tasted his saltiness, welcoming him back to the water. His heartbeat stopped and the last bubbles of air dribbled from his open lips as he sunk down to mangrove roots.

Pilar leaned her body on her hands to see into the water. "Amadahi," she called, watching the shadow of his motionless figure sink and fade. "He's gone," she whispered, as the body dissolved and washed away with the current.

"Give it time," his mother said as she stood, walking toward Pilar and pulling her off the ground. "Give it time."

Pete, the Professional Professional

Wyatt Robinette

THIRTY-FOUR HOURS AGO PETE GOODWELL WAS SUPPOSED TO CLOCK OUT AND leave All Time Everyday No Exception Convenience Store. When his wife, Samantha, dropped him off forty-two hours and fifteen minutes ago, he loved his family. He wanted to stay in their double-wide outside Marana, Arizona. But they need money to live. So Pete needs his job. Samantha doesn't let him forget this. She loves him. He remembers loving her. But she doesn't let him forget money and how they need it, damn it, they need it.

When Pete started his shift, the manager was heading to Europe for the summer and three more people were employed. Rick, the newest worker, was deported to Mexico two hours into Pete's shift. Pete didn't hear why from Rick's cousin who called to report what had happened. The other two eloped to Vermont to get gay married after their shift ended. Now, Rupert Martin is Pete's only relief. Now, Pete has to depend on someone that is fourteen years older (Rupert is forty-seven) and, in Pete's mind, a hundred times more unreliable. Unlike Rupert, Pete is six feet, four inches of strong, militaristic lines that define his cut features and expose his German and Russian heritage. They also hint at his heightened level of loyalty and dedication. His dead mother liked to say, "He looks like he'd call if he's going to be late."

Outside the glass doors, the world burns. Almost 110 degrees, the radio said. Gray and purple mountains sizzle on the horizon. Trucks, vans of families, and sedans of solitary figures pass on the highway. You can walk to All Time Everyday No Exception Convenience Store but no one does. It's located between Tucson and Phoenix. The closest neighbor is a rest stop that, because of an unfinished turnoff, hasn't rested a soul.

Pete stands by the door gripping the handle. He imagines taking off his yellow work polo, tossing it in the garbage between the gas pumps, and catching it on fire.

When Samantha arrives, she steps on the heels of her loose jeans and pulls at the edges of her shirt from her high school swim team. Her usually sharp features appear somewhat faded as she moves in and out of the light. She stops in front of the pay counter and smiles. Pete has a patchy five-o-clock shadow and smells ripe.

He says, "If Rupert comes, I can leave."

"Good," Samantha says in her soft voice. "It's getting lonely in the double-wide without you. It's so small. There aren't many seven-year-olds for Megan to play with."

When she speaks, Pete no longer hears the chop, chop of the clock behind him.

"Are you getting overtime?" she asks.

She holds one of his large, callused hands between her small ones. She can tell he's been pulling his blonde hair. If he kept it longer it might appear chaotic or troubled.

"Yes," Pete says.

She squeezes his hand with hers. He squeezes back and smiles.

"That's good," Samantha says. "Overtime is good."

After seventy-six hours, Pete realizes the store has everything one could need or want: snacks, toys, housewares, alcohol, diapers for all ages, perfumes, jerky, cheap sunglasses, hotdogs, first aid kits, a dairy cabinet, and quiet, earthbound fireworks.

Eight years ago, Pete's loyal persistence won Samantha over when he was single and she was engaged. It also assured her Pete would do what he had to to support her and the children they planned to have. He was the kind of man that saw things through. She cherishes this aspect of Pete. But she also knows his rigid, Purple Heart-wearing father—the person Pete inherited this trait from. Samantha forgot the number of times she heard how Pete's father held his face on the floor and dared him to get up. But, because of this man, Pete learned and prided his foolish stubbornness, even though it cost him many jobs and even more relationships.

The only TV is a small black-and-white that shows whatever the security camera perched behind Pete has in front of it. It usually displays the back of Pete, a customer (maybe), and the backside of the cigarette shelf that hovers over his head. Behind him, hidden behind his broad shoulders, are more cigarettes, cigars, nude magazines, and small, overpriced bottles of alcohol. Pete doesn't like watching the TV. He's scared to change the channel. What if he turns back and he's not there? Or someone else is?

The red lights outside the store that spell *All Time Everyday No Exception Convenience Store* never turn off. Pete can't see them, but he knows they're on. He feels their comforting hum in the soles of his feet and smiles.

There's still no word from the manager or Rupert. Outside it's day, but Pete thinks this is a mistake. His calculations might be wrong, but the calculator he keeps to the left of the register tells him otherwise.

The only things he knows for sure are that his relief hasn't come, the manager hasn't called, he wants to dream, he misses his family, and he has been at it for 128 hours straight, no sleep.

He remembers the .45 on the shelf under the cash register and the manager's instructions: Shoot to kill. The security camera isn't equipped with sound, and because of this Pete must shoot to kill. If he leaves a would-be robber alive, the robber can argue that he/she wasn't robbing the store but was asking Pete to admire his/her handgun. Pete spins the gun on his finger and checks the ammunition levels. There is only one bullet. He uses a Sharpie to write Rupert's name on it. The marker is big and what he writes isn't a word. It's a long, fat slash. Pete cleans the bullet with spit and thinks how Pete must shoot to kill. He doesn't know if he can, but he must. Those are the orders.

Pete's family comes in for the free milk, eggs, and bread he promised them. He recognizes them, but something is off. His wife wears dirty jeans and an undershirt. Her brown hair bounces and curls as she takes long strides from the glass doors to the pay counter. Megan looks like she's been crying.

He tells them about the overtime he—they—are getting. His tone is positive, which conflicts with his bloodshot eyes, sour smell, shaky hands, and frazzled half-beard. Megan pinches her nose and squints at her father as if his stink is a visible fog. He reminds himself to show the overtime chart. He thinks this will fix what was off. He shows the chart.

"That's not a chart," Samantha says. She says, "That's just 'Overtime is Good, Samantha Likes Overtime' written over and over again. I'm worried, Pete. You're scaring your daughter."

Pete drops the overtime chart. It takes a rack of over-the-counter caffeine pills with it. Both slap and bounce off the tile floor behind the counter.

"I'm doing this for my daughter," he says. "I'm doing this for you. You should understand Pete's responsibility. Pete's 110 percent attitude. You should know why he hasn't left after 196 hours, 23 minutes, and 17 seconds."

"We need you at home," she says. "Overtime is nice, but your family needs you. You look a mess. Your eyes are dark. You're losing weight—I've never seen your arms and cheeks so thin. Your hair looks like dreadlocks and smells horrible. You look lost in that stupid yellow polo. It's like I can barely see you." Her voice catches in her throat. "I love you and your dedication, but I'm scared. I don't know how much more of this I can take. Pete, you need to make a decision."

Pete turns his head and cups his chin with his thumb and pointer finger.

"If Megan watches the pay counter, we can have sex in the bathroom," he says.

Samantha looks at the floor and shakes her head.

"You're being stupid," she says. "You don't know what you're saying."

"Don't worry," he says with one eye closed. "Our daughter will be allowed to shoot to kill."

Samantha starts complaining. She says, "What the hell, Pete? What's wrong with you?"

Her brown hair's a mess, she's wearing new tennis shoes, her beauty seems elsewhere, and his daughter's scared of him. Her hand is in her mother's and her mother's grip is tight. Samantha paces while she complains. The heels of Megan's shoes squeak across the tiles. With her free hand, Samantha points at Pete or holds her large belly like its contents are about to spill out. Megan sighs and rolls her red, puffy eyes. When Pete tries to give his daughter a snack, his wife shakes her head and says, "That's bad for her," and complains more. "Our daughter is allergic to coconut. Do you want to kill her?"

When Samantha gives up and carries a teary-eyed Megan out the glass doors into the white light of the desert heat, Pete's skin feels loose. He tries running laps around the aisles. He passes an aisle of chips, one of jerky, but when he reaches the magazines he has to lie down and rub balm on his thinning calves. He wants to close his eyes but fears sleep. If the manager catches him sleeping, Pete loses the meager economic security he built for his family. He faces (if the job search is anything like the one that led him to All Time Everyday) up to six or more months of filling out applications only to be rejected. And then rejected. And rejected.

If that happens, he risks losing his family. He risks losing Samantha to her ex-fiancé, the restaurant manager, which was what she threatened during the months leading up to his hiring at All Time Everyday No Exception Convenience Store. He risks losing time with Megan and his unborn child. He wouldn't be able to read *Where the Wild Things Are* to them every night as they drift to sleep. Taco Sundays and Board Game Wednesdays would stop. The life he loved and worked for would end.

So, he stays.

The relief's phone and the manager's phone ring and ring and ring, but no one picks up.

While eating a hotdog, Pete bites into his finger and might've eaten the tip. Luckily, there are bandages. The store has everything. It's always open. No exceptions.

Sometimes Samantha and Megan are crouched over, snickering in the candy section. Sometimes they're cooling off in the corner to his right by the ice cream. Sometimes they're frowning at the back of the line where he can barely see them, or they're up in his face, inches from the register. He has chosen to ignore these mirages and focus on work. The work manual he reads and underlines passages from advises to professionally ignore any emotional stress inducers. By doing this he is working towards being a Professional Professional, who are the tip of the top—not in terms of salary—but in names a cashier can receive. As he ignores the mirage of Samantha slapping the counter with a loaf of bread, Pete wonders if Professional Professionals get a pin or a better nametag.

Pete makes a list of the new skills he's acquired after 250 hours. The list is ordered and clean, just like his aisles, just like his store (he likes to think it's his store).

This is the list:

Pete can go without blinking for five hundred seconds (this time is much shorter if he looks at the lights).

Pete can ignore an itch longer than he can ignore a customer.

Pete can clean the store until he can see his reflection in the floor tiles in less than two hours. (He thinks it's his reflection—the long beard, drooping sacks under his eyes, and curved-in, slumped shoulders confuse him.)

Pete can stand still and upright for four hours but then he has to sit for eight.

Pete can read a magazine he has already read and be surprised by the new things he finds if he waits sixteen hours between readings. If he waits any less he grows bored and recites the magazine to the magazine.

Pete must shoot to kill.

After 312 hours Pete has chosen to wear diapers. He doesn't relish not wearing jeans (they were too tight to wear over the diapers), but he has taken a positive attitude towards it. He will see his relief and manager if they visit. He won't be in the bathroom to miss them. He won't miss a customer stealing (the store hates theft). Once, when he was in the bathroom, he heard the door chime. When he came out, no one was there. He looked four hours for a missing item. Pete wanted to check the security tape but that would mean stopping the tape being used. He didn't know what would happen if he did. What if he watched and saw something he didn't remember? What if he caught Pete sleeping? Would he report Pete if he did?

A robber wearing a black ski mask strolls in after 352 hours and demands all the money and snacks his pockets can fill. The robber is dressed in black. Pete can only see his eyes and mouth. The robber looks unreal, like loose facial features floating through the night sky.

Pete tells the robber, "Pete is ordered to shoot to kill."

The robber says, "I don't care." Then he says, "Where are your pants?"

"Do your worst," Pete says. He believes he has made himself clear. Just in case there is a misunderstanding, Pete presents the gun and reminds the robber of Pete's policy. He says, "I've been ordered to shoot to kill. I'll kill you, even though I want to kill Rupert. Those are my orders."

Pete cocks the gun and scratches the robber's nose with the barrel.

Before the robber leaves empty handed, they stand in silence for a long time. Pete tells himself an agreement was made.

Later, he hopes the robber wasn't Rupert. If the robber was Rupert, Pete would've fired. Pete would've shot to kill.

After 456 hours, Samantha materializes with a line of customers behind her. While crying, she lets Pete know she isn't there for sex. He barely recognizes her. He only misses sex and if she were positive about the situation—like him—she would want sex too. She'd tell him how the overtime is greatly appreciated; she'd kiss his chapped lips, take off his diaper, and lead him to the bathroom. She doesn't do any of this. She says, "Come home. You look horrible. I barely recognize you. Your skin is turning yellow and I think I can see your ribs and spine through your work shirt. You don't recognize me . . . You don't even know how many times I've been here, do you? I've come every day. Tell me you know that," she says.

He says, "Pete can't leave. Pete's relief hasn't arrived. Pete has responsibilities." He says, "We never close."

Customers make faces, get nervous, embarrassed, and leave. Some with goods in their hands.

Samantha says, "It's your family or work, Pete. You have to make a decision. You can't go on like this. You're hurting your family. You're hurting yourself."

"Don't worry. I'm a Professional Professional. I know what I'm doing."

She says, "I used to think so. Now I don't."

When he calls home, a man answers and Pete hangs up. The man wasn't Pete. Pete knows this but isn't sure. His mind works in circles and he's not sure of a lot of things. He does remember to change his diaper though. This he does remember.

Rupert comes in after 736 hours. He drifts through the aisles with a thumb under his chin.

The gun is heavier than Pete remembered. His shoulder slumps from its weight like his hand is stuck in the ground. When he checks the gun's magazine, he finds the bullet has been replaced with a note. It says: "Rupert's dead."

When he looks up, the store's empty.

A short man in an expensive suit delivers divorce papers. Pete signs them. He asks if he was the man that picked up the phone when Pete called.

The man tells Pete no. Pete doesn't believe him. The man cleans his glasses with his tie. It's pink and looks like an elongated tongue. Pete says, "Pete doesn't miss his wife. He only misses sex. But, even this, he is learning to forget. Soon, sex will mean nothing to Pete."

The man slips the divorce papers into an envelope, smiles, and leaves. His brown shoes click on the floor long after he's gone.

Pete is growing tired of the tiny, sad voice that keeps calling and asking for Daddy or Dad. This prankster calls at least five times a day and when she does, Pete says: "This is Pete."

He points at his nametag when he says this.

"There is no Daddy or Dad here," he continues in the professional tone the work manual advises to use. "Pete is here. How can he help you?"

"I want my daddy," the voice says, cracking, as the prankster pretends to cry.

"Daddy isn't here. I've checked the store's records and no Daddy has ever been employed at All Time Everyday No Exception Convenience Store. Have you checked to make sure you're dialing the right number?"

"Stop it, Daddy. Come home, Daddy."

"There's no Daddy here. There's only Pete. He can help you. He'd be happy to help you. He's a Professional Professional. It's his job."

After God knows how long (maybe God doesn't even know), Pete's eyes move as if some grounding tether has been cut. They hover, linger, and bulge, but they don't ever close or shut. He doesn't remember the last time he ate or drank something. This doesn't matter. All that matters is the store, work, and for Pete not to sleep.

When he looks in the mirror or the TV, he doesn't see the bent and bearded creature he's become. He doesn't see the yellow skin that matches his uniform polo or the emaciated hips that poke over the top of his diaper like two doorknobs. He sees the store.

He likes to tell customers: "Come in, the store is open. Till the end of all things, the store will be open. You can come in anytime. I'll be here. Pete will be here."

When the end comes, Pete will be at the store and he'll know he can close it.

This will never happen.

The store will always be open. Pete will always be there. The lights will never turn off. They'll never turn off. Even after Pete is dead. Or gone. Or asleep.

Sunday Morning Breakfast

Taylor Crain

SUNDAY MORNING BREAKFAST GOSSIPED. SEMANTICS AND POLITICAL PIECES WERE subjects meant to be saved for later in the week; on Tuesdays, perhaps, when Tommy and Luke had oatmeal and one boiled egg, or on Wednesdays, when Mrs. Breiner hosted a tidy brunch for the other neighboring housewives.

Sunday simply made sense; let it be responsible for the all-important topics of household doings and considerations. The eggs were all present and sunny-side up, which is how they preferred themselves. The various meat products, who made a habit of being absent on the less-important weekdays, were all accounted for. There was toast, of course, potatoes, and this particular morning they were joined by the indulgent, yet highly respected opinion of thickly syruped pancakes. Mr. Breiner was to blame for the lushness of the banquet. It was the only morning he ate with the family, and Mrs. Breiner tried to make it a special occasion for him. He attempted to dissuade her on multiple occasions, using the phrases "I want you to relax," and "You never get to sit down and eat." Truthfully, after fifteen years of marriage, Mr. Breiner despised his wife's cooking. But he sat, Sunday after Sunday, with his black coffee, and on average managed to choke down a piece of rye toast and one or two greasy eggs without so much as a resentful grimace.

Breakfast knew this, and found a sort of vague delight in the dance.

It was a relaxed, sort of lazy ten o'clock. A purple mermaid sleeping bag lay crushed and crumpled at the foot of the living-room stairs, which could be clearly observed from the kitchen table. Francesca had spent the night; she was a new friend of Shelly's, and Dominican and Catholic besides, so the family found reasonable excuse to skip church services. Shelly's given name was Shirley Michelle, after Shirley Temple, and she was ten with blond hair her mother kept in braids. Francesca's given name was Francesca; she was eleven with black hair her mother chopped off at her ears. Last night she opened her purple mermaid sleeping bag and told Shelly that it was all right, that no one would know, and that it was just for pretend anyways.

Breakfast saw how Shelly's little white hands shook when they buttered her pancakes, how she had been so concentrated on last night, when Francesca pulled off her Frogger bottoms, that she had forgotten she did not care for hash browns and had two helpings. She screamed and let her knife clatter to the linoleum when Sampson licked between her legs.

"Out of my kitchen! Did you hear me? Out of my kitchen! Boys—take it outside!"

After being rejected by the youngest Breiner, Sampson had unwedged himself from under the table, and in the process crossed paws with Mrs. Breiner's heels. Elated with the prospect of being excused from the family meal, Tommy and Luke obediently leapt from the table and led the mutt out by his frayed collar.

"What're we doin' later, Tommy?"

"We? Nothin'."

"But I though you said—"

"I didn't say shit!"

"OK. I was just ask'n." Luke put his face into Sampson's back. "What're you doin' then?"

"Nothin'. Don't worry about it."

"How come I can' ever come?"

"'Cause you're too little, that's why."

Luke breathed in the rainy smell of the dog's fur until he heard Tommy go down the driveway to meet his friends, where they would surely smoke the pot and talk about pussy, and other things he wasn't supposed to understand. Luke understood. He was twelve and only two years younger than Tommy. He knew what pussy was. Connie Lisler was pussy.

First Court Appearance, 2009

Christopher Semel: *Brothers*

Only after moving away from home did I realize that my brother and I lived worlds apart. Other than an irrefutable genetic cocktail and mutual domestic frustration, we shared little else. To escape the frustrations of a dissatisfying home life, I sought sanctuary at my then-girlfriend's house. My brother, in turn, distanced himself by delving into a world rife with questionable friends, hobbies, and practices. *Brothers* is an ongoing investigation of Timothy Robert Semel, my younger brother. By documenting my brother's life, I am able to realign the orbits of the worlds we inhabit. This ongoing series is a chance for me to reconnect with him and better understand his world.

See more of Christopher Semel's work at **www.christophersemel.com** and **www.edelmangallery.com**.

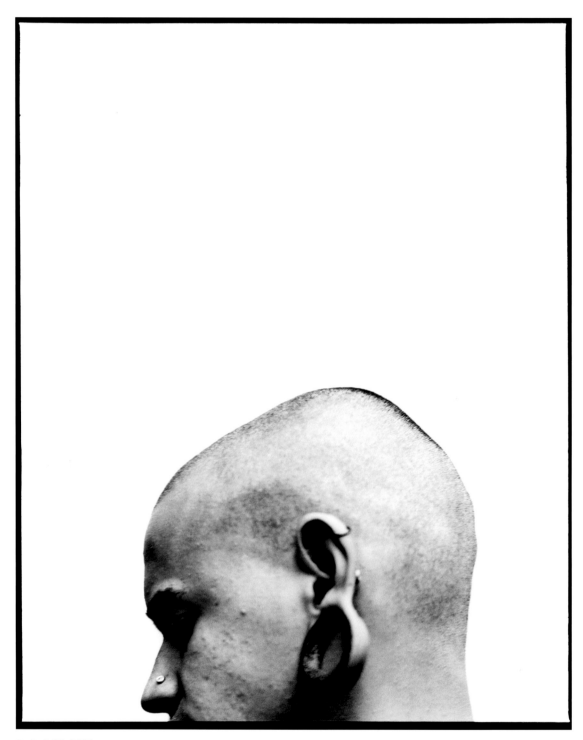

Portrait #2, 2009

Portrait #4, 2009

Smile, 2010

Mother's Lap, 2002

Sarah Faust: *My Mother*

I am fascinated by the beauty and resilience, yet fragility, of life. In photographing my loved ones, in particular, my mother and my daughter, as well as myself, I investigate this coexistence. In my photographs I attempt to explore this concept by highlighting physical gesture and the weaving of tension and flow between my subjects. I am intrigued by the idea that one's own memories and feelings may overlap from one generation to the next, and that through storytelling, personal artifacts, and shared experience, a legacy is created. This collapsing of time and intertwining of life and death is a large part of the human experience. In these psychological distillations, I hope to reveal the complexities of our existence.

See more of Sarah Faust's work at **www.sarahfaust.com** and **www.edelmangallery.com**.

Pink Sleep, 2004

Birthday Cake, 2007

Fawn, 2009

"He doesn't love you," he told the dog gently, reassuringly. "He doesn't love you," he repeated, when Sampson did nothing but pant in reply. He jammed his fist into its hind legs then, and the dog scrambled and growled but fell anyhow. Luke told him and told him, but all the dumb animal ever understood was fists and kicks.

"Mom! Sampson bit me again."

Mrs. Breiner examined her youngest son's wrists, and looked in vain for the elder. "Where was Tommy?"

"He left."

"You'll be all right, baby, you'll be all right. Go to the bathroom and in a minute I'll come up to bandage it. Just a minute." Once he shuffled away she looked to her husband expectantly, who did not look back. "That's one bite too many. There's something wrong with that dog. You need to take care of it."

Shelly looked up from her breakfast mush. "Take care of what?"

"Nothing, honey. Why don't you take Francesca outside and show her your new clubhouse?"

The braided head studied the plate again. "I don't wanna."

"Don't be rude. And don't say *wanna*."

The girls got up and went out the back door, one taking the other's hand before being shoved away. Mr. Breiner retrieved his hunting gun from its case in the den and was in the front yard, calling to the dog. With Luke waiting patiently in the upstairs bathroom, Mrs. Breiner quickly grabbed for the box nestled at the very top of the fridge. Inside there was nothing particularly expensive or secretive. She pushed aside envelopes and knock-off pearls to bury a faux gold brooch. It belonged to that bitch Clara Ashton—but it didn't anymore, did it? And she'd never have it back. It wasn't worth anything, of course it wasn't, but it had been her mother's and she wanted to give it to her daughter at her wedding next Saturday. She wasn't now.

"Ma!"

"Coming, sweetheart!" She giggled and closed the box with a kiss before returning it to its home—and breakfast saw.

When they were ten minutes into the wooded ridge behind the main street, Mr. Breiner stopped with the leashed dog and let it wander while he sat. He contemplated shooting the thing, he really did. His wristwatch, a Christmas gift from his wife, was nearing eleven. He considered the dog; then put the rifle into his mouth.

Breakfast heard the shot, as did Mrs. Breiner. With one of her children adequately bandaged and the other two safe with friends, she was in the process of scraping the eager meal into the garbage. "Good riddance," she muttered. The thing was always filthy.

By eleven fifteen she had finished clearing the table and cleaning up laughing, chanting eggs. *We know everything!* The trash rustled with glee, with gossip, with purple mermaid sleeping bags and faux gold brooches. *We know everything.*

Dear Sean

Stephanie Velasco

YOUR HAND WAS RIGHT THERE—INCHES AWAY FROM MINE. I COULD SO EASILY have brushed a finger against your hand and called it an accident. It would've been just like the first time we held hands, three years ago, watching *So I Married An Axe Murderer* in the basement of my parents' house.

When you, Nick, Jimmy, and I got to the sushi restaurant, it was all full except for the floor seating that was supposed to make us feel more "authentic." I was in Knoxville that weekend, visiting Jimmy at UT before my fall semester started in Chicago. He and I had been doing the long distance thing on and off for almost a year at that point. Nick was spending the night at your place on his way back to the University of Alabama. Though I would rather have spent my last evening in Knoxville in bed with Jimmy, it would have been rude not to see Nick, my family's honorary adopted white kid, at the very least for dinner. And he was staying with you, so I couldn't just see him and not see you.

So we all squeezed around a small, rectangular table, only a foot or so off the ground. You and I sat cross-legged, wedged between the table and the floor-to-ceiling windows, while Jimmy and Nick sat with their long legs stretched out in opposite directions, looking like life-size bookends.

"So Sean," Jimmy said, "how're the new housemates treating you?"

"Meh, you know Alex and Peter," you said, shrugging. "They're not really around much, so I get the place to myself a lot."

Jimmy nodded and then chuckled. "That's cool. So I'm still the best roommate you've ever had, right?"

"Oh, definitely," you said, without a moment's hesitation. "They don't even have Madden."

I glanced down at your hand again, then quickly looked up at Jimmy, across the table. He winked at me. I've always found it kind of creepy when people wink at each other, but somehow when Jimmy does it, I don't automatically cringe. He's a sturdy, good-looking guy—a bit of a jock, when it comes down to it—but somehow he can pull off the non-creepy wink. So when he winked at me then, I smiled back at him and tried to busy my hands with a more innocent objective.

I split my chopsticks apart, but one flew and landed on the floor between you and me. We both reached for it and our fingertips tangled briefly, just like in the movies. I was suddenly reminded of Scholars' Bowl and how you used to hold the buzzer with your left hand so we could hold hands under the table. And then I remembered how Mr. Schull separated us after we lost that round. I had forgotten, though, how cool and smooth your hand felt, and how adorably pale your skin looked in comparison to mine. I looked up to see if Jimmy had noticed the finger graze, but he and Nick were both engrossed in trying to figure out how to hold their own chopsticks.

"There you go," you said, sliding my rogue chopstick back on the table. The way you said it was like even you hadn't noticed the physical contact.

"Thanks," I said, without looking at you. Maybe I had imagined our fingers touching. But surely I wasn't imagining the old familiar fluttery jitters migrating from my stomach to my chest and back again.

After that point in the dinner, I was just looking for an excuse to touch you. I needed to confirm that we had, in fact, secretly brushed hands under the table. In case the first time was just an accident, I wanted to give you a chance to do it on purpose. In case you were just working up the courage to hold my hand again, I wanted to show you I was open to the idea—asking for it, even. But with my boyfriend sitting across the table from us, I'd have to be sneaky about it. When the server came with our food, I held the plate as awkwardly as possible so you would have no choice but to graze my hand when you took it from me. Somehow, though, your plate-grasping skills were far too advanced for such an elementary maneuver. I threw down the last of my beer.

"These tables were not made for normal-sized people," Jimmy said, struggling to maneuver his body into a more comfortable position. He ended up putting his legs straight out in front of him, so they fit under the table. His legs stretched out to my side of the table, so that I was sitting in between his ankles, his right leg creating a barrier between you and me.

"You can leave your legs like that, if you want," I told him, patting his shins, happy to have his legs act as a barrier between you and me. I thought his leg-wall would keep me from doing anything rash. I thought his leg-wall would remind me that I was with him now—that this was not high school anymore; this was not a football game where you and I would secretly share the pockets of my yellow coat. This was a sushi restaurant, and we were in college, and we were all supposed to be much more mature now.

"Nah, it's OK," he said. "I'm just stretching." And then he pulled his legs back to his side of the table, and the leg-wall was gone.

Didn't he notice that something was happening, or maybe, possibly about to happen here? Some months into Jimmy's and my relationship, we had confessed to each other that we were, at least in the beginning, each other's rebound people. We didn't talk about it after that, so I guess we both quietly assumed that he was over his ex and that I was over you.

"I'm paying," you said, halfway through a piece of tuna. The rest of us politely argued with you, but you insisted. You waved us off with that scrunchy "I'm serious" face of yours. "Happy birthday and Merry Christmas." I never could say no to that face.

So Nick, Jimmy, and I ordered another round of beers, and you asked for mochi ice cream. I asked for mochi, too, even though I wasn't quite sure what it was. You always were the more Asian one of the two of us, even with your bright orange hair and freckles.

"What's the point of sharing if we get the same thing?" you said faux-exasperatedly when I ordered green tea flavor, as well. I mumbled something about not realizing we were sharing and then ordered mango instead. Boyfriends and girlfriends shared desserts, not ex-boyfriends and ex-girl-friends. In case you were trying to send me a not-so-secret signal, I covered for the both of us by offering my actual boyfriend a spoonful.

"Jimmy, do you want to try some?"

He didn't want to, of course. He's not very adventurous when it comes to food. Sometimes it's kind of cute and makes me want to tousle his wavy brown hair, like he's a little kid. Other times it's not, like when I'm craving

Thai or Mexican or Indian food and all he wants is a burger. Or devastatingly plain cheese pizza. Nick passed on the ice cream, too.

"Watching your weight?" I joked.

"Yep," he said, patting his nonexistent belly with both hands.

He probably launched into some memorized stand-up bit about diets, but I didn't hear because you started leaning toward me. I inhaled and smelled your once-familiar scent of dryer sheets and worn teddy bears. I remembered how in the summer you always smelled like sunscreen. I wondered what happened to that bottle of sunscreen I bought just so I could smell you when I left for Chicago.

"Can I have a bite of yours?" you asked. It was almost a whisper, a secret.

"Yes, you may," I said, clearing my throat and sitting up straighter. I pressed the backs of my fingers to my face. I knew I was getting red. It was probably the beers.

Of course you and I ended up sitting beside each other on the ride home. Nick drove and Jimmy, with his long legs, got shotgun. To make matters worse, Nick's duffel bag and half a dozen other objects were crammed into one side of the car. There was no avoiding body contact; our legs and hips had to touch. I put my hands between my knees and compressed my shoulders and elbows together.

With every slight curve in the road, your arm brushed against mine. The place where the hair on your arm grazed the hair on mine burned and prickled. I took shallow breaths. I couldn't tell if it was an accident or if you were doing it on purpose. Then, when Nick took another curve, I felt the warmth of your lower leg against mine. On high school trips junior year, back before we were a couple, you used to make sure we sat beside each other on the bus, and you'd press your leg against mine, ever so slightly, when the bus swerved one way or the other. The windows of Nick's car started to fog up, and the air inside got warm and a bit moist.

"Sorry, guys," Nick said, "the AC's 'on the fritz,' as they say."

You shifted your weight to your left butt cheek, momentarily unsticking the right side of your body from me. That side of my body, the side you were sitting by, was sweating more than the side by the car door. I could see a sharp curve in the road up ahead, and I braced for impact.

I'd hoped that Nick would take the long way back to Jimmy's apartment—through downtown, past the Sunsphere and the Bijou Theatre where we'd seen Andrew Bird together senior year. I wanted the Bijou to remind you of how we drove four hours on a school night to see a man in striped socks play "Armchairs" on his haunting violin. I wanted you to remember how closely we stood that night—so close that I could feel your breath on the back of my neck. But none of that happened, because Nick took the turnpike, and we got to the apartment in seven minutes, flat.

"M'lady," Jimmy said, opening my door and sweeping his hand out in front of him. I knew he was getting horny, because he always gets particularly chivalrous when he wants some. We all said quick good byes in the parking lot, Jimmy repeatedly mentioning my early flight time.

"Yeah, I'd invite you guys in, but, uh, I've got to drive her to the airport reeeeeally early tomorrow. So we should probably get to bed soon. Since we've got to wake up so early, I mean."

You and Nick stood side by side behind the car waiting, I assumed, for the farewell hugs. We probably wouldn't see each other for several months, so hugs were definitely in order—at least from me, the token girl. I hugged Nick the way you'd hug a distant cousin: longer than usual, but still with a hint of obligation. When I side-stepped to face you, there was a moment of hesitation where we were both trying to decide between the intimate face-to-face hug and the friendly, but not too friendly, side hug. I opened both of my arms slightly, indicating the former, but you must've missed it because you mechanically turned your body and threw a casual arm around my shoulder.

"See you later," was all you said as you squeezed my torso. But then, when you let your arm fall, I could've sworn your fingers trailed down my bare arm. I shivered even though the air outside was as thick and humid as it was inside Nick's car.

"Don't leave, OK?" Jimmy had said after we made love that night. I knew he meant he didn't want me to fly back to Chicago in the morning, but when he said it, his voice cracked a bit, as if he were holding back tears. I'd never seen a boy cry before, and seeing my typically stoic boyfriend lose it scared me. He meant "don't leave *ever*." What I should've said was, "I love you. I won't ever leave you." But I didn't. I just kissed his wet cheek and said, "Shh." After he fell asleep, I got a text message from you. All it said was, "Two a.m., bedroom window."

That night, your dark silhouette appeared at the garden-view window of Jimmy's bedroom. I looked at the clock. Two a.m., just like you'd promised. I don't think you'd ever been so punctual in your life. I had left the sliding window cracked open for you. You slid your glasses down your nose, neatly folded them, and set them down on the asphalt in front of the street-level window. It was exactly the way you used to fold your glasses and set them in the armrest of my pick-up truck right before we made out in your parents' driveway. Every single time, it was exactly the same way: careful, as if you had all the time in the world to fold them just so.

I slowly peeled myself away from Jimmy's sleeping body until I stood eye to eye with your thin-rimmed glasses from inside Jimmy's bedroom. I looked down at Jimmy, sleeping on the twin bed where I was standing. He always sleeps facing the door, which means he always sleeps facing away from me. I read once in a women's magazine that a guy's sleeping position says a lot about how he feels about the relationship. According to the article, Jimmy was a "Commitmentphobe." To be fair, the article did say I should cut him some slack, because "he may just not know how to give you the closeness you desire." I like to think I'm an evolved woman and don't put much stock in those kinds of magazines, but for some reason I always think of that article when Jimmy and I sleep together. He's the deepest sleeper I know, and his eyelids don't even flinch when I try to flip him around to face me in his sleep.

"C'mon," you whispered, "I'll help you out." You swiped your head to the side, brushing your red hair out of your eyes as you knelt by the window, looking down into the bedroom. You stuck your hand through the window to help me up.

The first time I ever snuck out a window was to meet you at the Ridgefields playground. You were allowed to be out past eleven, but I still wasn't. "Foreign parents," we'd said, shaking our heads while crouching together in the child-sized tower. When your mom called, wondering what time you'd be home, you said you didn't know, and she seemed OK with that. When my parents called, wondering where the heck I could possibly be at midnight, I was grounded for a month.

The second time I crawled out my bedroom window in the middle of the night, you picked me up in your car at the end of my block. That was the time we drove out to an open field where there were no streetlights so we could see the stars.

The third time, you and I just sat in the back of the pick-up, and you wiped my snotty nose with your shirtsleeve. It was the night before you left for math camp. We hadn't spent more than a couple days apart before that. Six weeks seemed like forever back then.

I looked at your hand, thinking about how hours earlier all I had wanted to do was touch it, hold it. I looked back at Jimmy, who was tangled in the thin bed sheets. What would happen if I left and he woke up? I wouldn't be grounded, of course, but I knew he would be just as worried as my parents had been the first time I snuck out.

And now, here you were at the window. You were the one who had kissed my wet cheek when you had to leave. You were the one I had pleaded with never to leave. And now you were back, and you were asking me to sneak out with you. To leave Jimmy. I stared at your hand, as if the solution would write itself on your palm. I waited and waited, but nothing came. The lines on your hand just crossed and uncrossed.

Just then, Jimmy rolled over in bed. His shins met my heels, and I would've fallen backward had you not grabbed my hand. For a second I froze, leaning backwards with only your hand to counterbalance myself. Jimmy, true to form, was still fast asleep, and when I looked at you through the window, you let out a relieved chuckle. You pulled me upright, and I brought my face back up to the window, still holding onto your hand. I finally exhaled.

"All right, let's try again," you said, quickly reaching your other arm around to put a hand on my back. We looked like we were trying to ballroom dance through the window.

"I don't think I can," I said, shaking my head. The warm pressure on my back slackened, and you retracted your arm. I didn't want to sneak through windows anymore. We were older, and we were more mature, and sneaking out windows just was not something mature people did. I couldn't look you in the eye, so I just kept looking at our still-clasped hands. I knew that if I looked you straight on, I'd see exactly what I wanted to see—exactly what I'd been wanting to see ever since you broke up with me. And if I saw that look—that goofy grin you used to get when you looked at me across the room in Mrs. Harrell's calculus class—I knew I wouldn't be able to stop myself from hopping out that window right then and there.

So I squeezed your hand the way we squeeze hands in church after saying the "Our Father" or at Girl Scout meetings after singing "Make New Friends." I told my fingers not to linger, and miraculously they didn't. All I could say was "Bye." "Good bye" would've been wrong. "Good bye" was too final.

Without bothering to close the window, I carefully placed my body, piece by piece, back on the bed beside Jimmy. When I looked back, I could still see your shadow hovering right outside the window. For a while, everything was still. I silently challenged your shadow to a staring contest, but before I could say, "Go," you, your shadow, and your carefully folded glasses were gone.

I turned to my side to face Jimmy's sleeping form, and for once he was facing me. I kissed him in the place between the bridge of his nose and the corner of his eye—the place he always kisses on me. His eyebrows furrowed, and he slowly opened his eyes.

"Is it already time to go?" he asked, his voice soft and gravelly.

"No, no, go back to sleep," I said, scooting myself closer to him. "I'm not leaving yet."

Mike on the Fourth

Max Wentzel

THE NIGHT BEFORE THE FOURTH OF JULY PARTY, MIKE FAILED TO FALL ASLEEP. Again. Three nights of staring up at the bedroom's crossbeams and trying to get Dick Hartford's face off the blades of the ceiling fan had turned Mike into a twitching mess. When he quit trying, just before five in the morning, the sun and the moon were still switching places. There was a faint glow in the sky, neither bright nor dull, that made Mike feel like he was walking around the craters of the moon. It was bright through the bay window in the kitchen. He had to look through splayed fingers as he pounded to the fridge. He'd actually remembered to make coffee the night before, but because of a combined sense of sleep-deprivation, a sudden bout of depression, and blind patriotism, he felt the right thing to do was to crack open a Pabst on Independence Day.

He parted the screen door and stood in the middle of his long, slender deck that jutted out into the backyard like a plank over the Indian Ocean. Earlier in the week he'd confirmed a long-held suspicion that someone other than the man who raised him, Wally, was actually his father. That man was Dick Hartford, and the same face that smirked at Mike from the dusty photo in his parents' attic stared at him from the mouth hole of the beer can.

He blinked seven times. In his boxers, white tank, and slippers, he traced the sun's slow path as it crept over the mountains and colored the sky inch by inch. Mike shook Dick's smile out of the center of the sun, took a hearty gulp of beer, and yawned with the solar system.

The two picnic tables on the deck needed to be set, but Mike shambled across the yard to the edge, where the land sloped down into a bowl of trees and dry grass and dirt. Bounded by the five-foot slope of yard and the chain fence to their neighbor's tennis court, it was his own clubhouse, his sanctuary.

Near the back of that indented piece of land, Mike walked up to his set of quoit beds. "Hey babies," he said, and guzzled down his beer suds.

Quoits ran in the Wentzel family like food recipes ran in other clans. To the uninformed, the game of quoits was essentially the same as horseshoes, except the horseshoes were round. Well, Mike hated the uninformed almost as much as he hated horseshoes. Centuries ago, maybe even millennia, the ancient civilizations connected the ends of horseshoes to make round, metal hooks. The game started with the goal of getting the disc farther than your enemy, but someone smart came up with the idea to stick a pin in the ground as a target. It became about precision, hurling the metal donut across the eighteen feet to land as close to the pin as possible, and if lucky, pitching a perfect ringer.

Mike ripped the tarps off the clay of the quoit beds and felt a sense of importance. The game was primarily played in Pennsylvania, more specifically the Pennsylvania Dutch region, and not many other places. He was keeping the tradition alive after all the years of the damned horseshoes dominating America. To put it simply, it was hard to hang a ringer because the hole in the quoit was small. That's part of the skill. Well, in the 1920s, some asshole decided he wanted to only make ringers, so he just started throwing the horseshoes as they were. Only ringers! Of course it caught on. There was no hole, only an open space easily maneuvered around the pin. It caught on because ringers were more glamorous than just getting a quoit really close to a pin. As far as Mike and the rest of the Wentzels were concerned, there was no skill involved in horseshoes. It was like shortening a football field to twenty yards so the teams could make touchdowns on every play.

Cheap fuckin' bastards, Mike thought, as he pounded the clay of his beds into a compact, level surface with the metal stomper. The Wentzels, a family he had once thought of as his own, had preserved the tradition of the ancient game. Wally had taught all the boys when they were young, and Mark, Mike's nine-year-old son, had learned to pitch from the moment his little hands could grip the rim of the quoit. Mike wasn't sure if he was a Wentzel, but he was sure that he would hold onto that tradition no matter what he found out.

As the day wore on, Mike pounded the clay. Suzy set the tables, organized the food, laid out the Slip 'N Slide, picked up the Pabst and Heineken from Ron's Beer Depot, and greeted every member of the family as they walked through the hot grass to the back of the house. The whole time, Mike watered the clay, pounded it, washed the quoits, set up the grate in the barbecue pit, and sat in the shade on top of his cooler. He never once left the little indent of thick trees and quoit beds.

As with every party, Wally and Joan, the family elders, were the first to show up. Mike watched Joan, in her blue sweater and white cotton pants, leading Wally, in his suspenders and Navy-style cropped hair, around the side of the house from their blue Oldsmobile. Wally glanced down into the bowl in the yard and waved over Joan's silver curls. Mike took a drag of the lone cigarette he'd been hiding in his closet for weeks and leaned against the biggest tree.

"I thought you quit that shit," Wally yelled.

Mike stubbed out the final half in the dry dirt. "Just for old time's sake," he said. "I'll be right in." And he wanted so much to call him dad, to feel the way he felt when he was little Mikey, learning carpentry skills from his dad, his Wally. Now he was just Wally, not Dad. Mike bit his lower lip and breathed heavily through his teeth. He scratched his beard and grabbed another beer from the cooler.

Nearly two hours and six beers into the party, Mike was partnered with Steve, throwing an easy game against Joe and Bill. Partners threw at opposite quoit beds, so Mike felt the pressure building up as Joe swayed in the wind by his side. Joe's feet shifted in his brown leather sandals. As Bill and Steve each threw their last pitches in the opposite bed, Joe stared off at the empty tennis court next door. Mike knew he was thinking of paddling those tiny green balls instead of giving a shit about his own game.

"That's three points for me," Steve said, scratching his clownish, orange curls and pointing his Heineken neck at Bill's chest, "and two for you."

"Might as well be over," Bill said, scratching the sunburn around the waist of his blue swim trunks. His blond wavy hair, which had been tight and curly when they were kids, blew across his red, tanned face. "Mike, just get a quick point so we can start a new game."

Mike nudged Joe's fragile arm with the pulpy side of his fist. "Get goin'," he said. "You're up, young one."

Snapped out of his tennis trance, Joe bent down to pick up one of the quoits. An idea, partly fueled by his midday buzz, clicked in Mike's brain. He turned back a few steps and hoisted his body up onto the cinder blocks that made the barbecue pit. Luckily, no chicken was sizzling on the black grates, and no coals were burning under his feet, because he didn't even take the time to look. He felt his back heel merge onto the grates and then felt his weight push them down in the middle. He scuttled forward on the blocks before he could ruin the dinner for everyone. He glanced up and across the yard to the deck and saw that no one else at the party noticed his new height. Only the brothers, bent gloriously below him like peasants under the pope.

"Hey, hey," Mike said, loud enough for them to hear, but not enough to travel up to the deck and to the wives' game of Blitz.

Joe turned around, the muddy quoit rubbing against his dainty white pants above the knee. He squinted his small eyes, and his nose scrunched up like a bunny. "What is it?" He didn't seem to be amused, but Mike was.

"Cheer up, you little shit. You're lucky I even let you play in my holy quoit beds. You know how much time I spent slapping those beauties into the yard? Huh? A long fucking time, that's how long. I made sure the angles were perfect, that each side of each bed was three feet and not an inch below or above the clay. You know what you're doing to those beds right now, little Joey boy? You're making a disgrace out of them, turning them into fools. You suck, Joe. You have no skills."

Mike felt his voice start to rise. The kids still jumped through the sprinklers on the opposite side of the deck, Suzy and the ladies still played their game with their quarters clanging on the glass tabletop, and Wally still chopped the vegetables on the picnic table under the steaming sun. It was all clear. No one heard. Steve put his Rolling Rock on the shelf built into the tree and crossed his arms, giving Mike a silent "Go on . . ." So he did.

"I can't even remember the last time you got a ringer. When was it? Jesus, was it way back at uncle Phil's on Christmas Eve? Fuck. Yeah, the only reason you got it was you never cleared off the snow, and you went first, so of course your quoit was just gonna skim across the snow sheet and wrap around the pin." Mike noticed he was pacing the cinder blocks, bent forward like an old wizard telling a secret to a bunch of scared kids. "You prick. You cheat. You scum."

Bill stepped across the grass between the beds and held out his hand. His mouth was straight and tense like he was scolding his own kids. His voice was lower than Mike's. "You need to stop. We all know where you're going with this, and I can't think of a worse time than now to bring this shit out."

"What? I'm just talking about quoits here." Mike motioned with both arms like he was tossing in slow motion. He squinted his left eye and imagined a giant metal disc spinning around Joe's twig body.

Joe moved forward and into a sharp ray of light. He squinted but stayed, only a foot from Mike's face. "Please don't do this. Not near Sandy and the kids."

"Oh, don't get all scared. She can't hear me. Steve probably can't even hear me anymore. Plus, we all know you ain't got any fight in you. Just stay right here. Keep holding the quoit if it makes you feel any better."

Mike picked up the beer on the corner block, but looked at Joe the whole time. Guzzled, but stared down the can at the terrified eyes. "Damn, that beer sure does taste good. You know what, Joe? What's so funny about all this? You're the only one who doesn't even have quoit beds! Imagine that! A Wentzel without quoit beds. And to kick us in the ass even more, you play horseshoes with your fucking co-workers! Horseshoes: the easy way out. That should be that game's motto. Is it, Joe? Because I think it's yours, what with you not telling Sandy and all. Seems pretty easy to me. And here I think I'm the outsider. A man without a family. Well, let me tell you something, little special one."

Mike stretched out his hand so the whole quoit area lay under it, a puppet stage under its master's fingers. "I put these beauties in the minute I bought this house, way before I bought Suzy any mulch for her gardens. The precision I put into this, they could do pro tournaments right here at our own picnic. And we all know how amazing yours are, Steve. Shit, the way they straddle each side of your creek and the quoits go flying over the water, and holy fucking Moses, it's a sight for sure. And Bill, well, at least you tried."

Bill walked across the quoit beds and over to the cooler with the chicken bits inside, just to look busy. Joe stayed silent, but glanced over at the deck. Mike followed his gaze and saw that Suzy and Sandy were watching them as they scooped bean dip at the picnic table.

Mike watched Steve pat down the clay of the far bed with the metal stomper, whistling into the mud, and knew that his brother was trying to avoid looking suspicious. "Just get on down from there," Steve said, pounding away.

"What's gotten into you?" Suzy yelled over.

Surprised he'd gotten so far into it without anyone noticing, Mike jumped down, holding out his beer can so it didn't spill on his sneakers. "Just messin' around," Mike said, louder now. "Boys being boys."

The ladies balanced their loaded paper plates on their palms and walked back to the shade under the deck awning. In his own bowl of shade, Mike wiped a batch of invisible sweat off his forehead and flung it in the dirt. Both Bill and Steve were at the open cooler, unwrapping the chicken bits to get ready for the grill. Joe stepped away and grabbed a Coors out of the red cooler against the metal fence by the neighbor's tennis court. Baby Joey's hand trembled as he tried to pry a fingernail under the tab.

Mike saw a helpless fool, the same child he'd saved all those times growing up. Joe had soft hands, the delicate fingers of a real estate agent that only ever touched a keyboard or a pencil. The most extreme form of manual labor he ever encountered on the job was nailing a sign with his fake smile on the side of an empty house in Mt. Gretna or pounding wooden stakes into the ground. There was a point in Mike's life when he envied Joe's career: the security, the ease, the ability to actually hold a new couple's fate in his hands. But it had led Joe to a point where he couldn't build a quoit bed or open a goddamn beer, and it had led him into the muscular, manly arms of Debra when he should've been home holding the soft arms of his wife.

"What the fuck, Mike?" Joe said, as his nail popped from under the tab over and over. "Are you that drunk already?"

Mike stepped up to Joe and ripped the can out of his hands. Mike's hands were stiff and sturdy from years of construction work. He had calluses between every knuckle on his fingers and all over his palms, so severe that Suzy once made him wear gloves that were filled with lotion to bed. It lasted for an hour before Mike slipped them off and left them for the garbage man. His fingernails were so thick that clippers couldn't cut through them, and he had to keep them trim by filing them down every other day. They were long for a man, but covered in dirt and black specks, even after scraping them with industrial soap for three rounds of the birthday song. The thickness of his nails matched his hair.

He jammed his middle nail under the tab and crunched the tin seal. "Not drunk yet," he said, handing the beer back to Joe. He realized he'd been playful up on the cinder blocks. It must have been hard for the brothers to tell if he was having harmless fun or trying to be malicious. Well,

Mike wanted to make sure Joe wasn't confused anymore. He turned his lips so far the opposite of a smile that Joe couldn't even see them through the tangled, black beard. "Opening this can is the last thing I'm going to do for you."

Joe tried to counter the seriousness with a laugh. "Please, don't do this here."

Mike moved over to the cinder blocks and removed the metal grate. "I'm just trying to tell you that I'm done keeping your shit with Debra a secret. Well, shit, now's the time, Joey boy." He leaned the grates in the grass against the side of the barbecue pit and grabbed an open bag of coals with just the meat of his hands, knowing that Joey would have had to bear hug the bag just to get it off the ground. "What was that you told us back in May? What was that promise?"

"That I was done with Debra. And I am. We only see each other at work, and believe me, it's tough. But I think I'm going to be able to do it." Joe sipped the beer, arm still quivering.

Mike dumped the coals onto the tin foil that coated the bottom of the pit. "Yeah, but you were lying." He raised his voice over the clinking of the coals smashing the foil and each other, knowing with each word that Sandy was closer to hearing, and Joe was closer to losing his shit. "Bill, tell Joe what you told me."

Bill ripped the Saran Wrap off a breast and shook his head like he didn't want to have to say it. "Fuck, Joe, I saw you guys together at the Blue Bird on Thursday. The fucking Blue Bird! Why would you take her there, of all the bars in Lebanon?" He crumpled the Saran Wrap into a ball and threw it in a trash bag in front of the cooler.

Like a hawk hesitating in flight, Joe threw out his arms and lurched his neck forward. "We were on a business lunch. Holy shit. What the hell was I supposed to do? Harmless. I went home to Sandy and she home to her husband."

"You were holding hands the entire meal," Steve said, peeling the protection off a bundle of thighs.

As Mike dumped a second bag of coals on top of the first batch, he glanced over his shoulder to see Joe's mouth and his shoulder drooping all the way down to his belly button. "You're not going to mess up this family," he said.

"Seriously, Mike, why the hell have you turned into such an asshole today? What makes you Mr. Morality over here?"

Mike threw the paper bags against the metal fence and picked up the can of lighter fluid off the tiny, wooden table. "It's time for you to grow up. Over the past couple of weeks I've learned some stuff that makes me wonder who the hell I'm even supposed to be. I'm looking at lying in a completely different way now. I need to think what the hell family even means. So do you." He squeezed the tin fluid can and squirted the liquid all over the coals in zigzag patterns.

"What the hell are you talking about?" asked Bill.

"Oh yeah?" said Joe, resting a white Reebok on the grating. "Did you forget about five years ago, when you came this close," and he put his soft index nail right against his thumb nail, "to leaving Suzy for that skank?"

Mike's heart rate picked up, and he squeezed the lighter fluid can so hard that it crunched in the middle. Even though he'd been expecting Laurie to be brought up at some point, it didn't make it any easier to hear. He stared up at the deck because Joe's voice had been so loud, and he felt a little of what Joe must've been feeling the entire conversation.

Steve pulled out a matchbook from his back pocket and stepped between the feuding brothers. "Quit this right now." And he dropped a lit match into the pit, then another. The fire started in the middle and spread slowly to the corners before every coal was wrapped in orange flames.

Mike threw the bottle of fluid on the ground and trudged up the hill towards the deck. Laurie, Laurie. He hadn't thought about her in a long time, maybe a full year. That asshole just had to bring her up. As if he wasn't already worrying about enough shit, now he had to have that guilt refreshed in his skull.

"You're not gonna help with the chicken?" Bill called.

Mike took a long step from the grass to the deck and stared at Suzy, playing cards near the kitchen screen door. "Grill it yourselves."

Mike wasn't thinking straight. His mind was clogged with Laurie and Dick and Joe wrapped in muscular, woman arms. He snatched every beer can on the way to the kitchen, empty and full, until he had two arms full of warm tins like a homeless guy in August. As he passed the card table, none of the other ladies noticed him or the way he was acting, but he locked eyes with Suzy. He tried to smile. Suzy fanned her cards in front of her face and scowled at Mike. She knew him better than she knew the cards in her own hands.

When he got into the kitchen he dropped all the cans on the counter and started dumping the liquid into the sink, even when there were only suds bubbling over the sharp lips. Each bubble contained Dick's face, and the smile stayed trapped in the dome even as Mike turned the faucet on full blast and washed the tiny bastard down the drain. After four cans, he gripped the front of the sink and stared out the bay window to his deck and yard. There was so much around him, so many people, children, love, but he felt nothing. He watched Joan deal a new hand at the head of the table and saw lies. He looked to his left at Joe throwing the slimy thighs onto the black grates and saw cheats, scams, more lies. Even when he saw Suzy excuse herself from the table and stroll into the kitchen, it only reminded him of his own fuck-ups. He let go of the counter and hugged his chest.

Suzy scooted up behind Mike. He felt her huge, bobbing breasts push against the middle of his spine. Her arms slid up his ribs and over his elbows. It wasn't sexy or sensual. Mike had grown tired of those boobs decades ago. Her hug gave him a comfort that went back to his childhood. He dug his tense fingers into his collarbone and held on as Suzy squeezed his crossed arms into his chest. She swerved his bones across his body. She brought his elbows close together and threw them apart. She pressed her fingers into his bicep like she was dialing a quick number and palmed his forehead like she was opening a stuck jar.

Mike closed his eyes and saw only black. Dick Hartford didn't float in, and because of that Mike smiled. Suzy had been doing this for him since they'd started dating; she always thought it was a form of massage, something to relax him. In a way she was right, but Mike never told her the full truth. It would reveal things about Mike that he didn't want anyone to ever know, even Suzy.

He remembered that one night on the mountain as clearly as a Vietnam vet must remember the exact smells of the jungle. When they were kids, Wally and his brother Phil would take the Wentzel boys camping in the woods behind Phil's log cabin. On the top of one of the many hills scattered in the dense forests of Mt. Gretna, the men set up their camp. Wally made the boys, from six-year-old Joey to ten-year-old Mikey, carry all the supplies up the short trail through the thick pine trees. It wasn't long, only half a mile, but Wally wanted to teach them something about carrying their load, being responsible for their own futures. They mostly carried sleeping bags, although Mikey gripped the only tent, which was strictly for a rainy emergency. Their camping trips involved only the sleeping bags and the fire and the stars.

One night after they were all ready to go to bed, Wally started to tell a ghost story. The boys lay in their bags in a circle around the fire while Wally and Phil sat on an overturned log at the head of the trail. Phil had just told one about evil rabbits, but no one really bought the scares. It was Wally's turn.

"Way back, over two hundred years ago, there was a tribe of Indians who lived right in this very spot. Right here on Mt. Gretna. They were very superstitious, almost too spooked by every little thing that crossed their path. These beliefs caused their main tribe to banish them into this area around our campsite. Their main tribe moved on to other parts of the coast, but this one tribe of only thirty Indians made their home right here.

"One of their superstitions involved eagles. You know how there's really nothing more American than a big, beautiful bald eagle? Well, these guys, the Tomashaw, felt that the eagle was the most evil animal to ever grace the blue skies of Earth. Whenever they saw one soar across their village, they ran into their huts and threw spears at the sky as it flew away. See, the Tomashaw believed that if you were ever unlucky enough to have an eagle look you in the eye, that beast would steal your soul and feed it to its children. That's why they ran into their huts and closed their eyes, why they sent up constant smoke from their fires during the day: to keep the eagle from looking at their eyes."

Mikey, flat on his back, watched as Wally leaned on his knees through the vertical flames of the fire. He was muscular and had a voice that commanded everyone's attention, even people miles away who never knew the man. Back then, Mikey wanted to be just like Wally, and he remembered that feeling that day at his sink.

Wally continued, "After being here, so high up in the sky, prime flying grounds for eagles, more and more Tomashaw were getting stared at by passing eagles. They would be looking up a tree for a squirrel to eat and— BAM!— eagle looking them right in their eyes. Whether their souls were actually taken or not, those inflicted by the stare would die within three days. Cold sweats, throwing up, all the signs of the flu, but those Tomashaw knew what it really was: the lack of a soul. After a year there were only a dozen Indians left living.

"One day, a young Tomashaw about your age, Billy, was taking a nap in this very grass while the rest of the tribe was off hunting that night's dinner. This Tomashaw was dreaming about an eagle prying his eyelids open with its talons, staring so deep into his head that it stole his soul five times over. He woke up and, just when his eyes shot open, there was an eagle soaring across the sky right above his napping body. The eagle craned its neck and the boy saw the solid black eyes as they drilled into his soul and ripped it out of his body."

Mikey turned on his other cheek and saw all three brothers on their sides, fully captivated by the story, their hands cupping their chins. He saw them all shaking. Even though he didn't exactly feel frightened, his body started shaking anyway as Wally kept going.

"Now this was a smart Tomashaw. He knew he had three days to live and he didn't want to go out like all his people did before him. He saw the eagle circle the trees, scouting for more Indian eyes. The boy ran to the nearest tree and climbed, branch by branch, all the way to the top. There was the eagle, just one tree over. It seemed to taunt the boy, so he jumped from the highest branch and grabbed onto a sturdy branch on the next tree. He pulled himself up and saw the eagle in between both trees, just staring at him. It floated there as if on a string, clearly braver than any other eagle before it. The boy saw his chance and snapped off a thick, short branch by his feet. He held it over his head and ran along the big branch as if it were a plank, launched into the air, screaming for his soul, and sliced the smaller branch through the air where the eagle should have been. But just before the branch cut through the air, the eagle jerked up and flew off to its nest. The boy fell all the way to the ground, right on his back, right where you boys are sleeping. He died right here, never made it to the third day.

"Ever since then, the boy's soulless ghost roams the hills, looking for a good soul to steal. He only comes when you're sleeping, though, just rises out of the ground like steam. If you don't follow the rules, he'll rip your soul out of your body just like the eagle ripped his. And the only way to keep him from taking your soul is to cross your arms over your chest like an X. It's a cage that protects your body from the restless Tomashaw boy."

Wally slapped his knees. "All right, well, goodnight boys," he said, crawling to his own sleeping bag.

Mikey had been so engrossed in the story that he hadn't taken his eyes off the black of the sky. Mikey saw that each of his brothers had their hands crossed over their chests. All on their backs, all six arms crossed like the Tomashaw. Billy and Stevie had both fallen asleep at the end of the story, but Joey had his eyes wide open to the expanse of the sky. Only a few inches away, Mikey saw his little brother's body tremble.

"It's all right," Mikey whispered. "It was just a stupid story."

"I'm scared," Joey said without turning his head. "I wanna keep my soul."

Mikey brought his arms up so they crossed his sternum. "OK," he said back to Joey. "I'm just like you. If any of us moves our arms, including me, we all go down. OK? We're in this as brothers."

Joey just shook his little head. Mikey was the first to open his eyes the next morning. He looked at Joey and saw that his arms had shifted to his sides. He saw that his own arms had moved over the course of the night, and he wondered which of them had broken the pose first.

Over the next couple weeks, Mikey's brothers insisted on crossing their arms even in the safety of their own attic. He went along with it each time. He found himself hugging his chest whenever he waited to hear the results of a test or watched the climax of a horror movie, any time he wished his brothers were there with him. It calmed him down, even long after he left the house. It became engrained in his head as a way to focus.

As Mike stood there in the kitchen, he was ashamed that he still needed his arms crossed to relax. It reminded him of Joe. Fuck Joe. It reminded him of Wally. Who the hell was he, anyway? He kept thinking of Debra hugging Joe in the same way Suzy hugged him, those strong arms breaking Joe's tiny stems. He even saw Joan squeeze Wally, and then his stomach lurched when he saw Dick gripping his own arms, smiling at nothing.

Mike threw open his arms and stepped to the side. "All right, quit it."

"Did I hurt you?" Suzy said, backing up against the fridge.

Mike stepped out to the deck and only answered once he had the screen door shut. "I'm just done with that squeezing shit." And he stomped to the bean dip.

For the rest of the day, Mike kept mainly to himself. He leaned back against the tennis fence and watched as Bill and Steve flipped the breasts and thighs over the fire pit. They knew better than to ask for his help; they could sense that Mike was tucked into his mind again. He finished a beer, threw the can against a tree, and helped haul the top grate off the cooked chicken parts. "Come get it!" he yelled up to the deck. He burped, grabbed a chicken leg and another beer, and headed over to the Slip 'N Slide drying in the sun. The whole family passed him. They ran and bumped his shoulders. All twenty-five of them. He was a great white swimming through a school of carp. His son, Markie, chased his cousins to the food and never once looked at Mike.

Sandy and Joe were the last to step off the deck. Mike stopped in front of them. His body wavered as he took a gulp and the can clanged against the dimes in his pocket. Joe's face was sweating and Mike just wanted to slap the can across his cheeks so the cold sweat of the tin could mix with Joe's salt. Sandy's blond hair framed her smooth, thin face. Half a head taller than Joe, she was beautiful. She looked like a movie star from the

Golden Age, the ones Wally had been obsessed with, who had been dropped into the twenty-first century with a wardrobe of men's clothing. Even in Joe's blue Hawaiian shirt, which fit her better than it fit her slimy little weasel, Sandy looked like the kind of girl he would've run away with back when he was a two-timing pig. Sandy looked like Laurie, and it made his heart shift down two inches and crumble like wet Styrofoam.

She smiled. "Where you headed, Mike? Food's all ready."

Mike pushed the bottom of the can against the coins. Looking at the air above her head, he thought about it for a second and said, "You're way too pretty for little Joey over here. I ever tell you that?"

Sandy giggled with her lips closed and pushed his shoulder with a limp fist. "Always a charmer, Mike."

Joe grabbed Sandy's arm and tugged her toward the chicken pit. He was staying close to Sandy to make sure Mike couldn't speak to her, he could see that much. But he could also see the blind fear that turned Joe's eyes all white. As if he would tell Sandy right there in front of poor little realtor. Joe glared at Mike as he ambled away.

"You should've kept your arms crossed," Mike said, the can hovering under his chin.

Joe and Sandy stopped. "Say that again?"

"Nothing. We all dropped them, I guess. You were first, though." And Mike chugged.

Joe ushered Sandy forward by the base of her spine. "You're drunk, Mike. Get yourself something to eat." They walked down the hill to the chicken.

Mike wanted to throw the empty can at Joe's bobbing head, but he tucked it into one of Suzy's flower bushes lining the deck. Even though he'd had eight beers already, they'd been spread out since early morning. He felt heavy like a bear, slow like stone, not drunk. He ambled over to the Slip 'N Slide and picked up the hose by the middle so the nozzle dangled at his feet. He grabbed the metal with his other hand and sprayed down the plastic. The water rolled down the slick surface and picked up dirt and grass and gravel.

Mike looked across the deck and made sure everyone was still down at the chicken pit before he ripped off his shirt and kicked his shoes in the mud. He took a running start of only three feet and flopped his hairy belly onto the sleek yellow plastic. His skin rippled across his sides and he spit the water out of his beard as he glided the full twenty feet. He felt young, thought of Bricker Lane and the brothers and their bedroom in the attic of their childhood home. When his flabby skin hit the warm grass, he rolled over, and without realizing it, crossed his arms over his chest. The sky was a bright blue, and two skinny clouds floated over his eyes and crossed themselves. As they blended together, Mike twirled his thick chest hairs, understood that Joe was never going to tell Sandy, and closed his eyes. A second later he jolted at the sounds of the kids running back to the yard with their plates full of grilled legs. Before anyone saw him, his shirt was on, a beer was in his hand, and a plan was in his head.

As the darkness came over the party, everyone gathered on the deck to watch the fireworks. Even all eight kids, who had been running nonstop the entire day, settled against their mothers' legs and watched Mike and Joe set up the light show in the yard. It was their year to do it, and Bill and Steve could sit back and just watch without having to worry about finding the short wick in the dark.

Mike carried the last firework, a solid cube of sparks that was supposed to last for a full minute, from the back of his van to the grass at the head of the deck. He saw Joe's ass in the air as the tiny brother bent over and placed bottle rockets in a row of clear Rolling Rock bottles. Mike had stopped drinking a couple of hours before but started to feel dizzy when he bent down next to Joe. He plopped his fire cube so close to the first bottle that the shaking of the ground made it wobble in the grass.

Besides the four tiki torches burning around the deck, the only light in the yard came from a glow stick around Joe's girly, small waist. His fluorescent green body, hunched over, moved from glass to glass with such seamless fluidity that it looked like the grass had turned into a moving sidewalk. One bottle, plunk; two bottles, plunk; and so on. The fireworks he put in were small space shuttles with red stems twice as long that smacked all sides of the bottle when he dropped them in.

Mike flicked the first bottle. "This is the best you can do?"

"It was last minute," Joe said from down the line at the last bottle. "Asshole."

Mike felt the twenty pairs of eyes boring into his back, waiting for him or Joe to finally light something. He had to be careful. "Light yours first. If you couldn't even make the fucking trip down to Maryland to get some real shit, you don't deserve to get the finale."

He stood up and walked back to the deck. Sandy stood five feet away from everyone else, teetering into the yard. It was even more perfect than Mike could've imagined. He hopped up on the wood and let the toes of his shoes hang over the rim, balancing, proving to himself that he was sober. He was only inches away from Sandy, but he wanted to be closer. He took a step in and Joe's green glow turned around to stare.

Mike knew he was shaking in his glow stick. Sandy's arms were crossed. "I'm always nervous when you guys do this."

Mike heard the hushed whispers behind him, the kids' feet shuffling on the wood, the forks scraping on the paper plates. He couldn't see them, but he knew everyone was staring at Joe. Mike breathed deep like a skydiver in the plane's doorway and put his arm around Sandy's shoulder. Before he spoke, he saw Joe stand upright at the first bottle, flick a small flame from a lighter, and most likely shit his pants at the sight of his future possibly dying.

Mike was right up against her cheek, his nose pressed against the side of her nose, and he got the sudden urge to kiss her, to trace his tongue along the boundaries of her jaw, to bite her lower lip until it bled, to do it all while staring at Joe. It was Laurie; it was Sandy; it was Suzy watching. Instead, he moved his lips to her ears and whispered.

"There's something I gotta tell you." He shifted his eyes and saw her face slump, saw Joe's back get more rigid in the distance.

"Light the shit already, Joe," Bill yelled from behind them. They must have assumed Mike was telling her a joke.

He hadn't thought about what he was going to say, but he continued anyway. "When Joe was a little kid, I would find him jerking off into the toilet when he thought the door was locked. He looked at me and screamed and huddled into the bathtub so I wouldn't see."

Sandy tried to turn her face, but Mike's big head blocked it forward so Joe could see her reaction. "Mike, what?"

While still looking at Mike and Sandy, Joe bent down and lit the first rocket. It zipped straight in the air, just two inches from his arm, and sounded to Mike like the whistle Wally always made with his fingers. He heard the oohs and ahhs all around. He tapped Sandy's back like he was about to finish. "It happened more than once. And to most of us. I started to think he was leaving the door unlocked on purpose so someone would always catch him. It was probably some sick thrill of us seeing his wiener."

Mike pulled his head out of her space and saw Joe flicking the lighter over and over before he sent the next rocket whistling through the thick dark. He was suffering, dying to run over and punch Mike in the balls, whatever it took to stop him from talking to Sandy. She was just like Laurie and Mike couldn't figure out why he'd never noticed before. On the deck, as he patted a silent Sandy on the back and bounced over to Joe, he didn't know if telling Suzy about his Laurie affair all those years ago had made him feel more or less guilty, but he did know that Joe needed to make the same jump and figure it out for himself.

"I'll help him out," Mike called back to Steve.

Stopping in front of Joe's crouched body, Mike pulled out a book of matches.

He smirked and rubbed Joe's shoulder. "Let me get this next one."

"You think you're funny," Joe said, voice quivering.

Mike smiled; it worked. "That might be true. But I guess the question is if I actually am. Sandy sure didn't think so."

"You were just fucking with me. I know it."

A flick, a fizzle, a flash, a zip, and a whistle. Joe hobbled to rocket number four.

"Brother, you know me too well. Sandy is too sweet a person for me to ruin in front of the whole family. That's your job. In private. I was just telling her some family secrets."

Joe lit it and they both moved to rocket number five. All the kids gasped, even though the pop in the air was just a straight line of boring fire.

"So, what is it? Are you going to tell her, or am I gonna have to pay a visit to your house while you're at work banging away at Debby?"

"You're sick," Joe said, hobbling forward on bent knees.

"A lie kept me sick. I spent my whole life protecting you, preserving your image. Wally may not be my dad, and I know it's a different kind of lie, but shit, Joe, lies are lies, and I see how they fucked me up. I can't even sleep. Not in three days."

Joe sent the fifth rocket in the sky. "You know that's bullshit about Dad."

As Joe hunched and hobbled, Mike traced the same path with his back straight and arms over his bloated beer belly. "What if you keep this affair up and have some tiny little babies with Debby girl? Let's say you raise those babies and they never know about your other life. Matt and Andrew never know about these others kids and then when they're, say, fifty-six, they all find out. Different circumstances, sure, but still fucked up."

"You're not thinking straight."

"Maybe not, but it might matter if I gave a shit."

Joe went back for the sixth and final rocket, but Mike leaned in. He pushed Joe's hand away and struck a match, sent fire up the fuse. Joe fell back on his heels. Mike watched the fire spurt out across the black sky. Wally's whistle joined the cheers, and Mike joined Suzy on the deck, his mind on the cooler of beers by the kitchen.

Craven

Julia Plale

TO THE LESS DISCERNING EYE OF A MORTAL, I WOULD APPEAR TO BE A WOMAN
with no more than forty years behind her, but I assure you, my dear reader,
there is much more to me than it may seem. Though for the sake of polite-
ness I will not divulge my true age here, I will impart to you, with all sincerity, that for the better part of the last eight hundred years I have been the
keeper of an inn resting along a well-worn path behind the thin veil of one
of the Other realms of this world: one set between Man and the much older
spirits of Nature. As you may imagine, my life amid the phantasmagoria of
dream, myth, and story has brought me into contact with all sorts of grotes-
queries and characters that could make a grown man start back in fright, or
break down in sympathy, or—as is probably more common—stare motionless in curiosity with one eyebrow cocked as his brain makes a failing
attempt at comprehension. Some of these characters I've had the pleasure of
working with, many more I've had the bright fortune of knowing, and a few
I've had the terrible misfortune of stumbling upon by mistake in a shadowy
corner of the forest. However, quite possibly one of the most extraordinary
beings I have ever known arrived to me in the tragic form of Craven. He was
one of those men—I use the term loosely, as you will understand soon

enough—who managed to keep his origins entirely shrouded in mystery, which is quite a feat considering the number of seers and other readers of fortune and mishap that pass through the open door of my public house at any given moment. It would be quite impossible, then, to offer any sort of explanation for the curiosities Craven possessed, except, of course, for what I myself have witnessed and am able to surmise from what I was privy to, which admittedly, wasn't much.

Before I plunge into Craven's intriguing tale, however, I should take a minute to explain myself and the inn at large in order to give you an understanding of it, as well as accentuate the anomaly he really was.

Mainly, you must understand, I'm not the type to pursue grandeur. Many seem to believe that living in the fey lands, in the midst of all types of creatures born from tales and beliefs, would lend itself to all sorts of epic adventures and dangers, when in truth it is a rather quiet, comfortable existence for those, like me, who don't go looking for trouble and choose to be happy with simplicity. I have chosen my little corner of the enormous map of the world, so I treat it well and get plenty in return. Hundreds of explorers and wannabe heroes have been among the varied ranks of my guests throughout the centuries, and I guarantee not one of them would say an ill word toward me or my establishment. All anyone ever needs is good food, strong ale, and a soft place to sleep, the type of selfless service I have come quite near to perfecting. That is not merely my opinion: one young epic heroine claimed that without the warmth of my hearth and the unmatched down of my mattresses, she undoubtedly would have been overtaken by her enemy, and the task she was destined to accomplish left unfulfilled, which would have spelled disaster for the world as a whole.

Now, my inn is located within the hollowed stump of a huge, wide tree, the top of which had been struck by lightning during a torrential thunderstorm and had broken off, much to the dismay of those living along the road near its immense base. With the care of my own two delicate hands, I removed the debris, and helped the inside of this stump repair and mold itself into the cozy, three-story tavern that quickly became famous throughout multiple realms, due mostly to the large hearth shaped from a handful of small boulders occupying the majority of one wall of the dining floor. Guests come from miles in every direction simply to sit near the comfort of its hot gaping maw, smoking, reading, or drinking their cares away in the golden glow of its flames.

The time when Craven came to work for me was a period of great unrest throughout most of the human realm, as we saw a great influx of those who I like to call Straddlers, people who willingly cross from the Humans to the Fey on a regular basis, as well as Dreamers, most of whom end up in Faerie through their subconscious while sleeping and don't ever realize that what they saw or experienced wasn't merely an invention of their imagination. Whichever way those people wandered into my establishment never concerned me as much as why they were looking for an escape in the first place. You see, I don't normally concern myself with the sordid affairs of human beings, yet I feel as if I must, at the very least, point out the utterly depressing picture times like those paint of your piece of the world because, though good for business, the disenchanted masses moping into my cozy establishment during those times greatly dragged down the overall morale of my frequent customers as well as my staff. I almost feel obligated to beseech you, reader, to please keep the war and fear to a minimum, as they cause an unsafe number of customers in my bar and fill my rooms to capacity, overworking my exhausted staff.

At the time I first met Craven, I had in my service three dutiful employees: a bartender, a groundskeeper, and an errand girl. Though creatures as ourselves tend not to bother with specific names—usually because many of us end up being called a number of different things depending on the human time period and culture in which we are referenced—for the sake of clarity I will refer to the above-mentioned employees by the pet names I gave them out of a motherly type of fondness for each: Frisky, Grunt, and Dust Mite, respectively.

Frisky was a petite woman with black and purple hair, almond eyes, and a rather jagged look about her. Unlike me, she had been completely human at one point, therefore her perceived age was much closer to her actual age (about forty-five years old); however, she could have passed for younger if not afflicted with therianthropy, or shape-shifting, which is a physically and mentally taxing condition. It left Frisky with a slightly crazed edge to her dark brown eyes, though in truth she was very professional and skilled in her work behind the bar. It was really only after the sun slipped behind the trees, allowing the night full reign over us that the edginess in her demeanor intensified to the point of mouthing off to the customers in between anxious glances out the nearest window, which was when I often had to send her outside so she could go for a run in her tiger form.

Once, on the second night of the full moon, after Frisky'd broken yet another glass in her anxiety, I confronted her about the possibility that perhaps she should take those nights off every month for the sake of her health. "Oh, no no no. I swear, I'm good, really," she replied with a breathless smile and a small twitch in her fingers. "I just need to get laid is all. I mean, I can handle the moon, I swear. I just gotta channel all my energy into flirting or something." Her laugh was raspy as she made an awkward gesture, squishing her breasts up and together with her hands. I had little choice but to concede to her, because even in the Faerie lands there were plenty of lonely men and women who could use the confidence boost that came from the wink of a hot bartender on an isolated night. Marketing aside, Frisky was impeccable at her job. She knew how to make every drink anyone could throw at her and even created a few of her own on our slower nights. I did make sure, however, to handle any complex drink mixes myself on the nights the moon shone in ultra-white shafts through the windows, making long square phantoms along the dark wood floorboards that threatened to overtake my haggard barkeep.

My second employee, the aforementioned Grunt, was a very strong and sturdy centaur, pretty young even by human standards, and though he had the misfortune of not being that bright, he was well suited to the physical labor of groundskeeping and maintaining the stables on the other side of the back garden. However, his dueling natures of man and stallion plagued his mind with two potentially destructive forces: aggression and obsessive compulsion. The former very often sparked the latter, especially when it involved the vast number of gardening and grooming tools he kept in stacks and rows along one wall inside the stables. Often I would head out to see how his preparations for the day were shaping up, only to find him grumbling to himself in the midst of rakes, brushes, horseshoes, hammers, shears, shovels, and whatever else he kept at hand, all in disarray. If ever any precious object on one of his stacks was disturbed by anyone or anything, like an oblivious mule on its way out to the pasture, Grunt would be compelled to roughly dismantle his previous organizational system and completely start from scratch, spending hours to decide exactly how that was to be done. One day, everything could have been ordered from shortest to tallest, and the next it was lightest to heaviest, or newest to oldest, or once, shiniest to rustiest. Much like in the case of Frisky, I felt it would be a disservice if I were to let Grunt go because, in spite of his neuroses, he always took great care of the horses and other beasts of burden my guests left in his charge, and unlike most of his race, he held himself with a fair amount of dignity, taking the effort to keep his whiskers trimmed in a neat goatee and pull his dark blond mop of hair neatly back with a narrow thong of leather, and would even agree to put on a shirt when more respectable company was expected.

Thankfully, Grunt's compulsions tended to take hold of him only from the late morning until the few hours before dinner was brought to him, immediately after which he would slip into a mellowness equal to the strength of his previous anxiety. This afforded me some mercy as I wouldn't have to simultaneously corral both him and Frisky.

The third employee was my errand girl, Dust Mite. Sweet and helpful as most nymphs are wont to be, her duties were a bit more extensive than her title would lead you to believe, as she would not only run errands in and about town, but she would also provide assistance to me back in the kitchen on the rare occasions I needed any, and she would keep the rooms swept and dusted, as well as the bedding washed in between overnight guests. Her favorite, though unofficial, duty was to be the flower-bringer for the guests, myself, and Frisky. The flighty dryad would spend all her free moments walking barefoot through the garden, conversing with the gnomes and *kami* out amongst the flowers, and when she'd return, there would be a tiger lily tucked behind one ear and baby's breath braided through her long brown hair. More lilies, roses, and orchids would be bunched in her thin hands; she'd offer a flower to anyone who would take one (which was nearly everybody) and go fill every vase she could find with what seemed to be a never-ending bouquet.

Now I'll return to the reason I required the addition of Craven in the first place. As I mentioned before, it was during one of the busiest influxes of Straddlers and Dreamers I had ever been a part of, which meant my inn almost literally became a revolving door of overnight guests and passersby entering and exiting, checking in and passing out. It was becoming too much for even my highly capable staff to handle, so I spread the word that I would be looking for a jack-of-all-trades type of valet to be my second in command. Not long after, a tall, pale beanstalk of a man silently passed through the crowd into my chambers. I can recall looking up and seeing, in that long sallow face, a pair of emerald-green eyes so round with unspoken sorrows that to peer into them was to feel the weight of innumerable days and comfortless nights. This well-dressed phantom was Craven.

Making note to avoid eye contact with him as much as possible, our subsequent discussion proved Craven to be very respectful and organized, which softened the unsettling blow of his first impression. I hired him then, excited to have an employee with a consistent, palatable demeanor.

The ground level of the inn, as I should have explained more clearly before, was split essentially into three sections. The first was the wide-open front room I described before, with the enormous fireplace set into the left-hand wall, the curving polished bar situated at the back corner to the right, and our various dining tables and chairs nestled in between. Cracking the back wall in two was a long question mark-shaped hallway, which led directly to the back door and out into the toe path of Dust Mite's garden. At the mouth of this hallway, on the left, was the landing of a broad staircase which swept in a wide semicircle up to the second-floor bedrooms. Across the hall from the stairs and a short way down the inside portion of the hook was a wide swinging door to the kitchen and farther still, just before the tail of the punctuation, were my chambers, which took up much of the space behind and below the staircase. As my other employees had their own sections of the grounds to prowl and attend to, I set Craven up with his own armchair and table in a back corner of my study under an expansive window and the regal gaze of my polished bookshelf filled with impressively old volumes and artifacts.

From the beginning, Craven seemed a natural for the job. He took no notes, and yet I could tell that all the history of the place, explained both orally by me and textually within an ever-growing compilation proudly displayed on a shelf of its own, was being pulled in through his sharp ears and vacuum-like eyes, then locked away in his mind for safekeeping. Craven was also very useful at those times when we restocked supplies for the stables and kitchen—not that it was difficult for me to lift the necessary poundage of meat, feed, and produce into their respective places, but an extra pair of strong, nimble hands simply made the chore move along much more efficiently. I would have been immensely pleased had he shown some feeling of accomplishment in his part, but there was none. Neither would he complain. He just was; any opinions he may have formulated stayed shadowed behind those haunted eyes of his.

One occupational hazard of running an establishment such as mine is the contact we—mostly Frisky, Dust Mite, and myself—inevitably must make with customers and overnight guests, and as not one of us retains the ability to be in two places at once, a reasonable rotation has been developed so that those guests checking in or out will not be lost. It was on such a busy day not much more than a week after Craven started with me that Frisky, Dust Mite, and I were all indisposed with other business at the moment a pair of weather-worn old wizards clad in cloaks the color of moss and dust swept up the garden path, having relinquished their horses into Grunt's care. I had been able to guide them from there to my office as I was on my way back into the kitchen and assumed Craven would be able to show the pair to one of the double rooms up on the second floor without issue. I poked my head in the half-open door and speedily informed my new valet of this.

"I can't help them," was the dull statement I received in reply. Understandably, I had not been expecting this type of response at all and was taken so instantly aback that I stood staring, dumb and unblinking, at the heavily bent visage of Craven as he remained nose deep in the history text in his arms.

As no other coherent thoughts formulated in my mind as to how to respond to such bland rejection, I repeated myself, more slowly, though, in case I had spoken too quickly and caused some misunderstanding. But once again Craven monotonously returned, "I can't help them."

"What do you mean 'can't'? You have been reading that book for hours now with nothing else to do. If I interrupted you in the middle of a sentence, please go ahead and finish, but otherwise lead these magi up to their room." I flushed a bit as I had finally regained the use of my vocal cords and the words tumbled out of me, strung together with confusion.

"I can't help them."

I studied him for a long moment, searching for any sign of why he might refuse such a simple task. He looked comfortable enough as he leaned forward on his elbows, the heavy book cover propped up against his forearms. His brow was smooth and un-furrowed, the muscles around his eyes relaxed, his thin lips soft and slightly parted. There was nothing to suggest that he was in pain of any kind, and his voice had been void of any inflection, agitated or otherwise. It was very, very strange, and if anyone else had so completely defied me, I would have had no issue terminating their employment right then, even with guests watching. And yet, I could not do anything of the sort with Craven. He was like a stray kitten who had bitten me as I tried to give it a bath. It was intensely bizarre, but I had to continue on with my day, so I left him there in my study and bustled the wizards upstairs myself.

It was approximately a month later when a small, haggard band of adventurers found their way to me in the early afternoon. They were four in all, led by a tall rotund man with very large mirrored aviator sunglasses, a goatee, and hair a bright cherry red. Closely following him was a massive dragon-man with dark green scales, wearing dented, yet still intimidating, armor. Then a dwarf came, who more closely resembled a moss-covered boulder than anything human and smelled like a stagnant pond, and a three-foot-tall halfling, the only female among them, with a mass of black hair spiraling from her scalp in all its unwashed glory. Dust Mite and I settled them in, filling every washtub to the brim with fresh water, and then attended to other business. It wasn't long after that the dwarf, who had sadly ignored the bath and strong soaps so carefully arranged for him, inquired of the nearest postal service. I informed him it was only a five-minute walk, but seeing as he was so new to town I preferred him to go with someone who knew the area, and so called to Craven, who was polishing the top of an open coffee table in front of the fireplace. He did not look up, didn't reply. The smooth swirling strokes he made with the rag did not even stutter at the sound of my voice.

He must not have heard me, I thought, seeing how the dining room was about half full with customers making merry with their food and drink. I excused myself from the molding dwarf and weaved my way between the tables and straight up to Craven's shoulder. It was only then that he paused in his work, sighing himself up into a standing position as he blandly asked me, "What do you need?"

I relayed my need to Craven and added, "Quickly, if you please," as I noticed the foul stench of the dwarf gradually wrinkling the noses of those sitting downwind of him along the bar.

"I can't help him."

To be completely honest, I had not been expecting this type of response from him again. Did he think since I let it go once that he'd be able to pass off any sort of trivial duty with that melancholic phrase of his? "Craven," I commanded, "I know you have been to the postmaster and back more than a few times since your arrival, so there should be no reason as to why you can't do the same once again, just with a companion in tow. Now, please will you do your duty and assist one of our guests?"

"I can't help him." His face and voice were set, emotionless.

"Are your legs broken? Have you lost your wits and forgotten the way? I don't have the time to argue with you, Craven, so stop refusing to help this guest here." With anyone else I would, no doubt, have lost my temper by this point and cast them out my front door, but Craven . . . he unsettled me and intrigued me, so I was pushed only into a moderate frustration.

"I'm not *refusing* to help. I simply can't." I could tell by the slightest shift in Craven's ghostly green eyes that he had comprehended every request and weighed every question I posed to him, and still he seemed unable to offer me anything more. His words wouldn't connect with the logic in my brain, yet he said everything with such steadiness that I began to wonder whether I had skimmed over some essential piece of the puzzle. Was *I* the one speaking nonsense? I caught Frisky on her way back to the bar with some dirty glasses in her hands.

"Am I making sense?" I asked after a brief explanation of the situation. "I'm not expecting him to go far above and beyond his duties, correct?"

"Nah, you're cool," she replied with a relaxed half-smile. "Makes sense to me."

"What do you think, Grunt?" I queried after going out to the barn for a tertiary opinion.

"What do I think?" he replied with a snort. "I think he needs a good mule-kick to the head just before we let the door smack him in his bony ass on the way out!"

(Obviously the sun was still fairly high in the sky, so Frisky hadn't a care in the world, whereas Grunt was deep in the throes of his daily reorganization and not very tolerant of, well, anything.)

"Dust Mite," I called out the nearest window as I knew she'd be eavesdropping. She popped up from below the sill with an embarrassed blush on her cheeks. "What's your opinion on this whole thing?"

"Honestly, ma'am, I think he's part troll." This summation, though offered with a childish giggle, was the last bit of support I needed. I wasn't being unreasonable and was, in fact, speaking as coherently as ever, so I made my way back to the dining room.

"Every one of your peers here agrees with me, Craven, so please do your job. Go retrieve that dwarf and take him to the postmaster." He made no reply. His silence was like a vacuum that diminished even the great warmth of my fireplace as he turned slowly toward the flames, which reflected the intensity of his dead-man's stare. I hesitated there out of concern, but was once again obliged to take care of the duty myself and leave the questions gnawing on my gray matter for another day.

It wasn't until a handful of months later that I worked up the gall to confront Craven about anything once again. I had taken that time to observe him and his habits, or lack thereof, in hopes of understanding this enigma in our midst; however, doing so only deepened my concerns. He never seemed to eat, require a rest, or converse with the guests. In fact, Craven's diligence focused predominately on scrubbing and polishing: our floors, dishes, furniture, and silverware had never looked better. And yet, I felt guilty. I had not brought him on solely for janitorial work, and the great effort he put into these duties appeared to me to be a desire for something more involved or challenging or intellectually stimulating, but knowing he would never outright tell me anything of the sort, my need to pick his brain began to overwhelm me.

"Craven, are you happy here?" I asked him point-blank once when he was on one of his silent perusals of my bookshelf, standing still as death with his hands clasped behind his back. His only acknowledgement of me was a slow mournful inclination of his head as he mildly claimed that yes, he was happy. Needless to say, I was unconvinced. "Are you sure? You don't want more . . . challenging responsibilities?" He indicated he didn't. "Well, why not?" I could no longer help myself and let the question slip out from between my lips. All I got in return was a shrug. A shrug! Had he no drive? No ambition?

A little later, after the rest of us had finished dinner, I returned to my chambers to find Craven there polishing my desk. "Could I have a word?" I asked him, with an emphasis on my innocent curiosity so he wouldn't think I was there to reprimand him for something. I pulled a chair up to his table by the window and indicated with a smile that he should take his seat opposite me, a task he accomplished with such speed and lightness of limb that the cushion was hardly disturbed by his presence upon it. "I wanted to ask you—and forgive me if this is too forward, but—do you have any family or friends nearby? I mean only that you hardly seem to leave the inn, and yet I've seen no one come by for lunch or a cup of coffee with you. And, don't take this too much to heart, but even Grunt takes a few days off here and there for the sake of a friend in need of a good rampage."

"I can't help you," Craven quietly returned.

Fearing I'd insulted him, I went on apologetically, "I don't mean to pry into matters you'd prefer to keep private, Craven. I ask only out of concern for you. Even in a place like this with rooms full of people you manage to hole yourself up in the few solitary spots there are to find. I just want to make sure you feel comfortable in your position here, you realize, because we all work very closely together and I'd like to think a strong sense of camaraderie exists between us. Including you, Craven . . . if you'll allow it." I smiled encouragingly, though he didn't return it. He just stared at me— *through* me. Cat-like. Corpse-like—if a corpse could ever have such a gaze which held a man still as it stole the breath from his lungs.

My smile had fallen in the dead silence, and it wasn't until I ventured to speak again that I perked it up once more, hastily, unconvincingly, into my cheeks. "Well, Craven, I'm glad we got the chance to talk." It came out delicate as Chinese silk, and once I stood, I left my chambers in a jittery haste and spent the rest of the evening out in the garden.

Waking much earlier than usual the next morning, followed by the haunted feeling one gets from an eerie dream not quite remembered, I padded downstairs from my private chambers on the lofty third floor with a lantern swinging heavily from my outstretched hand. Having little else to do in the translucent blue hour or two before dawn's pink and orange blush powdered the treetops, I figured I'd get a jump on some chores before breakfast. As I reached the hardwood landing at the mouth of the question-mark hallway, however, my pale yellow bubble of lamplight illuminated a tall silhouette, motionless in front of the fireplace, which was already filled with a crackling blaze. A violent tremor of fright racked my body for a moment, causing the metal hinges on my lantern to release tiny versions of the scream I was holding in.

"Craven?" I inquired, after a handful of deep breaths. Upon further inspection (accomplished by moving a few cautious steps closer), I affirmatively answered my own question, as Craven, in his vigil, remained utterly silent. "What are you doing here so early?" I questioned to no avail. "Well . . . don't just stand there. You can help—you can give me a hand with breakfast. I decided to get an early start on things myself." I would have gotten more reaction from one of the logs currently burning in the fireplace. He scarcely seemed to breathe as he focused into the depths of the flames, one arm supporting his narrow head against the stone and the other bent perpendicular to his torso as it rested on his lower back. "Craven—"

"I can't help," he finally replied, in little more than a whisper.

"Oh? Are you ill, Craven? Exhausted?" Perhaps he needed a day off at last. "Don't worry about it, dear. You can have the day for yourself and then tomorrow—"

"I can't . . . help . . . I can't . . . ," he repeated despairingly.

He was making me terribly uneasy, so I tried to keep a soothing tone in my voice . . . for both our sakes. "I promise you, it's all right. Take the day off; you're far overdue." Craven still did not look at me, but was silent this time as the fire snapped and sparked. I hesitated, then took it as an agreement and slipped off to the kitchen to busy myself and impatiently wait for the sun to rise.

Craven spent the whole day—and the next day, and the next—in the exact spot and position I'd found him in that morning. He had ceased to acknowledge the existence of anyone who tried to speak with him, and didn't even bat an eye when Dust Mite slid a long-stemmed daisy into the fist at his back, an act I reversed, of course, as soon as I was aware of it.

"I don't get why you won't just fire his creepy ass," Frisky shot at me during the third night of Craven's perch at the fireplace.

"And how exactly am I supposed to accomplish such a thing when he's become a veritable statue, Frisky? It's not as if I could simply lift him up and out the window, or drag him through the front door. I'm not a barbarian." I wrung out a wash rag into the small marble sink under the bar ledge and began to remove and scrub each glass from a pyramid that had accumulated next to a large fox-man reading *Finnegan's Wake* at the end of the bar.

"Who says you can't? Hell, I'll go over there right now and kick his ass halfway back to whereverthefuck he came from!" Frisky slammed down the very tall, frosted-glass bottle of vodka she'd been gesturing violently with, shocking the hunched cloaks at the bar into the straightest sitting positions they'd been in in years.

I caught the back of her belt with my wet right hand as she went to make good on her tirade. "No, you won't." With very little effort, I held her in place until her growling and scratching-at-the-air fit was over. "You're going to stay here and take care of our lovely customers, and leave the Craven situation to me." I released her only after she'd poured herself a shot and downed it with a painfully satisfied "gahhh."

Then, from the other side of the dining room I heard: "Sir, I asked you about the painting here very kindly, and I'd prefer an answer in turn." A noble, aging knight with a crescent of thin hair spread from temple to temple, who I had seen admiring a large oil painting depicting the copper-haired Valkyrie, Brunhilde, begging the god Odin for mercy, which was situated on the wall to his right, seemed to have been attempting conversation with Craven at the fireplace and was not much pleased with the result. This last statement was made purposefully loud enough so the whole dining room would hear. Not surprisingly, Craven continued to peer into the blaze as if he contemplated diving deep beneath its searing blue depths. A magenta flush soaked the knight's cheeks with frustration and public embarrassment, which made the white of his goatee appear much too stark and wiry. The whole of the room's occupants had gone silent and watched with the corners of their eyes.

I was obliged, at this point, to leave my post at the bar and work my way across the room to ensure that the minimum amount of reputational damage was being done. As I neared, however, the knight snatched a chain-mail glove from his belt as if to swing it at Craven. Then, for the first time in days, Craven silently turned toward the man speaking to him, his face blank, eyes deep and dark. "I can't help you," he told the gentleman. The statement sounded like it came from a great distance, as if Craven had one foot in another realm and was speaking through the veil. With a long, steady stride, he stepped up to and through the noble old knight, who had been struck dumb in awe. Craven continued on to pass into the wall, leaving nothing but a breathless chill and wide-eyed wonder in his wake.

"Craven!" I called at the wall. There were crickets and frogs vibrating the air outside in the moonlight under our windows. They were the only voices I heard in that moment. I made eye contact with Frisky to let her know the audience within my establishment was no longer welcome, and I hurried down to my office. The guests' voices murmured into life behind me once Frisky announced how it was "such a beautiful night. You all should go enjoy it instead of wasting your lives hanging around here . . ."

The knob was cold in my palm as I flung the door open so hard it bounced off the wall, leaving a dent in the plaster that I would discover later. "Craven?" I stepped over the threshold. There was no hint of him or any sort of disturbance, except that the temperature had dropped about five degrees. Then a figure near Craven's chair slowly shifted into focus as if I'd been viewing it through a camera lens. It glowed with a creamy sort of light, and as the shape sharpened it took the form of a man, shorter and stronger-looking than Craven. He appeared to be walking toward me and yet covered no ground between us. His details sharpened and color came into the denim of his jeans and the green cotton of his T-shirt; the creamy glow settled into his arms and face, subsiding but not dying away. He solidified, and without breaking stride stepped up to me, holding purpose in every step.

"Ma'am," he spoke with a respectable resonant tenor which endeared him to me immediately, "my name is Liam. I'm a guide for lost souls. You need to come with me." Liam's eyes were a kind hazel gray and his touch, when I reached out to take the hand he stretched toward me, caused a sensation of warmth and comfort to encircle first my arm, then engulf the rest of my body. As Liam held my gaze, I began to feel myself lifting, almost as if my soul were slipping effortlessly from my body. When the motion slowed to a stop, the ground beneath me solid once again, Liam turned his attention to something off to my right side. I followed suit.

He and I were still standing inside my office—or so it would seem. Everything was as it always had been: my desk next to the door, bookshelves and all their inhabitants standing at attention along the walls, the big window with its shutters open at the back of the room. The difference became evident in the way everything was set in gray scale. Liam and I were the only spots of color in a sea of charcoal and clouds. And there by the chair and table at the back corner, as gray as everything else around him, was Craven. He stood with his back to us, his hands clasped behind him as he faced the window. The sun, casting him in silhouette, shined almost white through the small square panes of glass, splashing a long black shadow behind him on the floor boards. I dropped Liam's hand and the calm left with it. A haunting stillness bore down the back of my neck and caught my breath. We were in Limbo—the space between a heartbeat and eternity.

"I know you." Craven disturbed the quiet with a melancholy whisper. He did not turn around, and yet I felt the vacuum of those hollow eyes upon me.

Liam spoke softly in my ear, "Each time I've tried to talk to him, all he does is stand there. Most wander their space at the very least. He doesn't."

"What should I do?" I asked, without looking away from Craven.

"Help him. Help him let go."

I nodded to show my understanding and stepped to Craven's shoulder. "I know you," he repeated.

"I know you, too, Craven." I sighed, unsure of how to continue. "Craven . . . you need to go with this man, OK? His name's Liam. He'll take care of you, I promise."

"I can't help you." A deep sorrow filled his voice. I feared I had done all he'd allow me to do, but to my surprise, Craven turned to face me. His eyes were like bowls full of ash.

"I can't . . ."

"You don't have to help *me* . . . or Liam. We're here to help *you*, Craven. We can help you." He let me grasp his chilled hand. "I promise it will be all right. You won't be stuck anymore, Craven. You won't have to help anyone with anything. You'll have peace and quiet." That same comprehensive shift I had seen months before flowed through his features again. An almost imperceptible nod pulled his chin down for a beat. I heard Liam step up behind me, and I allowed him to take my place. Craven's hand slid limply from my fingers.

Liam clasped him by the shoulder, and his glow reawakened to enshroud them both in warmth. In that moment, pane by pane, the window began to dissolve away. The sill stretched down to the floor and the white sunlight filled the space with intensity and radiance. Bookshelves and chairs began to dissolve as well, replaced by the beautiful emptiness slicing through the open spaces between Liam and Craven's arms and legs. They ventured forward together into the gate. With each step, Craven faded, until the whiteness finally permeated him and took his place. I closed my stinging eyes and hung my head in mourning for poor Craven.

When I opened them again, the color was restored to my office, and the sky outside was still black as ink. A single shaft of moonlight shot down from the upper left corner of my window, illuminating Craven's former armchair like an icy spotlight.

"Ma'am?" Dust Mite was behind me in the doorway. I now noticed I had been supporting myself with my right hand on my desk. I took a steadying breath, straightened up, and found her confused little face. Frisky was next to her with a frown at her lips and brow. "Where's Craven?" she asked.

"With kings and counselors," was all I could reply.

Colophon

HAIR TRIGGER 34 WAS PRODUCED ON A DELL STUDIO 1737 WITH INTEL Pentium Dual-Core CPU (T4200 @ 2.00 GHz) using QuarkXPress 7.31. The cover and photograph pages were produced on an Apple Macintosh G5 using InDesign C53 and Adobe Photoshop X53. They were submitted to McNaughton & Gunn, Inc., Saline, Michigan, camera-ready on CD-R for printing.

The cover image was provided by the photographer in digital format, as were the images in the photo insert. All images were submitted to Lake County Press, camera ready, on CD-R for printing. All photograph titles are Franklin ITC Pro Bold Italic.

The cover copy is Franklin ITC Pro Light and Thin. The text on the first photo page is Franklin ITC Pro Bold and Light. All photo titles are Franklin ITC Pro Bold Italic.

Body copy is Sabon 11 point. Author names are in Franklin Gothic Book Compressed 14 point. Page footers are in Franklin Gothic Book Compressed 9 point.

Paper stock for cover is 12 PT Kallima C1S. Paper stock for photo pages is 100# Opus Dull Text. Print specs for photo pages are black plus overall aqueous satin coating. Print specs for cover are four-color process and one PMS color with matte laminate.

Print run 1,000.